STREAM FLOW

MEASUREMENTS, RECORDS AND THEIR USES

by

Nathan Clifford Grover

and

Arthur William Harrington

With a New Introduction by

VEN TE CHOW
University of Illinois,
Urbana, Illinois

DOVER PUBLICATIONS, INC.
NEW YORK

Published in Canada by General Publishing Com-
pany, Ltd., 30 Lesmill Road, Don Mills, Toronto,
Ontario.
Published in the United Kingdom by Constable
and Company, Ltd., 10 Orange Street, London
W. C. 2.

This Dover edition, first published in 1966, is an
unabridged and unaltered republication of the second (1949) printing of the work originally published by John Wiley & Sons, Inc., in 1943.
This edition also contains a new Introduction
by Ven Te Chow, University of Illinois, Urbana,
Illinois.

Library of Congress Catalog Card Number: 66-24128

Manufactured in the United States of America
Dover Publications, Inc.
180 Varick Street
New York, N. Y. 10014

This Dover Edition is dedicated
to the memory of
NATHAN CLIFFORD GROVER
(January 31, 1868–November 29, 1956)
and
ARTHUR WILLIAM HARRINGTON
(June 7, 1888–June 29, 1964)

INTRODUCTION TO THE DOVER EDITION

In this decade we are witnessing rapid and extensive progress in the fields of hydrology and water resources development. This activity is exemplified on the international level by the commencement of the International Hydrological Decade in 1965 and on the domestic front by the quick passage of some important water legislation, including the Water Resources Research Act of 1964, and the Federal Water Projects Recreation Act, Water Resources Planning Act and Water Quality Act of 1965. These developments are creating great interest in techniques for collecting hydrologic data.

Stream-flow measurement is the most extensive and expensive of all the programs for gathering basic hydrologic data. In the United States, major stream gaging began in 1851 with the famous survey on the Mississippi delta by the Bureau of Topographical Engineers of the War Department. The scale of this program exceeded that of all previous hydrologic works. The report on this survey, made in 1861 by Captain A. A. Humphreys and Lieutenant H. L. Abbot, immediately won world-wide attention and respect.

In 1888, instruments and methods of stream gaging were studied and personnel were trained at the Embudo camp, New Mexico, established by Major J. W. Powell, then Director of the U. S. Geological Survey; this was a significant first step in the systematic work of collecting records of stream flow in this country. In 1894, a nation-wide stream-gaging program was launched by Mr. F. H. Newell, organizer of the Water Resources Branch and later a chief engineer of the Survey. Up to 1930, this program was essentially consolidated throughout the nation.

The U. S. Geological Survey currently carries on practically all stream gaging in the United States, either independently or in cooperation with other Federal agencies and with states, counties, and cities. At present (end of 1965), the Survey maintains about 3000 primary gaging stations, about 2000 secondary stations, about 8000 partial record stations, over 3000 water management stations, about 2000 quality-of-water stations, and 38 benchmark stations.

The authors of this book were both veteran hydrologists of the Geological Survey and are well-remembered contributors to the art of stream gaging. The senior author, Nathan Clifford Grover, was the chief hydraulic engineer from 1904 to 1939, and contributed to many important publications. He was co-author, with J. C. Hoyt, of *River Discharge*, an excellent textbook on American methods of stream gaging published in four editions from 1907 to 1916 by J. Wiley & Sons of New York. He contributed to an invaluable monograph, *A History of the Water Resources Branch of the United States Geological Survey to June 30, 1919*, privately compiled by R. Follansbee, which tells the interesting and heroic history of the American engineers pioneering in stream gaging.

This present book contains a wealth of information on stream-gaging techniques that were developed largely by the engineers of the U. S. Geological Survey in all sections of the country. It represents the art and practice that have been evolved over a period of many years and that have stood the test of time under a great variety of conditions. Such information is particularly useful and beneficial to many developing countries, where engineers can use this readily available material without having to go through the long and tedious process of producing it.

In the United States and other developed countries, numerous new techniques have been developed since publication of this work in 1943. Nevertheless, the book embodies many basic principles and much knowledge that is almost everlasting and should be learned by all engineers and students in hydrometry. In addition to the art and practice of stream gaging, the book covers the physical and chemical phases of the hydrological cycle as well as the legal and administrative aspects of river development. Therefore it can be used as a textbook or as a major reference for students in hydrology and water resources, and this reprint edition should be a welcome addition to any hydraulic engineer's library.

The science of stream-flow measurement is generally known as hydrometry. In its broadest sense, however, hydrometry includes all types of hydraulic measurement. Anyone who wishes to master this subject would do well to choose this book as the text for a first course in his program of study. He could then extend his reading to many other publications in the field. For his interest, several important references written in English may therefore be mentioned.

Although the basic principles and knowledge of stream gaging are essentially universal, the procedure of stream gaging may vary with the agency that conducts it. For the methods and practices followed by the U. S. Geological Survey, the reader should refer to *Stream-Gaging Procedure: A Manual Describing Methods and Practices of the Geological Survey*, prepared by D. M. Corbett and others in 1943 as the Survey's *Water-Supply Paper 888*. This is an official manual of the Survey's Water Resources Branch for field hydrometric work. Similar manuals for irrigationists include *Manual for Measurement of Irrigation Water* and *Water Measurement Manual*, both issued by the U. S. Department of the Interior, Bureau of Reclamation, in 1947 and 1953, respectively. The United Nations Economic Commission for Asia and the Far East (ECAFE) also issued two manuals entitled *Standards for Methods and Records of Hydrologic Measurements* and *Field Methods and Equipment Used in Hydrology and Hydrometeorology* as ECAFE's Flood Control Series No. 6 in 1954 and No. 22 in 1962, respectively. (The latter work was published in cooperation with the World Meteorological Organization.) These manuals are frequently used as guidelines for international practices in hydrometry.

Up-to-date basic information on the practices, arts and techniques of stream-flow measurement is given by my colleague, Mr. M. C. Boyer, Natural Resources Coordinator of Fresno County, California, in Section 15 on "Streamflow Measurement" of the *Handbook of Applied Hydrology*, which was edited by me and published by the McGraw-Hill Book Company of New York in 1964. This presentation summarizes the present status and offers suggestions for improving the accuracy and efficiency of stream-flow computations.

In addition, there are many books on hydrometry in foreign languages. One important treatise written in Polish by A. T. Troskolański in 1957 has been translated into English by J. Bertholdi and others and published by Pergamon Press of London in 1960 as *Hydrometry: Theory and Practice of Hydraulic Measurement*.

The history of hydrometry is a fascinating story of man's adventures and explorations in unlocking nature's secrets in streams and rivers. The reader will find an enlightening and inspiring American story told by my former great friend, Dr. Steponas Kolupaila, late professor of civil engineering at the University of Notre Dame, in his paper "Early History of Hydrometry in the United States," published in the Journal of Hydraulics Division, *Proceedings of the American Society of Civil Engineers*, Vol. 86, No. HY1, pp. 1–51, in January, 1960. Dr. Kolupaila also compiled a monumental *Bibliography of Hydrometry*, which was published by the University of Notre Dame Press in 1961.

During the past twenty or so years, numerous advances in the technology of stream-flow measurement have been achieved. Of particular importance are the developments of new instruments, the automation of stream-flow records, and the new concepts of stream-gaging networks.

Among the new instruments are the electromagnetic flowmeter, the ultrasonic flowmeter, the bubble gage, the surface follower, the sonic sounder, the velocity-azimuth depth assembly (VADA), and the two-speed timer. Detailed descriptions of these instruments are given in the Geological Survey *Water-Supply Paper* 1669-Z entitled *Selected*

Techniques in Water Resources Investigation, compiled by G. N. Mesnier
and K. T. Iseri.

The electromagnetic flowmeter operates on Faraday's principle that
when an electrical conductor—in this case, water—passes through a
magnetic field a current is generated within it. The generated current
is gathered by two electrodes set with their axes at right angles to both
the direction of flow and of the magnetic field. The current is then
recorded and converted to stream-flow record. The acoustic or ultrasonic flowmeter works on the principle of the Doppler effect on ultrasonic waves passing through water. A transmitter directs a signal
toward a receiver some distance upstream. Sound waves moving upstream are compressed and those returning downstream are attenuated.
The magnitude of this effect can be recorded and related to water
velocity. Both electromagnetic and ultrasonic flowmeters record velocity continuously. They contain no moving parts in the water to be
fouled by debris.

The bubble gage and the surface follower record continuously the
water stage in a stream without need of expensive and troublesome
stilling wells and intakes. The bubble gage utilizes the purge technique,
involving nitrogen gas bubbles to transmit the water pressure to a
servometer that operates a recorder. The surface follower, which also
operates a recorder, follows the fluctuation of the water level in a pipe
that is mounted vertically in a stream.

The sonic sounder is an assembly of a depth recorder operating on
acoustic reflection and a Price current meter. It permits measurement
of depths and velocities in river channels without lowering the assembly
to the stream bottom. This is particularly suitable in flood measurement where relatively great depths are encountered and where debris
carried by the stream is a frequent menace to the equipment. The
VADA is a combination of a sonic sounder with a remote-indicating
compass and a Price current meter. This device permits measurement
of the direction of flow as well as the velocity and depth at any point
in the stream or in a tidal estuary.

A two-speed timer has been developed for use on small flash streams,
where it is desirable to automatically expand the time scale of the
recording of high water to several times the low-water scale.

Stream-flow records are ordinarily recorded in terms of water stage
in the stream on a strip-chart recorder. For a stage-discharge relation
that is defined empirically by current-meter measurements, or computed
by approximate hydraulic methods, the discharge is determined. This
procedure of data reduction involves many steps which require tedious

and time consuming manual work and provide much room for errors of all kinds. Trained hydrographers, competent to make stream-flow measurements and to convert them into figures of discharge, are becoming relatively scarce in view of increasing demands for such personnel. At the same time, modern inventions of great sophistication, such as electronic computers, have become available to perform their functions automatically and accurately. An analysis was made that indicated an overall savings of about ten per cent of the costs can be achieved when the automation system is applied to 2000 gaging stations. With advances in computer technology and automation science, advantages of the system will undoubtedly increase greatly in the future. As a result, a system for automatic computation of daily discharge records has been developed by the U. S. Geological Survey during the last decade. As of February 1, 1966, there were 2,996 automatic digital recorders in operation at about twenty-five per cent of the total number of stream-gaging stations. By 1968, it is planned to have 5000 of the gaging stations automated. This program will ensure significant manpower savings, increased accuracy, and accelerated compilation and publication of useful data.

According to the description given in *Automation of Streamflow Records*, Geological Survey Circular 274 (1963), the automation system consists of a digital-stage recorder, a paper-tape translator, and a general-purpose digital computer. The digital-stage recorder is a battery-operated, slow-speed, paper-tape punch which records a digit on a paper tape at preselected intervals of time. This device is used basically for coding and recording the position of an input shaft, but it can be adapted to accept a voltage input, to record several variables in sequence, or to transmit data by wire or radio. The paper-tape format is a unique configuration which requires rearrangement by a translator before input to any high-speed digital computer.

New concepts in stream-gaging network include the developments of the vigil network, the hydrological benchmarks, and the network design. The vigil network is intended to detect subtle or dramatic changes in the hydrological environment resulting from conditions that arise naturally or are imposed by man. For this network, for example, observation stations are set up in watersheds that are subject to uses such as farming, grazing, deforestation, afforestation, urbanization, and other activities of man. Intermittent observations are therefore made to detect changes that occur with time in the hydrologic parameters involved. It has been planned that many of the vigil network basins in the United States will be located along east-west and north-south transects. Also, a system of vigil basins, uniformly spaced along latitudinal and meridional lines, will gauge the effects of gradually changing climatic regimens on hydrologic factors.

Hydrological benchmarks record the evolutional effects caused by natural phenomena alone. Thus, these stations are established at such places as national and state parks, where there is the least chance that works of man will cause changes in hydrologic regimens. The records of the benchmark stations can be used to adjust those of regular stations in the region of hydrologic homogeneity so that the latter can be corrected for the influence of man's activities and thereby kept consistent over the years. A network of one hundred benchmark stations is planned for completion within the next decade in the United States.

In order to obtain the maximum useful information from stream gaging for a given effort, new principles and procedures of design are being developed to optimize the efficiency of the gaging network. This scientific design of stream-gaging network is of particular importance to new programs of water resources development in which there is always competition for available funds and best operation.

Despite all the new developments, every hydrographer must still learn certain fundamental knowledge in stream gaging. As this book contains much of such information, I am indeed happy to see it reprinted and hence made available to the engineering profession. When Mr. Hayward Cirker, President of Dover Publications, Inc., invited me to prepare an introduction to this new edition, I considered it a great privilege and gladly accepted, although I feel that many of my colleagues are better qualified to undertake this significant assignment. Finally, I wish to express my sincere gratitude to my colleagues, Dr. Luna B. Leopold, former chief hydrologist, and Mr. E. L. Hendricks, acting chief hydrologist, both of the U. S. Geological Survey, for supplying information on the Survey's stream-gaging programs.

VEN TE CHOW

Urbana, Illinois
March, 1966

PREFACE

The procedure involved in obtaining systematic records of river discharge is based primarily on the natural laws which pertain to the flow of water in open channels. In the abstract, these laws and their mathematical expression are relatively simple. Stream flow, however, is affected by many factors related to temperature, turbidity, viscosity, slope, depth, and condition of channel that cannot possibly be expressed directly in equations or formulas. Its theoretical evaluation must depend, therefore, on the use, within the basic formulas, of inexact coefficients that must be applied through the exercise of judgment. Theoretical considerations related to hydrology and the hydraulics of stream flow are thus attended by an almost unlimited variety of disturbing factors and approximations.

Through the art of stream gaging, records of stream flow are obtained by practical means with, in general, only minor reference to theoretical considerations. Though these records are not exact, they are generally sufficiently accurate to serve the purposes for which they are to be used. As in other situations of this nature, there is no one limit of accuracy that may be set, but each refinement introduced for the purpose of increasing relative accuracy generally increases the cost, and the economic law of diminishing returns puts a sharp limit of practicability on the refinements that may thus be made. Stream gaging has, therefore, practical limitations in costs which must always be studied in their relation to the relative accuracy of the records needed in any region for any purpose.

In the gradual development of the art of stream gaging, considerations of cost have always been of controlling force. As the work has developed, the demand for greater accuracy of results has grown, and fortunately the available funds have kept reasonable pace with the increasing cost of the more accurate records. The art has, therefore, been improved gradually in both technique and facilities but always at increased costs that could at no step be greater than would be warranted by the increase in the number of records and the improvement in their quality. The development of methods, instruments, and equipment utilized in measuring and recording stream flow has proceeded and must continue to proceed on the basis of the relation of cost to relative accuracy.

This book treats primarily of stream-flow records and describes in an elementary way their collection, computation, publication, and subsequent use. Related phases of occurrence, control, and administration of water have also been presented briefly. The text has been designed to show, in Chapters 1 to 7, why records of the quantity and quality of the discharge of surface streams and of ground water are needed as a basis for stable local or regional development; in Chapters 8 to 14, how sites for gaging stations are selected and the stations themselves established, equipped, and operated; in Chapters 15 to 18, how the results are computed and published or otherwise made available to the public; and, in Chapters 19 and 20, how stream gaging is organized and financed in this country in cooperation between federal, state, and municipal agencies. The collection, computation, and publication of records, Chapters 8 to 18, are described with reasonable thoroughness in terms of the present best practices. The remaining chapters, which are brief and broadly informative, are planned to serve as a background against which the main theme will appear in a proper light for its appreciation and correct evaluation.

The authors have had long service in the field and office work of the Geological Survey related to the collection, computation, and publication of records of river discharge. They have assisted in the development of the methods, instruments, and equipment that are used and that are accepted as standard in this country and in foreign countries. In this book, many references are necessarily made to the Geological Survey and to the conditions that affect various practices in that organization, even though some of those conditions may not be strictly applicable to similar work in another organization, especially those conditions that are involved in fiscal matters, cooperative arrangements, organization in field and office, publication, and in recruiting personnel through the United States Civil Service Commission. The presentation of those phases which appear to relate wholly to the regulations of a particular federal bureau or department, however, may not be without suggestive value in other connections.

The authors are, of course, greatly indebted to the many engineers who have preceded them or have been associated with them in the Geological Survey and who have contributed in varying degrees over many years to the development of the instruments, equipment, and procedures utilized in the collection, computation, and analysis of stream-flow records. A few of these engineers have been mentioned in the text of the book in connection with particular phases of the work, but it is obviously impossible to name all of them or, in general, to give proper credit for their individual contributions to the art of stream gaging. However, the authors wish to pay tribute to Dr. Frederick Haynes Newell, who, by his pioneer work, broad vision, courageous optimism, untiring energy, and never-failing enthusiasm under great difficulties, laid the foundation of modern systematic stream gaging.

Acknowledgment is made to numerous engineers, geologists, and others, whose helpful suggestions and kindly criticism have been invaluable. The great assistance of Miss Margaret Elizabeth Woods in the preparation of the text of this book is also acknowledged.

NATHAN CLIFFORD GROVER

ARTHUR WILLIAM HARRINGTON

March, 1943

CONTENTS

CONTENTS

CHAPTER 1

PRECIPITATION AND RUNOFF

The Hydrologic Cycle. Water is precipitated to the earth from the atmosphere in various forms, such as rain, snow, and dew. Part of this water returns almost immediately to the atmosphere by evaporation; part is evaporated from water surfaces; part flows over the ground as surface water; and part enters the ground, whence it returns to the atmosphere by transpiration from growing vegetation or by evaporation from the moist earth. Some of this water comes to the surface again through springs and seeps to join the surface water and to form creeks and rivers that flow to the oceans or to inland seas, from which it is again evaporated. All water so evaporated and transpired becomes atmospheric water and as such is again available to be precipitated. There is thus a never-ending cycle, commonly called the *hydrologic cycle*, of water moving from the atmosphere to the earth, over and through the earth, and to the atmosphere again.

In the hydrologic cycle, the mean rate of flow of water or its equivalent in water vapor appears to be of the order of magnitude of 500,000,000 cubic feet per second, which is roughly 200 times the flood flow of the lower Mississippi River. This estimate has been made on the basis of an average annual rate of evaporation from the oceans (about 139,000,000 square miles) of 39 inches [1] in depth and of evaporation and transpiration from land surfaces (about 58,000,000 square miles) of 18 inches in depth. That amount of water moving constantly through the hydrologic cycle corresponds to an average annual precipitation of about 32.5 inches over the total surface of the earth (about 197,000,000 square miles), and to an apparent average rate of runoff from land surfaces of 0.5 cubic foot per second per square mile if on the average 20 per cent of the precipitation appears as runoff. A basis for comparison is afforded by the records of runoff in the United States (about 3,000,000 square miles) where the average rate of annual runoff is about 2,000,000 cubic feet per second or about 0.7 cubic foot per second per square mile. This evaluation of the hydrologic cycle is significant only in emphasizing the magnitude and

[1] Bibliog. 1·20.

1

importance of the flow of water in that cycle, the enormous amount
of solar energy involved in evaporating, transpiring, and lifting water
into the air, and the insignificance of any possible general effect of
the activities of man on this process of nature.

The quantity of water in or on the earth varies widely, not only
from region to region, but also from season to season in every region.
Variations with respect to place result in humid, semiarid, and arid
regions; variations with respect to time result in floods, normal stages
of water, and droughts. Water, whether in the air or on or beneath
the surface of the earth, is always moving. Surface water can be
retarded temporarily but it cannot be conserved in the sense of being
saved as other minerals or the soils or forests can be saved. For the
earth as a whole, neither evaporation and transpiration, which determine the amount of flow in one direction in the hydrologic cycle, nor
precipitation, which represents the return flow in the cycle, can be
materially changed by man. Man does, however, make changes
which affect the local availability of water and local evaporation and
transpiration but without affecting appreciably the earth's hydrologic
cycle. For example, storage of water in reservoirs serves to change the
natural rates of discharge and so to increase the utility and value of
rivers, but the resulting retardation of flow increases the opportunities
for evaporation or transpiration or both and, instead of conserving
water, increases the local transfer to the air and so decreases the supply of water in surface streams.

Water is essentially pure as it comes to the earth from the clouds.
However, it is a natural erodent and solvent and, immediately after
reaching the earth, begins to collect foreign matter, in suspension in
surface waters and in solution in both surface and ground waters.
The quality of the water changes, therefore, in accordance with the
erodable and soluble substances with which it comes in contact. The
nature and quantity of the suspended and dissolved materials vary
with the topography and geological characteristics of the land over
and through which the water flows. Water also collects many bacteria, some of which are harmless and others pathogenic. Water, both
on and beneath the surface of the earth, is, therefore, widely variable
not only in quantity but also in physical, chemical, and bacterial
quality.

Although constant interchange takes place not only between water
vapor and fluid water but also between ground water and surface
water, the total amount of water in and on the earth and in the
atmosphere is believed to remain essentially constant. The transfer
by evaporation and transpiration of water from the liquid form on the

earth to the vaporous form in the air, and the reverse process, are under way at all times. The interchange between surface water and ground water is likewise continuous. Water passes from the surface of the ground into the soil in nearly all places whenever opportunity offers, and, similarly, water flows from the ground to the surface at numberless seeps and springs. Consequently, the relative quantities of ground water and surface water in any region are constantly varying, but whether the totals for the earth of each class of water are essentially constant or widely varying is not known.

Although the rivers that flow over the surface of the land represent only a minor phase of the hydrologic cycle, they are nevertheless of the utmost importance to man because of their use in connection with municipal supplies, navigation, irrigation, power production, industrial processes, and air conditioning. Ground water, which constitutes another phase of the cycle, is, compared with rivers, only a minor source of water for man's use. It is, however, a very important source for all the uses indicated for rivers except navigation and hydraulic power. The repeated transit of water through the hydrologic cycle and its recurring purity as it reaches the earth give it a value, particularly to man, that is greater than that of any other natural resource.

Sources of Atmospheric Water. Because of their great areas, the oceans are doubtless the principal sources of atmospheric water and therefore of the water that is precipitated on the land. Large quantities of water, however, are carried into the air from land surfaces by evaporation and transpiration, and this water is mingled with that derived from the oceans in proportions that vary with the movement of air currents, with the topography of the land surfaces, and with distances from a seacoast. The precipitation which comes in storms that move over large regions is derived from moving air masses of great extent, and the water thus precipitated may be, and probably generally is, carried into the air in regions far removed from those in which the precipitation occurs. Not all precipitation occurs, however, in connection with wide storm movements. A considerable part, varying from time to time and from place to place, reaches the earth in local showers which may have derived a substantial part of their water from relatively local sources. Although it obviously is not possible to determine the source of any particular water vapor or the relative proportions of ocean-derived and land-derived water that is in the air at any time or place or that may be precipitated in any storm, it is evident that each of these proportions may have significant value, especially in the interior of continents. It may be assumed that some portion of the water of precipitation on all lands is derived from inland evaporation and transpiration; further, that such portion, when compared with the portion derived from the oceans, is relatively small near a coast and increases toward the interior of a continent, and, similarly, that it decreases with the distance over the ocean from the shore, and perhaps is essentially zero in parts of the great oceans.

The runoff from a drainage basin is probably a direct measure of the net quantity of water that is brought through the atmosphere into that basin from outside sources. If the net amount that returns to the basin exceeds the amount that flows from the basin, there will be increasing humidity in the basin, and if less, increasing aridity.

There is much interchange of water through the atmosphere between different basins as well as between continents and oceans, and the smaller the drainage basins or continents, the greater the proportion of probable interchange. The runoff from a drainage basin affords no measure of the amount of the interchange but does indicate the net difference between the precipitation on the basin and the loss of water from the basin by evaporation and transpiration.

Water Supply and Precipitation. The wide variations in the quantities of surface water and ground water, that is, in the quantities of water available for man's use, are due primarily to fluctuations in precipitation. Humid regions are well supplied with both surface water and ground water; arid regions have relatively little of either. Rainy seasons produce high stages in rivers and high ground-water levels; droughts have the opposite effects. During periods of heavy rain or of rapidly melting snow, much of the water in surface streams flows directly over the ground surface or becomes ground water for only short periods of time. Therefore, it contains but little dissolved matter and is relatively pure chemically. It may, however, carry in suspension much material that has been washed from the surface of the ground or eroded from the slopes and channels. Wide variations with respect to dissolved or suspended matter may result from differences in geological characteristics, soils, vegetation, slopes, intensities of precipitation, or from the variable temperatures that cause different rates in the melting of snow. These variations affect the utility of water for many purposes, its storage and control, the silting of reservoirs, maintenance of channel capacities, treatment of the water to change its chemical quality, and the costs of utilization for all purposes. Knowledge of the quantity and quality of water is, therefore, essential to all development and to the welfare of man.

Snow Storage. Precipitation in the form of snow, its storage as snow accumulates on the ground, and its eventual release as water are all related to temperature. Snow accumulates on the surface of the ground as long as precipitation continues while temperatures remain at or below the freezing point. It gradually consolidates with the advance of winter because of the increasing depth and weight of the accumulated snow and because of the formation of crusts or layers of ice by the freezing of water derived from brief thaws or from rain and held by the snow as a result of its sponge-like action. Water in the form of snow and ice is, therefore, temporarily stored on the surface of the ground, but such storage is dependent on regional temperatures and is beyond the control of man.

Snow as it falls varies greatly in its water content. It may be light, or low in water content, if the temperature is considerably below freezing when the snow falls; or it may be heavy, or high in water content, if the temperature is near the freezing point when the snowfall occurs. The average water content of newly fallen snow is about 0.10; that is, 1 inch of water is equivalent to 10 inches of snow. However, in heavy snow or old snow the water content is considerably higher, and in late winter, when the accumulated snow and ice approaches the density of solid ice, the ratio of water to depth of snow is still higher. The limiting value, of course, is 0.92, the specific gravity of ice. When such heavy snow has a depth of several feet, it holds a great amount of water in temporary natural storage, the equivalent of 12 inches or more of water over part or all of a drainage basin being not uncommon.

If such an accumulation of snow melts rapidly as a result of continued high temperatures, and especially if such temperatures are accompanied by heavy rain, the potentialities of a flood are present. If, however, there are daily thawing and nightly freezing for a considerable period of time, such stored water may run off gradually without causing river stages that are excessively high. Where there are heavy accumulations of snow, therefore, the regimen of the spring runoff is controlled largely by temperature. In the high mountains of the far West, daily thawing and freezing occur during the spring, and the resulting runoff, varying widely within each twenty-four-hour period but not greatly from day to day, continues into the summer and is of great economic importance for irrigation and for the development of hydraulic power. The daily fluctuations of such runoff from the high snow fields are recorded as sine curves on the sheets of graphic recorders (Fig. 1). At the edge of such a snow field, the low flow occurs in the night or early morning and the high flow in or shortly after the warmest part of the day. Below the snow field, the high and low stages will occur at later hours, the amount of lag depending both

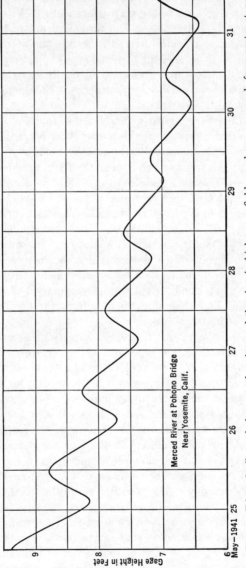

FIG. 1. Diurnal effect of alternate freezing and thawing in high snow fields as shown on graph from water-stage recorder.

on the distance from the snow field and on the velocity of the stream; and at any place of observation, the times of high and low water will be progressively later as the season advances and the distance from the front of the snow field to the place of observation becomes greater as the snow melts and retreats.

Fluctuations in Rivers. Fluctuations in the stage and discharge of rivers result from variations in precipitation and temperature. Such fluctuations are influenced by the rates of snow melt, the intensity and areal extent of rain, the slope and geological characteristics of basin, soil, vegetal cover, stage of ground water, and the season of the year with relation to vegetal growth and to freezing temperatures that seal the ground and cause precipitation to occur as snow.

The rate of melting of snow and the intensity of rainfall are probably the factors which affect the fluctuation of rivers most directly. Rainfall of low intensity in the growing season yields little or no runoff as all the water of precipitation not directly evaporated goes into the ground, is utilized by growing plants, and is largely returned to the atmosphere by transpiration. High rates of rainfall cause heavy runoff and flood discharges of small rivers and increased stages of all rivers to which such runoff is tributary. Between the precipitation which causes no runoff and that which causes floods, there are all gradations in intensity and duration that produce the ordinary variations in stage and discharge.

The accumulation of snow on the ground is important in relation to several aspects of rivers: (a) seasonal low flow, since the accumulated snow represents water that is temporarily withheld from runoff, the runoff during periods of frost being largely derived from ground water, so that in winter rivers may reach the lowest stages of the year if freezing is protracted; (b) seasonal floods, since the rate of melting of the accumulated snow may have a large effect on the magnitude of the spring floods; (c) the availability of the runoff for use, especially where the heaviest precipitation in high mountains occurs during the winter; and (d) losses of water to the atmosphere, since any delay in runoff increases the opportunity for evaporation, because, remarkably enough, there is appreciable evaporation directly from snow, apparently without transition through the liquid form.

The steepness of the slopes, the texture and depth of the soils, and the nature of the underlying rock strata intervene to affect the relations between fluctuations in precipitation or snow melting and fluctuations in stages and discharges of rivers. In general, the steeper the slopes and the less pervious the surface of the ground, the more direct will be the relation of river discharge to the rates of precipitation. A steep slope of solid rock will yield promptly nearly 100 per cent of the rainfall. A sandy plain covered with vegetation will slowly yield only a small percentage of the rainfall, in extreme instances approaching zero. Between these extremes, there are infinite variations.

The vegetal cover of a drainage basin affects the flow of the rivers of the basin in several respects; it decreases the runoff by checking the surface flow, thereby increasing infiltration and evaporation; it decreases the runoff by the transpiration of the water needed for plant growth; it decreases the rates of runoff by preventing or retarding the formation of channels and so delaying the transit of the water to the streams; and it decreases the rates of runoff throughout the growing season because of the water used in transpiration, and thereby its effects on infiltration probably tend to produce a more uniform river flow. These effects are generally greater during periods of active plant growth, during periods of no frost when there is no sealing of the ground by an ice cover, and during periods of no snow, when the sponge-like effect of the accumulated snow is lacking. Although vegetation tends to decrease total runoff, it may in some instances serve to increase the value of a stream by producing more uniform rates of flow and so increasing its utility.

The stage of the ground water may have a great effect on the relation of the rates of rainfall to the flow of surface streams. If the ground is already saturated with water, there can be no further infiltration, with the result that the ground is practically impervious and all water of precipitation must flow over the surface, a condition that is probably never fully attained in nature. If the ground water is low, there is full opportunity for infiltration and therefore for greater or less delay in the flow of the rain water into the stream channels. The ground constitutes one of nature's great reservoirs for storing water, and the quantity of water that passes into and through the ground is large, varying, of course, with many factors. The gradual release of water to the stream channels produces all the low flow and a portion of all medium and high flows, the proportion of ground water to surface water decreasing as the stages of the rivers increase.

Natural Function of Rivers. Rivers act as natural drains and as such carry to the oceans or inland seas the surplus water that remains from precipitation after some part, and in arid and semiarid regions the major part, has been evaporated and transpired into the atmosphere. They carry also to the seas the "wash" of the lands and transport the eroded materials to the flood plains and deltas.

In the natural order of events, rivers fluctuate in stage and discharge in accordance with variations in rainfall and with the storage or melting of snow; they fluctuate in chemical quality, that is, in the quantities and kinds of dissolved matter, with the geology of their drainage basins and with the relative proportions of ground and surface waters; and they fluctuate in turbidity, that is, in the kind and quantity of suspended matter, with the geological characteristics of the basin and with variations in the vegetal cover protecting the soil surface.

Rivers are always naturally polluted and in some degree turbid, and such pollution and turbidity will continue regardless of man's activities. Man, however, adds greatly to the natural pollution of rivers by discharging sewage and industrial wastes into them, and to their turbidity by agricultural practices which cause or promote erosion. Man may modify these additions to natural pollution and turbidity by treating sewage and wastes before discharging them into rivers, and by checking erosion by more conservative agricultural practices.

Runoff a Residual of Precipitation. The runoff from the land is the residual from precipitation after a large part of such precipitation has been returned to the atmosphere by evaporation and transpiration. In regions that have 25 inches or more of annual precipitation, the total of annual evaporation and transpiration from land surfaces and evaporation from inland water surfaces varies within comparatively narrow limits. As between evaporation and transpiration, it is difficult to state by which means a greater part of the water will be returned from the continents to the air. Evaporation from water surfaces is much greater than from land surfaces, and transpiration varies with different types of vegetation. The governing conditions are decidedly variable in different areas. The sums of the two quantities range, within the United States,[2] from an average of about 20 inches in depth in northern areas to about 30 inches in southern areas. These figures have been determined for drainage areas in the eastern humid states from the Canadian boundary to the Gulf of Mexico by subtracting the total measured runoff from the total measured precipitation over as long a series of years as records are available. Records covering long series of years are necessary in order to obtain a proper average over the whole period which will largely eliminate the error that otherwise would arise because of differences in initial and terminal stages of both surface and ground waters. Long-term records are also necessary to reduce the errors that might result from the great variations in annual values caused by the great yearly variations in several controlling conditions. The figures cannot be exact, no matter how long the records may be, because the total

[2] Bibliog. 1·17.

precipitation on the basin can never be known exactly, the total run-off is not always measured, and errors due to the fluctuations in surface and ground waters cannot be entirely eliminated. The differences will also vary somewhat because of variations in the times and intensities of precipitation from year to year and from basin to basin. In any event, a method is thus provided for estimating runoff from records of precipitation.

Although this method of estimating runoff can never take the place of actual runoff records, it is of value in estimating the water yield of those rivers or regions for which no long-time records of runoff are available. It will give fairly consistent average annual values and is safer in its application than the method of estimating runoff directly from rainfall by means of a coefficient or percentage of the precipitation. If, for example, the annual rainfall is 50 inches and the average annual losses by evaporation and transpiration are equivalent to 25 inches, the residual, 25 inches, which is the runoff, is 50 per cent of the precipitation; if the precipitation is 40 inches and the losses are 25 inches, the runoff is 38 per cent of the precipitation; or, if the rainfall is 30 inches with the same rate of losses, the runoff, 5 inches, is only 17 per cent of the precipitation. Generally, one will not be grossly in error in estimating average annual runoff by the method of differences, but he may often be seriously in error by using the method of percentages.

Neither of the two methods can be applied in regions where the precipitation is less than the normal rates of losses through evaporation and transpiration, that is, in regions where the precipitation is less than about 25 inches. In such regions, the amount of runoff is largely incidental and depends on the rate of melting of the snow and on the intensity of the rainfall. If such rates and intensities are low, there will be no runoff as all the water will be returned to the atmosphere by evaporation and transpiration. However, in seasons when the accumulated snow melts rapidly or in periods when the rainfall intensity exceeds the rate of infiltration, runoff will occur. It is a matter of record that runoff in such regions may vary in different years from minima of less than $\frac{1}{2}$ inch in average depth over the basin to 2 inches or more in years of unusually intense precipitation.

Climatic Variations. There is a widespread popular opinion that the climate is changing, and its truth or falsity is important as relating to the amount of water that comes to the earth from the atmosphere and is made available for use by man. If the precipitation is actually either increasing or decreasing, man's activities and the value of his hydraulic works may be affected. Statistical meteorological informa-

tion collected in many countries over periods of several decades shows
that climate varies widely. from year to year and over periods of years,
and that there have been years and series of years of high precipitation and corresponding years of low precipitation; that some winters
have been colder and others warmer than the average; that there have
been hot summers and cool summers; and that severe storms have
occurred at uncertain and unpredictable intervals of time. These
facts, which are commonly recognized, serve to explain in part the
origin of the widespread belief that the climate is changing. The belief is also probably explained in part by the difference in human impressions as between youth and maturity and by the human tendency
to remember most clearly the unusual events of a lifetime.

The history of the earth as recorded in the rocks and unconsolidated
strata and interpreted by geologists tells of great changes in climate
that have resulted in a succession of ice ages, the cause of which has
not yet been acceptably explained, when the polar icecap has extended
into regions that now have temperate climates, and in alternating
ages of greater heat when animal and vegetable life that is now found
in temperate or even torrid climates has extended northward to sub-
polar and polar regions. It cannot safely be assumed that such
swings in climate have come to an abrupt end and that the world
climates of today will continue indefinitely. Rather it must be assumed that swings in climate, perhaps of less and perhaps of even
greater amplitude than those represented by the geologic ice ages, are
still taking place. If this assumption is valid, at what point in one
of these swings is the world of today? Is it moving toward an age
of greater or of less heat? Of greater or less precipitation? Statistical records are too short to answer these questions with certainty, but
they furnish some clues.

A recent report by Francois E. Matthes [3] relates to the advance and
recession of glaciers. This report sets forth the conclusions that many
small glaciers of western United States, Europe, and Iceland are not
remnants of much larger glaciers that have persisted since the last ice
age; that all those glaciers, except perhaps a few of the largest, disappeared within a period of 6,000 years following that ice age during
which the climate in the western United States and presumably in
other parts of the northern hemisphere was much warmer and drier
than at present; that within the last 4,000 years the climate in those
regions has been cooler and moister than in the preceding 6,000 years;
that within the last 4,000 years all or nearly all of the small glaciers

[3] Bibliog. 1·1.

of western United States, Iceland, and parts of Europe have been formed; that there have been several advances and recessions of these glaciers, the last advance having ended about 1850; and that since that date there has been a period of 90 years in which somewhat higher temperatures have caused a gradual recession of the glaciers that appears to mark a minor fluctuation in the "little ice age" within which we are now living. The records reported by Matthes of glacial activities in this country, Europe, and Iceland indicate by the recent recessions of the glaciers that the climates of those regions during the last 90 years have been somewhat warmer than they were prior to 1850.

The United States Weather Bureau has shown by a statistical study [4] made by J. B. Kincer, using 20-year moving averages, that an upward swing in temperature has been in progress for more than half a century. S. T. Harding [5] has furnished corroborative evidence of climatic swings by a study of the lake levels in the Great Basin area. W. G. Hoyt,[6] using 10-year progressive averages, has studied long-time Weather Bureau records and has reported differences in trends in precipitation in different parts of the United States. Knapp, Kennedy, and Crawford [7] have furnished other information as to swings in the amounts of precipitation. T. C. Main,[8] using 20-year progressive averages, has studied trends in annual temperature in Alberta and Saskatchewan. Prof. A. E. Douglass [9] has studied the rings of the trees of arid and semiarid southwestern United States. By means of overlaps and the identification of peculiar sequences of rings within the overlaps, he has succeeded in producing a chronology of tree growth in that region that extends back for nearly or quite 1,000 years. This chronology indicates series of drought years and others of more than normal precipitation. It discloses many consecutive years that seem to have been much drier than any that have been observed since the Spanish missionaries went into that country more than 400 years ago. It indicates relatively long-time swings in precipitation such as are shown by the fluctuations in lake levels and the advance and retreat of glaciers. The evidence of tree rings [10] is, perhaps, not as definite as that afforded in other ways because other factors than the annual precipitation may affect the growth of trees, and there are differences in the rings of trees that grow in humid countries where the roots reach the water table. However, it tends to corroborate other evidences of long-time swings in climate.

4 Bibliog. 1·2.   6 Bibliog. 1·4.   8 Bibliog. 1·5.
5 Bibliog. 1·3.   7 Bibliog. 1·7, 8, 9.   9 Bibliog. 1·23.
10 Jessup's statement re precipitation and tree growth in Bibliog. 2·28, pp. 10–13.

Hugh M. Raup [11] has studied the possible evidence of climatic changes in New England and New York, including the pre-colonial forests, the zoological evidence, evidence afforded by coastal subsidence, and the changes in forest types, in an attempt to ascertain, if possible, whether climatic changes have recently taken place or are now in progress. He includes also evidence obtained in Greenland. He concludes that in those regions there have been positive swings in climate within the last thousand years.

The evidence to which reference has been made is cumulative and seems to indicate that the kinds of changes or swings in climate that have occurred in the past may still be in progress. It is probable that swings in climate have always moved slowly and gradually over periods of centuries and that the world is now, as always, within some phase of a slow-moving swing. It appears, therefore, that there still are changes or swings in climate but that the rates of change are so small that many years, even centuries, are needed to produce results that are of sufficient magnitude to affect greatly the problems related to the available supply of water or man's use of it. The progressively higher temperatures of the last 90 years cause greater evaporation and transpiration and, therefore, less runoff from the same precipitation. The decrease in rainfall that has accompanied the higher temperatures, especially during the last decade, has already depleted the runoff to a notable extent in some sections of the United States.

BIBLIOGRAPHY 1

1. F. E. Matthes, Report of Committee on Glaciers, *Trans. A. G. U.,* 1940, Part II, pp. 396–406.
2. J. B. Kincer, Is Our Climate Changing? A Study of Long-Time Temperature Trends, *Monthly Weather Review,* September 1933, pp. 251–259.
3. S. T. Harding, Changes in Lake Levels in the Great Basin Area, *Civil Engineering,* Vol. 5, No. 2, pp. 87–90 (February 1935).
4. W. G. Hoyt, Studies of Relations of Rainfall and Runoff in the United States, *U.S.G.S. Water Supply Paper* 772.
5. T. C. Main, Water Conservation in the Prairie Provinces, *Journal Eng. Inst. Canada,* Vol. 18, pp. 212–218 (1935).
6. H. M. Raup, Recent Changes in Climate and Vegetation in Southern New England and Adjacent New York, *Journal Arnold Arboretum,* Vol. XVIII, No. 2, pp. 79–117 (April 1937).
7. G. S. Knapp, Water Resources of the Mid-Continent Area, *Civil Engineering,* Vol. 10, No. 10, pp. 653–655 (October 1940).
8. R. E. Kennedy, Weather Cycles—Again? *Civil Engineering,* Vol. 11, No. 1, pp. 45–46 (January 1941).

[11] Bibliog. 1·6.

9. L. C. CRAWFORD, Trend in Rainfall Records Confirmed, *Civil Engineering*, Vol. 11, No. 1, p. 45 (January 1941).

10. J. C. ALTER, The Mountain Snow Survey: Its Genesis, Exodus and Revelation, *Trans. A. G. U.*, 1940, Part III, pp. 892–900.

11. MERRILL BERNARD, Weather Bureau's Mountain Snowfall Work, *Civil Engineering*, Vol. 9, No. 5, pp. 173–175 (March 1939).

12. Symposium, Internat. Assoc. of Scientific Hydrology, *Bulletin* 23, Trans. Internat. Comm. of Snow and Glaciers, at 6th Gen. Assem. at Edinburgh, Sept. 14–16, 1936.

13. R. K. LINSLEY, Extending the Forecasts of Temperature for the Prediction of Stream-Flow from Snow-Melt, *Trans. A. G. U.*, 1941, Part III, pp. 722–726.

14. C. S. JARVIS, Floods in the United States; Magnitude and Frequency, *U.S.G.S. Water Supply Paper* 771.

15. C. S. JARVIS, Flood Stage Records of the River Nile, *Trans. Am. Soc. C. E.*, Vol. 101, pp. 1012–1071.

16. Symposium, Evaporation from Water Surfaces, *Trans. Am. Soc. C. E.*, Vol. 99, pp. 671–747.

17. G. R. WILLIAMS, Natural Water Losses in Selected Drainage Basins, *U.S.G.S. Water Supply Paper* 846.

18. J. W. MANGAN, Natural Water Losses from Pennsylvania Drainage Basins, Dept. of Forests and Waters, Commonwealth of Penna.

19. WILLIAMS and CRAWFORD, Maximum Discharges at Stream-Measurement Stations, *U.S.G.S. Water Supply Paper* 847.

20. H. V. SVERDRUP, The Unity of the Sciences of the Sea, *Sigma Xi Quarterly*, Vol. 28, p. 105 (Autumn 1940).

21. C. F. MERRIAM, Long-Term Constancy of Rainfall, *Trans. A. G. U.*, 1941, Part III, pp. 703–708.

22. THORNTHWAITE and HOLZMAN, A New Interpretation of the Hydrologic Cycle, *Trans. A. G. U.*, 1938, Part II, pp. 595–598.

23. A. E. DOUGLASS, Climatic Cycles and Tree Growth, Carnegie Inst. of Washington.

CHAPTER 2

GROUND WATER

General Principles. Ground water, as defined by geologists and engineers, comprises only that portion of the water in the ground which lies within the zone of saturation or below the water table.[1] It does not include the suspended water which is held in the ground above that zone but does include the water which lies below a perched water table. Water above the zone of saturation and near the ground surface is of major importance in connection with agriculture because of its relation to plant growth. Much of this water, of course, is utilized and transpired by vegetation and is thus returned to the atmosphere without penetrating deeply below the surface or becoming a part of the body of ground water. Not all water, therefore, that enters the ground becomes ground water, since only a part, and in some places only a minor part, reaches the zone of saturation.

Two general conditions of ground-water occurrence are recognized: (1) water table or unconfined conditions in which the water is under atmospheric pressure, and (2) artesian or confined conditions in which the water is under pressure produced by an overlying impervious confining layer. In many areas following heavy rain or in the spring of the year a *perched water table* may exist above the main water table. Such a condition, which is generally temporary, is produced by the presence of relatively impervious layers above the water table.

Ground water, like surface water, flows as a result of differences of pressure; if the surface is not confined, the difference in pressure is the result of surface slope; without slope (or differences of pressure), neither ground water nor surface water can have lateral motion. As applied to surface water, slope relates to the free water surface; as applied to ground water, it relates either to the water table (surface of the zone of saturation) or to the piezometric surface (the surface to which the confined water rises in open wells). The movement of either surface water or ground water tends to be in the direction of the greatest slope. The velocity of flowing surface water is determined by the steepness of the slope, the quantity of water, the size and shape

---

[1] Bibliog. 2·1.

of the channel, and the friction on bed and banks. For any slope, the velocity increases with the mean depth and with the quantity of water. Similarly, the velocity of flowing ground water is dependent upon the steepness of the slope and the size, number, and nature of the subsurface interstices through which the water passes, which are determined by the porosity, permeability, structure, and solubility of the contiguous earth and rock. Because of the much smaller and more tortuous channels and the resultant greater frictional resistance to flow in the ground than in surface streams, the rate of movement of ground waters is very small as compared with the velocities of surface waters actuated by slopes of the same steepness. Ground-water velocities are normally of the order of tens of feet a day rather than several feet per second, as with surface water. Large quantities of water, however, may move through the ground when the aggregate cross section of the subsurface openings through which the water flows is great.

The ground has capacity for storing water as well as for allowing flow through it, and commonly the two capacities are combined; that is, the waters stored in the ground generally have sloping water tables or piezometric surfaces and so are moving slowly through the storage basins in the directions of the slopes. Such flow is generally laminar; that is, each particle of water tends to move in a straight line, which is parallel to the directions of movement of adjacent particles. The storage capacities of many ground-water basins or reservoirs are very great, but none is unlimited. The usable storage capacity of any such reservoir is its gross capacity less the volume therein of solids, such as rock, gravel, sand, and finer particles, and less the capacity represented by the water held by capillary and molecular forces within the pores of and attached to the solids from which water may be withdrawn. The effective storage capacity of a ground-water reservoir is therefore only a small part of its gross capacity. Its usable capacity is limited also to the amount of recharge. If the average rate of withdrawal from it consistently exceeds the average rate of recharge, depletion of the supply of stored water ensues and its complete exhaustion will follow if such withdrawal is continued indefinitely.

Interrelation of Ground and Surface Waters. The interchange between the water in the ground and the water in surface streams,[2] at least as it affects the medium and low flow of rivers, relates to ground water, that is, to water within the zone of saturation. Ground water may reach the surface either naturally, by discharge through springs [3] and seeps [4] and by capillarity into the root-zone of plants, thence by

[2] Bibliog. 2·14.   [4] Bibliog. 2·8.
[3] Bibliog. 2·15, 17.

transpiration into the atmosphere, or artificially, by withdrawal from wells. The water that flows naturally in surface streams at low and medium stages is derived principally from springs and seeps. As the stage of a stream declines, the discharge-time graph flattens; that is, the rate of lowering decreases while the discharge progressively decreases, approaching zero as its limit. The discharge reaches that limit only when the ground water from which it is derived reaches the level of the lowest thread of the stream. Any discharge-time graph of a natural surface stream shows this trend during periods of drought. The lower the ground water at the beginning of a drought, the lower will be the rates of discharge as the drought progresses; an initially low stage of ground water will inevitably lead to lower discharges as the drought continues.

During periods of heavy rain, much water may pass into the ground, move for short distances through it, and enter surface streams without reaching the zone of saturation and becoming a part of the body of ground water.[5] Flood flows include, therefore, water that flows over the surface of the ground, water that passes through the upper layers of the ground without reaching the zone of saturation, and, finally, water that comes from springs and seeps that are fed from the zone of saturation. The water that flows through the shallow ground channels (subsurface storm flow or perched water effluent) at times apparently does not lose the essential characteristics of surface water, either as to its relatively rapid concentration in surface streams or as to its chemical quality. Most of the water of a stream in flood comes to the channel over the surface of the ground or through shallow subsurface channels, and but little comes from the zone of saturation. At high stages of all rivers and at all stages in some rivers or parts of rivers, the flow of ground water may be reversed and, instead of a discharge of ground water into the stream (typical of humid regions), water may be discharged from the stream into the ground. The slope of the ground water is then downward away from the stream, being opposite to the usual slope, which at medium and low stages in humid regions is downward toward the stream. In intermediate stages between those of floods and droughts, the ratio of surface water to ground water decreases as the stage declines, becoming zero when all the water that has entered the stream over the surface or through shallow subsurface channels has flowed away.

Operators of hydraulic works that depend on river flow are, therefore, interested in ground-water stages within the basin, especially if

[5] Bibliog. 2·39, 40.

the amount of available storage in surface reservoirs is small and reliance must rest principally on natural flow. Experience has shown that, as available supplies of water are becoming more completely utilized, records of the fluctuations of ground-water stages are in ever-increasing demand.

The effect of ground-water flow on the maintenance of river flow varies with the geologic characteristics, vegetal cover, slopes, and agricultural activities of the basin. Geologic formations with open, porous surfaces and subsoils as well as large bodies of sand, gravel, or porous or cavernous rock, generally sandstone or limestone, will absorb water freely, store it in considerable quantities, and release it gradually as river stages decline. Geologic formations consisting of clays and other tight soils absorb and yield water slowly even though a large quantity of water may be held in the ground, with steep ground-water slopes. Between the extremes of open gravels or sands and tight clays, all types and combinations of soil and substrata occur, each of which has its own peculiar capacity to receive and discharge water.

Recharge, Discharge, Depletion, and Safe Yield. Ground water, like surface water, is derived primarily from precipitation. It is limited in quantity by precipitation both as to amount and as to the nature of its occurrence. The quantity of water that enters the ground affects the amount that reaches the zone of saturation and thus becomes available for withdrawal and use. No water will reach the water table and enter the zone of saturation until no more can be held in the ground above that zone, and vegetation will take a heavy toll from such water during the growing season. After a period of drought, there must be several heavy rains before any water will reach the water table. The runoff in surface streams is the residue of precipitation that is left after evaporation and transpiration have returned to the air all that the conditions of the time and place have permitted; similarly, ground water is the residue left from the water of infiltration after vegetation has taken all that it can use and the soil water deficiency has been satisfied.

The natural recharge of water into a ground-water basin takes place partly by downward percolation of water that has been precipitated on the overlying surface as rain or snow, partly by lateral and downward movement from surface streams and other bodies of water, from the edges of which the ground-water table slopes downward away from the stream, and partly by lateral movement from varying distances as a result of artesian pressure or of slope of the ground-water table. The relative amounts of recharge from these three sources vary with differences in the geologic structure, nature of the soil and subsoil, vegetal cover, and the works of man. In general, probably the greatest proportionate amounts reach the ground water as a result of direct downward percolation from the surface. This is not the situation, however, in all sections, and especially is it not true in the recharge of artesian basins from the surfaces that lie directly over them. The recharge may be artificially increased by spreading water over the surface of the ground, as in irrigation, by spreading water over gravel beds, as is done in southern California, by promoting in other ways the infiltration of surface water into the ground, or by the artificial withdrawal of ground water, as in connection with municipal supplies, thereby creating capacity in the ground to receive and absorb more water, which may be supplied either naturally or artificially.

The discharge of ground water takes place naturally through springs and seeps. It may take place artificially through flowing (artesian) wells, by pumping from nonflowing wells, or by lowering the points of ground-water discharge as would result, for example, from dropping the levels of surface streams into which the discharge occurs or from the construction of drainage channels and ditches. Neither recharge nor discharge is definitely limited to natural amounts, and, although the augmentation of either may tend to increase the other, such increase is relatively small and commonly inconsequential except in connection with irrigation and water spreading for the purpose of increasing infiltration.

Withdrawal of water from the ground always produces a local lowering of the water table or a reduction of the pressure in an artesian basin, and the resulting effect varies with the rate of withdrawal. In many areas of heavy draft, the lowering, which may already have been great, will continue as long as the heavy draft continues. Over broad regions, ground waters probably have not been greatly lowered or depleted by man's activities. This is indicated by the fact that the low water discharges of rivers have in general not decreased materially since the time of the earliest records of stream flow. Meinzer's discussion of McGee's report [6] is of interest in this connection. The systematic records of the fluctuations of water level in several thousand wells distributed unevenly through most of the states now collected and published by the Geological Survey will not only throw light on the fluctuations of the ground water in many sections but in time will also give information with respect to a progressive or permanent lowering of ground water, if such is taking place as a result of man's activities or from other causes.

[6] Bibliog. 2·11, 12.

The depletion of ground water caused by man's activities is ordinarily strictly local as a result of local drafts on the ground-water supply. In some sections, the depletion is extensive and serious, but from the information available at this time generalizations are not warranted and may be greatly in error.

The continuous yield that can be relied upon limits stable development in all activities that depend on ground water, and information concerning its amounts and fluctuations is becoming increasingly important as the demands for ground water increase. Because the uses of ground water may also be served by surface water, although in some instances at greater cost and less efficiently and satisfactorily, the safe yield of ground water is closely related to the use of the water of rivers.

Vegetation may affect the quantities and stages of ground water in several ways and consequently has a more or less definite bearing on the flow of rivers. Bare ground from which water flows quickly contributes to streams a maximum proportion of the water of precipitation, since it offers a minimum opportunity for evaporation and infiltration and none at all for transpiration. By the accumulation of vegetal matter on the ground and by breaking the ground surface and the shallow soil with roots, vegetation improves the opportunity for infiltration, thereby tending to increase the amount of ground water. On the other hand, vegetation utilizes great quantities of water from the ground which is lost through transpiration in the process of plant growth. Various kinds of vegetation differ in the amounts of water transpired as well as in the protection afforded to the ground surface from the effects of evaporation. The effects on ground water appear to vary, therefore, with different types of vegetation, as is evidenced, for example, by streams that have flowed perennially in forests and that become intermittent if the forest cover is changed to grass in fields or pastures.

The effects of vegetation on the quantity of water that reaches the ground-water table vary widely with the nature of the soil surface. If the soil is sandy, the effect will be at a minimum since a major part of the water of precipitation would enter the sandy soil even if there were no vegetation. With clayey soil, the effect will be at a maximum because, although the delay in runoff caused by vegetal matter and the opening of the ground by roots will increase the opportunity for infiltration, nevertheless a clayey soil under the best conditions of vegetation will not absorb as much water as a sandy soil under the poorest conditions. Between the extremes of clay and sand there are infinite varieties of conditions and infinite variations in infiltration. There appears, therefore, to be no definite rule regarding the effect of vegetation on ground water and the resulting low water discharges of surface streams.

There is a popular belief, which may be expressed in three parts, that vegetation tends, first, to increase total runoff, second, to decrease floods, and third, to increase low water discharges, all of which would mean higher ground-water stages and more ground water. The first part is certainly not in accordance with either theory or experimental results, and it is probable that the other two parts are not universally correct although doubtless true in some areas.

The safe yield of any ground-water basin is limited by its capacity to receive and retain water, by the amount of infiltrated water, and by the drafts made by growing vegetation on the water that, having entered the ground, is suspended in the upper layers or is en route to the zone of saturation. In arid and semiarid regions, the safe yield will be small because little water reaches the water table. In moister climates, the amount of ground water, along with the amount of surface water, will increase as the precipitation increases. The determination of safe yield of any ground-water basin that is to be utilized as a source of water supply is, therefore, important as a basis for safe planning.

Recovery and Use. Ground water, except as it comes to the surface in springs or becomes a part of the low flow of rivers or is utilized by growing vegetation, is recovered for man's use by means of wells or such modifications of them as underground galleries, sumps, or drains. The wells are widely distributed and vary greatly in their characteristics: in depth, from a few feet to 2,000 feet or more; in size, from 2 inches or less to several feet in diameter; in capacity, from a few gallons per day to several cubic feet per second; in equipment, from a bucket and rope to pumping plants of great power; and in type of construction, from dug wells, generally with brick, concrete, or stone masonry lining, including the many kinds of galleries, collecting basins and channels, to bored, driven, and drilled wells with or without metal casings. These variations are brought about by differences in the quantities of water needed in regions of different geologic and hydrologic characteristics. The depth of a well is determined by the distance below the surface of the ground of a satisfactory water-bearing stratum; the diameter, by the type of well and the quantity of water sought or obtainable; the capacity, in some places by the quantity of water needed and in others by the quantity of water obtainable, of which the limit may be set by the amount of recharge of the water-bearing stratum penetrated or by the rate at which water can enter the well from that stratum; and the type of construction and equipment, by the quantity of water to be taken and the height through which it is to be pumped.

Dug wells have been used throughout all historic time, and even now they are the most common of all types. They cannot be used, however, in connection with artesian supplies or, generally, with non-artesian supplies at depths that greatly exceed 50 feet. They are far more common in humid regions where water is obtainable at relatively shallow depths than in arid regions where water is likely to be found only at considerable depths. Other types of wells have been developed to meet conditions imposed by depth, strata to be penetrated, and the quantity and chemical quality of the water sought. A gallery may be used if the depth and nature of the water-bearing stratum permit and when large intake capacities are necessary because great quantities of water are needed, as for municipal or irrigation supplies. All wells should be so finished at the top that there will be no inflow from the surface of the ground because of the dangers that any water thus admitted will be polluted by pathogenic bacteria and that the well will become clogged by silt or other debris. Many wells must be so lined and finished at the bottom that water below the surface will enter only from certain geologic strata, and that as much water as possible will continue to enter without decrease as the result of clogging, at least up to the limit of probable needs. The wide variations in conditions produce many problems related to the construction of wells, many of which are described and discussed in the technical literature pertaining to ground water.[7]

Wells may be flowing or nonflowing. Nonflowing wells are better known than are flowing wells, because they are more common and more widely distributed throughout the country. They may be constructed and may be economically practicable where the water table is not too far below the ground surface and the water is not too highly mineralized. Flowing wells (Fig. 2) are possible only where the ground water is under such pressure that its piezometric surface is higher than the ground surface or, in other words, that the water will flow at ground surface from an open well that penetrates a water-bearing stratum underlying impervious confining strata. Artesian water occurs only in regions where water-bearing strata are confined by relatively impermeable overlying strata, with intake areas at sufficiently high elevations to produce enough pressure to force the water

[7] Bibliog. 2.

above the water table, or even above the ground surface through open wells. Such regions are widely distributed, but each is limited in extent and in its supply of water. There are many of them in the United States, and they are largely utilized as sources of water for domestic, municipal, industrial, and irrigation purposes. Whenever the discharge of water through the flowing wells in an area exceeds the recharge, the pressure decreases and the wells finally cease to flow.

Fig. 2. Flowing well in Roswell artesian basin, New Mexico; flow, 3,190 gallons a minute. Photograph by A. G. Fiedler.

This change has been experienced in many of the great artesian areas of the country, as in the Dakota Sandstone of North Dakota,[8] and the Roswell artesian basin in New Mexico.[9] In each of these regions, the wells were not capped for many years, but were allowed to flow freely and continuously. The resulting waste of water was doubtless largely responsible for the gradual reduction of the pressures and contraction in size of the flowing-well areas. As a result of these and similar experiences in other artesian basins, the capping of wells and the repair of well casings to prevent leakage[10] of water into overlying formations are now commonly required by state laws and enforced by state officials in order to prevent the waste of this valuable resource. In all artesian basins, wells are commonly pumped

[8] Bibliog. 2·36.   [10] Bibliog. 2·22.
[9] Bibliog. 2·33.

after they have ceased to flow, but, of course, at an increased cost of the water obtained.

Pumped wells exist in all parts of the country. Many of them, although of small capacity, adequately serve domestic and farm needs. It is estimated that nearly or quite 50 per cent of the people of the country, including a much higher proportion of the rural population, obtain water supplies for all purposes from the ground. Many villages, towns, small cities, and a few large cities depend, in part at least, on water pumped from wells for their public supplies, notably New York City in part, with its Long Island well fields,[11] Atlantic City, N. J.,[12] Memphis, Tenn., Miami, Fla., Savannah, Ga., Dayton, Ohio, and El Paso, Tex. Much agriculture by irrigation also is made practicable by the use of ground water from both pumped and flowing wells.[13]

The capacity of any well, large or small, to yield water is limited by the permeability of the water-bearing formation. Such capacity may sometimes be increased by deepening the well, but there is always a limit beyond which such capacity cannot be economically increased. This limit may be fixed by the water-bearing geologic stratum, which may not be water-bearing below some definite depth, either because of a change in the nature of the stratum itself or because of the normal tightening of the formations as the result of higher pressure caused by the increasing weight of overlying strata at greater depths. This limit may be fixed also by the economic height of pumping or by the chemical quality of the water, which may become more highly mineralized as it is drawn from greater depths.

As indicated in Chapters 1 and 3, ground waters are commonly more highly mineralized by dissolved matter than surface waters. This mineralization differs in kind and amount with the nature of the strata through which the water flows and the length of time the water has been in the ground. The chemical quality of the water of rivers, especially at medium and low stages, varies with the geologic characteristics of the basin and in degree of mineralization with the stages of the river, usually being most highly mineralized at the lowest stages.

Ground water is used not only for domestic and municipal supplies and for irrigation but also for industrial processes and for air conditioning. It is sought for industrial processes in which clear water is important, provided that the chemical quality is acceptable or can be made so by appropriate treatment, and provided, too, that the

[11] Bibliog. 2·37.   [13] Bibliog. 2·29.
[12] Bibliog. 2·34, 35.

water so obtained is cheaper and more satisfactory than a surface water supply that might be utilized after necessary control and treatment to remove color and turbidity and perhaps to improve chemical quality.

Ground water is more efficient than surface water for modern air conditioning because of its lower summer temperature. The rapid expansion of air conditioning by its application to hotels, office buildings, theaters, commercial and industrial establishments, apartment houses, and, most recently, to private dwellings is greatly increasing the drafts on ground-water sources of supply and threatens to bring about the eventual lowering of ground-water levels near large cities. To help in forestalling such a contingency, it is now required in some areas where ground-water levels are critically low because of over-development that the water pumped for cooling purposes from newly constructed wells be returned to the ground, generally to the same water-bearing stratum from which it was pumped. In such situations, the water, after passing through air-cooling pipes, is returned to the ground through recharge wells. After having been used for cooling purposes, the water may be several degrees higher in temperature than when it was pumped from the ground. The return to the water-bearing formations of large quantities of warmer water will eventually operate to increase to a slight extent the prevailing temperatures of the entire body of ground water in that formation.[14]

It appears, therefore, that man's use of ground waters may affect surface streams,[15] either increasing their flow by bringing to them greater quantities of water than would naturally reach them through springs and seeps or decreasing their flow by taking from their drainage basins water that would naturally reach them through underground channels.

Rights in Ground Water. The legal rights to the use of ground water [16] are important, but they are as yet neither well defined nor well established. The doctrine of the common law that the ownership of land extends indefinitely downward and entitles the owner to take whatever water he needs and can obtain from wells situated on his land without reference to the damage he may cause by lowering the water in his neighbor's well is still generally applied with respect to all uses of ground water in humid regions and with respect to small uses everywhere. There appears to be a need, especially in arid and semiarid regions, for some definition of the rights of priorities and for an administration [17] of the allocation of ground-water supplies

[14] Bibliog. 2·42.
[15] Bibliog. 2·30.
[16] Bibliog. 2·21, 22.
[17] Bibliog. 2·18.

among many users, similar perhaps to the administration of priorities that is applied to surface waters and which is discussed in Chapter 5. New Mexico [18] has already adopted a policy of appropriation of ground waters, and the Association of Western State Engineers has suggested a draft of a uniform law [19] relating to the acquirement and administration of rights in such waters in the western states. This important aspect of ground-water control and utilization, which is still in the early stages of development, does not fall within the scope of this book. It is presented and discussed in some of the reports and papers listed in the bibliography.

Investigations and Records. The intimate relation between stability of development and the proper use of ground water has made necessary the intensive and continuing study of the quantity, quality, and availability of such water. As with surface water, all studies of quantity of ground water are based on records of stages or levels and artesian pressures, which fluctuate naturally as the result of variations in climate and vegetation, and artificially as the result of man's withdrawal and use of ground water. Added to the fluctuations caused by the artificial removal of water from the ground, there are in most regions marked seasonal fluctuations which are the result of the same hydrologic conditions that essentially affect the fluctuations in stages of surface water, namely, precipitation, temperature, evaporation, and transpiration. These fluctuations, which occur in all sections of the country and which may not be related in any way to the use of water by man, are made evident by systematic records of ground-water levels and artesian pressures. In order to be of great value, such records must be made continuously or at reasonable intervals of time in widely distributed wells, many of which must be constructed solely for observational purposes. Frequently, abandoned wells, if properly situated, may be utilized as observation wells. Preferably, the wells so utilized should not be subjected to pumping, and if possible they should not be situated within the cones of depression of wells that are pumped. If wells used for observational purposes are pumped or are situated within the cones of depression of other wells, this complication must be taken into consideration; otherwise, recorded fluctuations may represent primarily variations in pumpage rates and not true changes in natural ground-water levels. If the water levels in the wells selected for observation fluctuate because of variations in barometric pressures or because of the influence of ocean tides, appropriate correction of the observed levels must be made. Obviously,

[18] Bibliog. 2·19.
[19] Bibliog. 2·20.

access to the wells must not be unduly difficult, and the observations at each well must relate to a fixed datum plane, which may be mean sea level or, commonly, an assumed local datum. The stability of the plane, of course, is obtained by proper use of a measuring or reference point directly over the well or a bench mark of permanent elevation.[20]

Records of stage are obtained by means of a water-stage recorder, properly housed (Fig. 3) and installed over the well, which yields

Fig. 3. Steel shelter over observation well, Westbury, L. I., N. Y. Note water-stage recorder.

continuous graphs, or by periodic observations made by means of a steel tape (Fig. 4) that is lowered from the reference point to the surface of the water in the well. Water-stage recorders utilized for recording ground-water levels generally have relatively large height or stage scales and relatively small time scales because of the slow changes in stage of ground water, except where the water table is within the reach of plant roots,[21] and many of them must be equipped with special floats designed for use in wells of small diameter. Figure 5 shows a typical recorder chart from an observation well. The steel

[20] Chapter 14.
[21] Bibliog. 2·6.

tape commonly used in this work is of ordinary design. Many different methods of measurement have been used, the most common of
which consists in chalking the lower few feet of the tape, which is
kept taut by a small weight on the lower end. When the bottom part

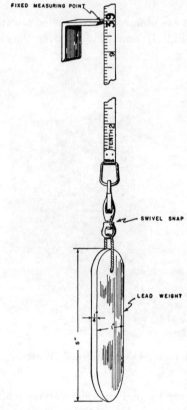

FIG. 4. Sketch showing measuring point, steel tape, swivel snap, and weight
used for measuring water levels by wetted-tape method. (Bibliog. 2·43.)

of the chalked portion of the tape is lowered into the water, a distinct
wetted line is produced which can be easily read to the nearest hundredth of a foot.

Water levels in wells which are subject to artesian pressures may
be measured by the same methods as ordinary ground-water wells
provided that the artesian pressure is insufficient to bring the water
to the ground surface. If the piezometric water surface is but a

short distance above the ground surface, the water levels may be measured by extending the well casing several feet above ground and installing a water-stage recorder thereon. Artesian wells under high pressure require the use of a pressure gage with which to measure pressures rather than water levels.

The recording of ground-water levels has not been standardized to as great an extent as the recording of river stages. Even in published records, ground-water levels are recorded in various ways. They

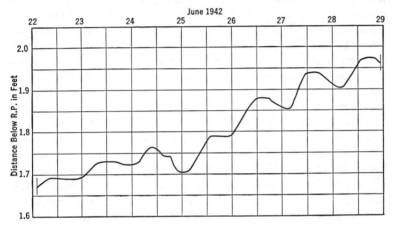

Fig. 5. Typical weekly recorder chart from observation well. Note stage scale used.

may be shown as distances below the measuring point, as elevations above sea level, or as elevations referred to an arbitrary or assumed datum. Records of ground-water levels are generally of greatest utility and value when plotted as a continuous graph for each year of record, thus facilitating studies and comparisons of the records for different years or different parts of the same year. Mean daily elevations are occasionally used, but under normal conditions one or two elevations daily, obtained either by direct observation or from the water-stage recorder charts, give sufficient data for the construction of a satisfactory graph.

Since the safe yield of a ground-water basin sets the limit of utilization in that basin and since continued draft in excess of recharge leads always to loss or to disastrous results, a prospective user of ground water for whatever purpose should seek to obtain reliable advice as to the amount of water that can be assured as a continuing supply. It is no longer sufficient merely to know that water can be obtained, but, since every supply of ground water is limited in quantity and is more or less highly mineralized, data on quantity and quality are indispensable.

Modern investigations of ground water, therefore, must yield not only records of ground-water levels but also specific and quantitative information that can be safely used as a basis for the design of water-supply systems, industrial plants, or irrigation developments with adequate assurance that the completed works will serve the purposes for which they were planned. A surface stream may be measured and its flow recorded with a high degree of accuracy, but the recharge of a ground-water basin cannot be directly measured, and the best determination possible can never be nearly as accurate as the record of flow of a surface stream. However, one or more of the methods of approximate determinations of recharge [22] may be applied in any investigation to determine the safe yield. These methods include the measurement of the precipitation on the surface of the ground-water basin as a basis for estimating the downward infiltration, the indirect measurement of the inflowing water by ascertaining the differences in flow of surface streams above and below intake areas, estimating the losses by transpiration, the measurement of the outflow through springs, the measurement of the accretions to surface streams within the region of discharge, and the running inventory of all inflow and outflow to obtain estimates of both recharge and discharge and to evaluate errors.

Investigations of the occurrence, recharge, safe yield, discharge, and the recovery and utilization of ground water are made in many parts of the country by the Geological Survey, generally in cooperation with states and municipalities with joint financing of each project by the parties so cooperating. The results of these investigations are prepared for publication by the geologists and engineers of the Survey and are published in part by the Survey in the series of *Water Supply Papers* and in part by the cooperating states. The work usually consists of local cooperative investigations that are continued for periods varying from one to five years or until approximate results are obtained. These investigations are then wholly abandoned, with no provision for the continuing of observations over a longer period in order to obtain information as the long-time fluctuations or trends. The strength of the plan consists in the pooling of funds and efforts, in the efficiency obtained by the utilization of men who have been trained in such work and who devote their full time and energies thereto, and

[22] Bibliog. 2·3, 6.

in the assurance afforded·by the proffer of local funds that only worthwhile and needed investigations will be undertaken.

Investigations with respect to ground water are made also by many consultants and agencies in all parts of the country, especially by state geologists, state engineers and similar state officials, and by officials of municipalities that use ground water for public supplies. Commonly, only part of the information thus obtained is published. Many such investigations are less likely to be continuing than similar programs carried on by the Geological Survey.

In addition to those specific cooperative investigations carried on by the Geological Survey, which are local in scope, the Survey conducts a broad program of systematic and continuing observations of fluctuations of ground-water levels and artesian pressures. This broad program is needed to obtain information relating to long-time fluctuations in ground-water levels and to permanent depletion of ground waters at any place or throughout the country, as well as to serve as a basis for evaluating the results of short-time investigations in terms of long-time trends in both ground- and surface-water supplies. The results of this program have been published annually since 1935 in the series of *Water Supply Papers*.[23]

BIBLIOGRAPHY 2

1. O. E. MEINZER, Outline of Ground-Water Hydrology, with Definitions, *U.S.G.S. Water Supply Paper* 494.
2. O. E. MEINZER, Plants as Indicators of Ground Water, *U.S.G.S. Water Supply Paper* 577.
3. O. E. MEINZER, Outline of Methods for Estimating Ground-Water Supplies, *U.S.G.S. Water Supply Paper* 638-C.
4. O. E. MEINZER, The Occurrence of Ground Water in the United States, with a Discussion of Principles, *U.S.G.S. Water Supply Paper* 489.
5. C. F. TOLMAN, *Ground Water,* McGraw-Hill Book Co., New York, 1937.
6. W. N. WHITE, A Method of Estimating Ground-Water Supplies Based on Discharge by Plants and Evaporation from Soil—Results of Investigations in Escalante Valley, Utah, *U.S.G.S. Water Supply Paper* 659-A.
7. L. K. WENZEL, The Thiem Method for Determining Permeability of Water-Bearing Materials and Its Application to the Determination of Specific Yield, Results of Investigations in the Platte River Valley, Nebr., *U.S.G.S. Water Supply Paper* 679-A.
8. MEINZER and others, The Channel-Storage Method of Determining Effluent Seepage, *Trans. A. G. U.,* 1936, Part II, pp. 415–418.
9. MEINZER and STEARNS, A Study of Ground Water in the Pomperaug Basin, Conn., with Special Reference to Intake and Discharge, *U.S.G.S. Water Supply Paper* 597-B.

[23] Bibliog. 2·32.

10. O. E. MEINZER, The Value of Geophysical Methods in Ground-Water Studies, *Trans. A. G. U.,* 1937, Part II, pp. 385–387.
11. W J McGEE, Subsoil Water of Central United States, *U. S. Department of Agriculture Yearbook for 1911,* pp. 479–490.
12. O. E. MEINZER, Review of the Work of W J McGee on Ground-Water Levels, *Trans. A. G. U.,* 1936, Part II, pp. 386–390.
13. Symposium, Fluctuations of Ground-Water Level, *Trans. A. G. U.,* 1936, Part II, pp. 337–390.
14. L. L. HARROLD, Relation of Stream-Flow to Ground-Water Levels, *Trans. A. G. U.,* 1934, Part II, pp. 414–416.
15. O. E. MEINZER, Large Springs in the United States, *U.S.G.S. Water Supply Paper* 557.
16. HEWETT and CRICKMAY, The Warm Springs of Georgia, Their Geologic Relations and Origin, a Summary Report, *U.S.G.S. Water Supply Paper* 819.
17. STEARNS, STEARNS, and WARING, Thermal Springs in the United States, *U.S.G.S. Water Supply Paper* 679-B.
18. HAROLD CONKLING, Administrative Control of Underground Water—Physical and Legal Aspects, *Trans. Am. Soc. C. E.,* Vol. 102, pp. 753–837.
19. New Mexico, Underground Waters—New Mexico Law, *The Future of the Great Plains,* Appendix 14, p. 185, 1936.
20. State Engineers, Uniform Law Suggested by a Committee of Western State Engineers, *The Future of the Great Plains,* Appendix 14, p. 190, 1936.
21. TOLMAN and STIPP, Analysis of Legal Concepts of Subflow and Percolating Waters, *Trans. Am. Soc. C. E.,* Vol. 106, pp. 882–933.
22. THOMPSON and FIEDLER, Some Problems Relating to Legal Control of Use of Ground Waters, *Journal American Water Works Association,* Vol. 30, No. 7, pp. 1049–1091 (July 1938).
23. A. G. FIEDLER, The Au Deep-Well Current Meter and Its Use in the Roswell Artesian Basin, New Mexico, *U.S.G.S. Water Supply Paper* 596-A.
24. A. J. ELLIS, The Divining Rod, a History of Water Witching, with a Bibliography, *U.S.G.S. Water Supply Paper* 416.
25. MORRIS MUSKAT, *The Flow of Homogeneous Fluids through Porous Media,* McGraw-Hill Book Co., New York, 1937.
26. O. E. MEINZER, Bibliography and Index of the Publications of the United States Geological Survey Relating to Ground Water, *U.S.G.S. Water Supply Paper* 427.
27. S. W. LOHMAN, Hydrology of the Wichita Area, *Civil Engineering,* Vol. 10, No. 11, p. 725 (November 1940).
28. PIPER, ROBINSON, and PARK, Geology and Ground-Water Resources of the Harney Basin, Oregon, *U.S.G.S. Water Supply Paper* 841.
29. CARL ROHWER, Putting down and Developing Wells for Irrigation, *U. S. Department of Agriculture Circular* 846.
30. C. V. THEIS, The Effect of a Well on the Flow of a Nearby Stream, *Trans. A. G. U.,* 1941, Part III, pp. 734-738.
31. MEINZER and WENZEL, Present Status of Our Knowledge regarding the Hydraulics of Ground Water, *Economic Geology,* Vol. 35, No. 8, pp. 915–941, abstracted in *Trans. A. G. U.,* 1940, Part II, pp. 648–649.
32. MEINZER and WENZEL, Water Levels and Artesian Pressures in Observational Wells in the United States, with Statements concerning Previous Work and

Results, *U.S.G.S. Water Supply Papers* **777** (1935), **817** (1936), **840** (1937), **845** (1938), **886** (1939), **906–911**, incl. (1940).

33. FIEDLER and NYE, Geology and Ground-Water Resources of the Roswell Artesian Basin, New Mexico, *U.S.G.S. Water Supply Paper* **639**.

34. D. G. THOMPSON, Ground-Water Supplies of the Atlantic City Region, *Bulletin* 30 of Dept. of Conservation and Development, New Jersey.

35. BARKSDALE, SUNDSTRUM, and BRUNSTEIN, Supplementary Report on the Ground-Water Supplies of the Atlantic City Region, *Special Report* 6 of State Water Policy Commission of New Jersey.

36. H. E. SIMPSON, Geology and Ground-Water Resources of North Dakota, *U.S.G.S. Water Supply Paper* **598**.

37. W. F. LAASE, The Present Condition of New York City's Long Island Sources of Water Supply, *Journal American Water Works Association,* Vol. 30, No. 2, pp. 298-301 (February 1938).

38. D. G. THOMPSON (Chairman), Reports of Committee on Underground Waters, *Trans. A. G. U.,* 1939, Part IV, pp. 545–555; 1940, Part II, pp. 433–439; 1941, Part III, pp. 948–950.

39. C. R. HURSH, Storm Water and Absorption, Committee Report on Absorption and Transpiration, *Trans. A. G. U.,* 1936, Part II, pp. 301-302.

40. HURSH and BRATER, Separating Storm-Hydrographs for Small Drainage Areas into Surface- and Subsurface-Flow, *Trans. A. G. U.,* 1941, Part III, pp. 863–870.

41. LIVINGSTON and LYNCH, Methods of Locating Salt-Water Leaks in Water Wells, *U.S.G.S. Water Supply Paper* **796-A**.

42. M. L. BRASHEARS, JR., Ground-Water Temperature on Long Island, New York, as Affected by Recharge of Warm Water, *Economic Geology,* Vol. XXXVI, No. 8 (December 1941).

43. LEGGETTE and others, Committee Report on Observation Wells; A Preliminary Manual of Methods, *U.S.G.S. Mimeographed Circular,* May 1935.

CHAPTER 3

QUALITY OF WATER

Variations in Quality. Chemically pure water does not occur in nature. Even rain water, which probably is the least impure, contains dust and chemical pollution from the air. Upon reaching the earth, the precipitated water begins to accumulate additional impurities, both soluble and insoluble. The longer the water is in contact with soluble matter on the ground or beneath the surface, the more of such matter is contained in solution; the more erodable the surface over which the water flows and the greater the volume of flow, the greater is the erosion and consequently the suspended load. Although spring water that is called pure may not contain pathogenic bacteria or deleterious chemicals, it may otherwise be chemically very impure and thus impaired for use in degrees that vary with the kind and amount of such impurities and the nature of the proposed use. Similarly, the water in rivers may be impaired for practical use by matter both in solution and in suspension in amounts that vary widely as the result of many conditions.

Natural water as used by man for many purposes is, therefore, either chemically or physically impure, or both. Such impurities affect its utility and the cost of its utilization. Those impurities which are not man-made are generally beyond his control, but they also may affect the economic utilization of water for many purposes. Knowledge of such natural impurities as well as of those related to man's activities is essential to the most efficient use of water. Man-made pollution occurs generally as sewage and industrial wastes, which are discussed in Chapter 6. Such pollution, which is within man's control, is most important because it may bring into the water pathogenic bacteria and stable or unstable chemical compounds, with the result that the polluted water may become offensive to sight and smell and its value for many uses may be affected. Sewage and industrial wastes may be treated to remove their dangerous or offensive elements before they are allowed to enter the streams, and the amounts of suspended matter that have been increased by the removal of forests or by improper agricultural practices may be checked or decreased.

34

The steps taken to prevent or decrease pollution or to improve quality are not accomplished without cost. As the resultant increase in value of the water or the value of by-products recovered by the reductions in the pollution may not be economically justifiable, treatment procedure must always be considered in terms of the cost and of the values that may thereby be obtained. Such costs and values vary widely with different kinds of pollution and with the uses that are proposed to be made of the water. There is no common criterion to be applied, no one rule to be followed, and no one result to be sought.

Dissolved Matter in Arid and Humid Regions. Water in arid and semiarid regions is generally more highly polluted by soluble matter than in humid regions. In arid and semiarid regions there has been much less washing and leaching of soluble matter from the soil than in humid regions and little or no vegetation to utilize soluble soil material in plant growth; consequently, there is much easily soluble chemical matter in the ground. In comparison with conditions in arid regions, water in humid regions has relatively little natural pollution. The lands in humid regions have been washed and leached throughout the ages and have always supported a more or less luxuriant vegetation that has taken much soluble matter from the soil. These soluble materials in the decaying vegetal matter on the ground surface are well situated for washing and leaching. The lands in such regions, therefore, have been more nearly exhausted of soluble matter than the lands in arid regions. In general, both the ground water and the surface water of humid regions are consequently of better chemical quality than the waters of arid regions.

The nature of the dissolved matter in the waters of any region is determined very largely by the geologic formations, since ground water and river water contain soluble matter derived from the geologic structures of the basin. The chemical characteristics of the water of a river draining a small basin of simple geologic structure will always be the same, inasmuch as the geologic nature of the formations does not change. The concentration of the dissolved matter, however, will vary widely, being greatest at low stages when all the river flow is derived from the ground water, having had long-continued contact with soluble materials, and being least at high stages when the greater part of the water has had much shorter contact with the soluble substances in the ground.

The waters of large rivers with many tributaries carry a great variety of chemical impurities. Such impurities vary with the changing proportions of the waters derived from the several tributary basins. These basins may have different geologic structures, and their runoff may fluctuate unevenly because of differences in precipitation over the subbasins. The waters of such rivers always reflect the nature of the geologic structures of their basins, but the mixtures and variations are much more complex than in rivers which drain small basins.

Suspended Matter in Hard-Rock and Soft-Rock Regions. Water is a great eroding and transporting agent. Rivers carry drift, litter, and dirt washed from the earth's surface and sand and silt eroded from various parts of their basins. Erosion is neither new nor caused solely by man's activities. It is "as old as the hills"; in fact, erosion has made the hills, by carving them from the lands that have been raised above the surface of the ocean, and it will not cease until the lands shall have been worn down to sea level. However, man's activities have expedited erosion in many places, and in some places the erosion has greatly reduced the value of the land for agriculture by removing the fertile top soils. Erosion has also affected adversely the river channels, which have been clogged and filled by the eroded materials carried into them.[1]

It is thus necessary to distinguish between the erosion that results from natural processes, which can neither be prevented nor greatly modified, and the erosion that results from the activities of man, which can be controlled or modified by him. It should be recognized that man will continue to use land for agricultural purposes and that, though such use will perhaps tend to expedite erosion, a reasonable balance must be reached between use and erosion that will prevent undue waste of the country's great natural resource in soils. Especially is this true of the soft-rock regions where the soils and subsoils are eroded most readily.

Although erosion is in progress everywhere, it is most active in regions of soft rocks, as is evidenced by the greater turbidity of rivers in such regions. In hard-rock regions, the streams are relatively clear and generally colorless; in soft-rock regions, the streams are turbid and are either yellow or brown, depending upon the color of the rocks from which the suspended matter has been derived. The variations in the amounts and nature of the suspended loads produce differences in river slopes, channels, valleys, and deltas. Rivers in hard-rock regions generally have solid banks and beds and small deltas; the St. Lawrence, Connecticut, Hudson, and Columbia Rivers may be cited as examples. Rivers in soft-rock regions have soft beds, caving

[1] Bibliog. 3·10.

banks, and large deltas, of which the Rio Grande and the Mississippi and Colorado Rivers are examples.

The differences both in suspended loads and in dissolved matter affect the utility of rivers from the standpoint of man by modifying the costs and details of construction work and of the treatment needed for their proper utilization. Such differences affect also the problems of measurement of the flowing water and the interpretation of the field observations into systematic and continuous records of discharge.

Relation to Agriculture in Arid Regions. The chemical matter carried in water may have great significance in irrigation.[2] Since all water contains dissolved matter which will accumulate in the soil if not carried away by outflowing water, drainage is intimately related to irrigation. The amount of dissolved matter carried away from an irrigated district must at least equal the amount of such matter brought into the district by the irrigating water; otherwise, the district is doomed to eventual ruin through the accumulation of excess salts or alkalies. Therefore, even with complete use, the total quantity of water brought into an irrigated district cannot be consumed by the growing crops since there must be sufficient return water to carry away the soluble salts that have been brought to the lands.

Many different kinds of salts are carried in irrigating waters, varying with the geologic characteristics of the drainage basins from which the water flows. Of these, sodium carbonate produces "black alkali"; all others produce "white alkali"; and all are injurious to growing crops to a greater or less degree. All these deposits may be reasonably controlled by drainage of such sort that the water table is kept at a greater distance below the surface than the height to which water will rise by capillarity, by such occasional washing of the surface as will dissolve and carry to the water table any alkali that may have accumulated as a residue from evaporation, and by the passage out of the irrigated district of the drainage or return water with its proper load of salts. Without these conditions, there will be an accumulation of salts on the surface that is sufficient to retard plant growth or an accumulation of salts in the ground which will ultimately be sufficiently great to destroy profitable agriculture, or a combination of these two conditions.

The more highly mineralized the irrigation water may be, the more highly impregnated with salts are the soils and the greater will be the quantity of water needed to wash the alkali from them. It follows that under these conditions the amount of water needed for irrigation

[2] Bibliog. 3·3.

will be substantially increased since the wash and drain waters are as necessary for successful irrigation as the water consumed in plant growth. In other words, the poorer the quality of the water, the greater the quantity needed for crops and the greater the danger of the deterioration of the irrigated lands by the accumulation of salts therein, and the more important becomes the efficient drainage of such lands in order to carry the salts away and to prevent water-logging and the deposition of alkali on the surface.

There are other forms of chemical pollution that have some local importance. For example, boron is present in such quantities in some irrigating waters in California that citrus trees are injured by an accumulation of boron in the leaves, which causes their premature dropping. In other sections of the country, selenium is carried by the water into the grasses and other forage crops in such amounts as to kill or impair the health of grazing stock. Waters that contain poisons are generally so rare as to have no wide significance or importance. Alkali, which in its various forms is widely distributed, causes one of the greatest problems in agriculture.

Relation to Industry. The fitness of water for process uses in industry relates largely to hardness, alkalinity, and corrosiveness, but in some instances its usefulness may also be affected by temperature, color, turbidity, or pollution by organic matter.[3]

Hardness, which is generally determined by the content of calcium and magnesium, is recognized as a major source of trouble in the use of water. It is commonly reduced or eliminated either by treatment of the water with lime (with or without soda ash) or by an exchange-silicate softener. By such treatment, water may be softened to any desired degree.

Alkalinity is determined by the amount of acid required for neutralization; it is generally expressed in terms of calcium carbonate, which is chemically equivalent to all the compounds that cause alkalinity.

Corrosiveness may be due to various causes. Water may contain free carbon dioxide in excess and may sometimes carry appreciable quantities of acid, or of salts such as magnesium chloride, which cause corrosive action. The treatment of corrosive water may be accurately adjusted to the cause of the corrosiveness.

Scale, including its formation, characteristics, prevention, and removal, is of major importance in many regions in connection with the operation of boilers, water pipes, and water containers. It is com-

[3] Bibliog. 3·6, 7, 8.

monly formed from hard water, and it may result from one or several different dissolved chemical compounds. The formation of scale may be avoided by removing the scale-forming constituents from the water, by treating the water with a hexametaphosphate (Calgon), or by some other preventive treatment.

Each industry has its specific problems relating to the quality of water, in addition to the general problems already mentioned. Canneries must consider the effects on the canned products of different chemicals in the water. Brewers and producers of carbonated beverages must have clear water, free from iron or chemicals that may affect flavor or keeping qualities. Manufacturers of ice must have colorless water of the same general qualities as a satisfactory municipal supply. Operators of laundries must have soft, clear water that is free from iron. Textile manufacturers require clear, soft water with other qualities that may vary with the kind of textiles produced.

Relation to Domestic Supplies. Water for domestic use should be free from pathogenic bacteria. If such bacteria are present in the supply, several possible courses of action are open. The source of supply may be changed; filtration may be resorted to in order to remove the bacteria, or sterilization by the addition of chlorine or other chemical to destroy them. As a last resort, the water may be boiled. Certain allowable limits on chemical impurities, such as lead, have been set. These important bacteriological and chemical aspects of water supply are closely related to public health.[4] The literature covering this subject is large and easily accessible to those who are interested.

Water for domestic supplies should be reasonably soft because of its effect on the consumption of soap. If the domestic supply is derived from a municipal supply, softness or other change in chemical quality may be obtained by general treatments of the municipal supply; if it comes from an individual or group source, such as an isolated or small-community well, the desired softness may be obtained by means of an appropriate water softener in each household.

If municipal supplies are used for both domestic and industrial purposes, obviously consideration must be given to both the industrial and the domestic needs.

Relation to Spas. There are many mineral springs in the country, that is, springs of which the water is valued because of its unusual mineral content. The waters of several of these springs were at one time widely advertised because of their supposed medicinal properties.

[4] Bibliog. 3·9.

Such advertising has now been stopped as a result of federal prosecutions under the Pure Food and Drugs Act on the ground that these waters did not possess the curative properties claimed for them. Many springs yield water that is radioactive in some degree, and this property has been believed by many to be valuable in the treatment of disease, a belief which has now been generally abandoned.

Several springs have been developed and are operated as spas, notably Poland Spring in Maine, Saratoga Springs in New York, French Lick Springs in Indiana, Virginia Hot Springs, and Arkansas Hot Springs. These spas and others are well patronized. Warm Springs of Georgia is operated as a spa, with special emphasis on the treatment of infantile paralysis. In this treatment, the use of weakened muscles is promoted by suitable exercise in warm water while the weight of the body is largely supported by the water.

Belief in valuable special therapeutic properties of the mineral matter dissolved in water has now been generally abandoned, inasmuch as it appears probable that the principal value of treatment at spas is derived from a supervised diet, exercise, and the drinking of liberal and scheduled quantities of water rather than from the effects of the dissolved minerals.

Relation to Stream Gaging. Substances which cause turbidity in water affect the collection of records of river discharge in at least two ways. First, current meters used in turbid waters must generally have pivot bearings rather than journal or ball bearings, because silt in journal or ball bearings affects the rating of a meter, and silt cannot be excluded from meter bearings that are operated at widely varying depths. The greater the depth of submergence in turbid water, the greater the certainty that silt will be forced into the bearings and that the meter rating will be changed by unknown amounts. Second, finely divided suspended matter affects the quantities of water as measured by current meter and therefore the accuracy of discharge records, since the discharge measured and recorded as water is in reality water plus silt, and no correction is commonly made for silt content. Under ordinary conditions, the error arising from this cause is not great since the silt load is generally less than 1 per cent by volume; however, the error is always of the same sign and thus is never compensating. Flood flows may contain as much as 10 per cent by weight or even more of silt, and, though under such conditions the recorded discharge should properly be corrected for the silt content of the water, no satisfactory method of applying such correction has yet been devised. Turbid water affects the measuring and recording of river discharge in other ways which are cited elsewhere in this book in connection with descriptions of the equipment and operation of gaging stations.

The quantity of silt carried in water is determined in terms of weight of dried materials. The engineer may wish to know how much space will be occupied by a specified weight of silt after having been deposited in a reservoir. The space to be occupied varies with the specific gravity of the deposited materials, with the length of time that has elapsed since deposition took place, and with the depth (and consequently weight) of the superimposed water. There is no definite general answer to such a question; only approximations are possible.

Drift, as distinguished from silt, may also affect current-meter work because its presence involves not only the possibility of damage to the meter by impact but also the danger of complete loss by entanglement in large pieces of drift. Fibrous drift may collect on the moving parts of the meter, thereby impeding its motion, and on the supporting line, thereby increasing the drag of the current, with a resultant misplacement of the meter during the periods of observation. The lodgment of drift in the control section for a gage may frequently disturb the stage-discharge relation at the gage and so lead to errors in the recorded flow.

Transportation and Deposition of Silt. One of the important natural functions of water relates to erosion and the transportation and deposition of the eroded materials. It is a continuous process, being responsible for land forms, for the water-borne fertile soils of valley bottoms, and for the deltas which form valuable agricultural areas. It is also responsible for the loss of valuable soils from cultivated areas, with a resultant decrease in productivity and therefore a decrease in the value of the land itself.

The natural laws governing erosion, transportation, and deposition are only partly known and to that extent are described in contemporary literature; in part these laws are unknown and are still the subject of research, and active investigations along these lines are now being carried on.

Density Currents and Stratification. The failure of water to mix readily, either in flowing streams or in reservoirs, has long been a matter of common observation and constitutes an interesting and important phenomenon with respect to the use of water. Its cause appears to relate, to some extent at least, to differences in density due to salts or other substances in solution, to silt in suspension that is so fine as to be almost in a colloidal state and so to settle very slowly, or to variations in temperature of different currents or strata of water.

The literature on this phase of hydrology appears to be extremely limited.

The principal phenomena that interest engineers appear to be the passage of water through reservoirs,[5] for example, Lake Mead and Elephant Butte Reservoir, and the stratification of water of different densities so that, in deep reservoirs at least, the water does not have the annual temperature inversion which has been generally assumed to cause such a thorough mixing that the outflowing water will have the same chemical quality as the average of the inflowing water. It is now found that this is not realized in all instances and that the quality of the water discharged may be either better or poorer than the average of the inflowing water.

The failure of waters of different densities to mix, therefore, may have a bearing on the rate of silting of reservoirs, on the design, location, and operation of reservoir outlets, and on the chemical quality of the water that may be withdrawn from storage reservoirs.

Investigations and Records. Investigations of the quality of water are made for various purposes and by many governmental organizations. Many cities make chemical and bacteriological examinations of the waters entering the municipal supply systems in order to determine the proper treatments, followed by supplementary examinations of the same qualities of the waters after treatment. Records of such observations are not generally published except perhaps in summaries. State and municipal public-health services also examine the waters used and proposed for use in public supplies. These results may or may not be published.

The Bureau of Plant Industry examines the chemical quality of waters with reference to their utility in agriculture and publishes the results, partly as summaries. The Soil Conservation Service examines waters with reference to erosion, transportation, and deposition, usually in connection with specific projects, and publishes the results. It also studies and reports on the natural laws related to these phases of soil erosion and on the instruments and methods to be used in observational work. For many years the Geological Survey, generally in cooperation with states and municipalities, has investigated and reported on the chemical quality of both surface and ground waters, with particular reference to their utility in industry and agriculture. Reports on these investigations and on general studies of the chemical qualities of the nation's water supplies are published in the series of *Water Supply Papers*.

[5] Bibliog. 3·13.

BIBLIOGRAPHY 3

1. COLLINS and HOWARD, Index of Analyses of Natural Waters in the United States, *U.S.G.S. Water Supply Paper* 659-C.
2. HERMAN STABLER, Some Stream Waters of the Western United States, *U.S.G.S. Water Supply Paper* 274.
3. C. S. SCOFIELD, Recent Studies in the Quality of Water for Irrigation, *Trans. A. G. U.*, 1938, Part II, p. 662.
4. C. S. SCOFIELD, Quality of Water in the Upper Rio Grande Basin, Nat. Res. Comm., *Regional Planning*, Part IV, Upper Rio Grande.
5. W. D. COLLINS, Temperature of Water Available for Industrial Use in the United States, *U.S.G.S. Water Supply Paper* 520-F.
6. COLLINS, LAMAR, and LOHR, The Industrial Utility of Public Water Supplies in the United States, *U.S.G.S. Water Supply Paper* 658.
7. W. D. COLLINS, Relations between Quality of Water and Industrial Development in the United States, *U.S.G.S. Water Supply Paper* 559.
8. W. D. COLLINS, Water for Industrial Purposes, *American City*, July, August, and September 1937.
9. J. H. GREGORY, Water Purification and Public Health, *Civil Engineering*, Vol. 7, No. 9, pp. 621–624 (Sepember 1937).
10. J. C. STEVENS, The Silt Problem, *Trans. Am. Soc. C. E.*, Vol. 101, pp. 207-246.
11. WILLIAMS and others, Selected Bibliography on Erosion and Silt Movement, *U.S.G.S. Water Supply Paper* 797.
12. O'BRIEN and CHERNO, Model Law for Motion of Salt Water through Fresh, *Trans. Am. Soc. C. E.*, Vol. 99, pp. 576–609.
13. GROVER and HOWARD, The Passage of Turbid Water through Lake Mead, *Trans. Am. Soc. C. E.*, Vol. 103, pp. 720–790.
14. AMERICAN WATER WORKS ASSOCIATION, *Manual of Water Quality and Treatment*, First Edition, 1940.

CHAPTER 4

PHYSICAL CONTROL OF RIVERS

Objectives. Two principal objectives are sought in the physical control of rivers: first, the prevention of loss of lives and damage to property by floods, and second, improvement in values by increasing the quantities of water available for municipal supplies, irrigation, generation of power, industrial processes, or navigation. Of these two objectives, the attainment of the former, which is the more spectacular, is generally accomplished by the use of governmental funds; [1] the attainment of the latter, which is the more common, is largely the result of private financing and initiative, although much improvement in river regimen in relation to utilization has been secured in recent years at governmental expense. Although these two objectives are not in themselves conflicting, the methods of operating storage reservoirs may, in many instances, put them into competition for reservoir capacity when such storage is planned both for flood control and for improvement in river regimen.

In considering the problems of flood control, it should be recognized that floods occur as natural phenomena, that the rivers make their channels for ordinary annual high water but not for the high floods which occur at long intervals of time, that flood plains are built by floods, that the occasional submergence of these plains is a natural and necessary phase of their building, that damage to man's property and hazard to his life result from his encroachment on the river channels and flood plains, and that, in attempting to control floods, whether by building hydraulic structures of any kind or by promoting selected vegetal growths, man is pitting his ability and strength against the powerful forces of nature. It may well be that the better course for him to follow in some river basins is to recognize the needs of the river for an adequate channel, perhaps in part over a flood plain, and to make his own activities conform to such needs.

Flood losses [2] are commonly prevented either by levees, planned to restrain the water from overflowing selected parts of flood plains, or

[1] Bibliog. 4·8; 5·5.
[2] Bibliog. 4·1.

by reservoirs designed to store part of the flood waters with a resulting decrease in flood stages and discharges. These two types of control have long been used and are of demonstrated and calculable value. A suggestion has recently been made to the effect that flood flows may be decreased and the regimen of rivers improved by controlling the vegetal cover of the drainage basins and by adopting better agricultural practices. This proposal is undemonstrated either as to quantitative results or as to the costs which must be incurred in attaining such results, and the values of the effects that may be so obtained have not been shown.

Storage of water may be employed to improve the regimen of flow by decreasing high stages and increasing low stages of rivers below the reservoirs, by changing the daily regimen of flow to meet the varying needs of water-power plants or other hydraulic structures, or, in extreme instances where there are great storage capacities in proportion to the total yields of water, by completely controlling the flow and so changing the regimen as to meet the most widely fluctuating daily or seasonal needs.

Reservoirs. Reservoirs are built and operated in order to change the regimen of rivers.[3] As already stated, they may serve either or both of two purposes: first, to control floods, and second, to improve the utility of a stream. These two purposes may be in competition with respect to the operation of reservoirs. Reservoirs for flood control should be so operated that the capacity required for storing flood water shall be available whenever needed; this objective can generally be accomplished by emptying or partly emptying the reservoir as soon as practicable after the flood passes. On the other hand, the greatest effectiveness of reservoirs for increasing the value of the stream for utilization is realized by keeping the reservoirs as nearly full as possible. There must thus be some compromise in operation between these two conflicting purposes if a reservoir is to perform both functions.

The storage of water in reservoirs decreases total runoff by increasing the area of water surface exposed to the air so that evaporation losses are increased. This effect increases as the surface area of the reservoir is increased and is relatively most important in broad shallow reservoirs, where the surface area is great in relation to the quantity of stored water. The limit is reached when the surface area is so great that the evaporation is equal to or exceeds the total runoff. This condition, which obtains at inland seas that have no outlets, such

[3] Bibliog. 4·6, 7.

as Great Salt Lake and all "sinks" in arid and semiarid regions, is possible only where the depth of annual evaporation greatly exceeds the depth of annual precipitation.

The effectiveness of a reservoir in controlling the regimen of a stream increases as the reservoir capacity is augmented and is always measured by the ratio of capacity to total runoff. A reservoir must generally be so designed and so situated that the quantity of inflow that is available for storage ordinarily equals or exceeds its capacity. Its effect on the regimen of flow in any part of the stream varies inversely with the distance from the reservoir because of the time of transit involved, because of natural losses, because of the fluctuations in flow of the intervening tributaries, and finally because of its decreasing relative effect as the flow of the stream is naturally augmented with increase in drainage area.

The feasibility of controlling flood flows by means of reservoirs depends on the availability of reservoir sites properly situated with respect to that part of the river basin where floods cause damage, on the cost both of the land within the reservoir area and of construction, and on the value of benefits resulting from the lowering of flood stages as measured by the decrease in damages to property and by the reduction in hazards to life.

The economic aspect of controlling rivers for utilization by means of reservoirs is largely affected by the availability of possible reservoir sites [4] where dams can be built at costs commensurate with the possible fillable storage capacities. Such sites are more likely to be found in the upper reaches of a river system than farther downstream, although there are important exceptions to this general rule. The use of reservoirs for augmenting utilization values has, therefore, very definite limitations which vary widely in different river basins, with respect to the value of the water in its uses, the cost of constructing the dam and control works, and the value of the land within the reservoir areas.

Natural lakes commonly furnish excellent sites for storage reservoirs either for flood control or for improving the regimen for utilization because relatively low dams may create great storage capacities. For this reason, glaciated regions are more likely to offer good opportunities for river control by reservoirs than nonglaciated regions. The river systems of New England, New York, Michigan, Wisconsin, and Minnesota afford many examples of the successful use of reservoirs for regulating river discharge, especially in connection with the generation of hydroelectric power.

[4] Bibliog. 4·4.

Levees. Levees are used to protect flood plains from overflow during floods rather than to control the regimen of rivers. Their effects are the reverse of those produced by reservoirs. They decrease the storage of water by eliminating the river's natural overflow basins on the flood plains; they expedite runoff and tend to increase its total amount by decreasing the opportunities for evaporation; they contract the channel and so increase flood stages within, above, and below the contracted channels. The more completely the natural basins on the flood plains of a river are cut off by levees, the higher will be the stages in the river channel. The limit of protection will be reached if and when the levees are raised to the height of economic building, either because of the cost in relation to the values protected by them, or because of the limit of capacity of the underlying stratum, generally alluvium, to sustain the weight of the materials of which the levees are constructed. As the levees are increased in height to restrain the flood stages which they tend to augment, breaks in them become more and more disastrous.

Levees serve in another way to increase flood stages; by preventing overflow of flood plains they prevent deposition of silt thereon and cause the silt which would naturally be so deposited to be carried to unprotected parts of the flood plains and to the outer edge of the delta, thus expediting the lengthening of the river and causing increased stages, especially in the delta region, because of the greater elevation of river surface needed to carry the water over the increased length of the river.

Reservoirs vs. Levees. Flood control, whether by reducing the flow by storing water in reservoirs or by protecting flood plains from overflow, always constitutes a local problem of which there is no general solution. On some rivers, levees may serve best; on others, reservoirs; and on still others, combinations of reservoirs and levees may give the most satisfactory control. Each situation must be studied with reference to practicable reservoir sites, costs of reservoirs and levees, costs of lands to be flooded by the reservoirs, and the value of the results that can be obtained by appropriate hydraulic structures.

Many localities in this country suffer from flood damages, and it is probable that levees serve best for protecting the majority of such places. The Mississippi and its tributaries in their lower courses offer stupendous problems in river control. Although reservoirs may have some small possible effect in reducing flood heights in the Mississippi valley, levees are and must always remain the principal means of protection.[5] Opportunities for reservoir construction are relatively

[5] Bibliog. 4·6.

few in the region from which the flood waters are derived (the eastern and southern tributaries, especially the Ohio) and in the Mississippi valley below the mouth of the Ohio; furthermore, the distances from practicable reservoir sites to the basins to be protected are so great as to make effective timing of releases of water practically impossible, and, perhaps most important of all, the quantities of water to be dealt with are entirely too great to be susceptible of reservoir control.

By-passes, Cutoffs, and Fuseplugs. Among the auxiliary works that may be adopted for local control of floods are three, at least, for the lowering of stages—by-passes, cutoffs, and fuseplugs—all of which have been used in the Mississippi valley.

By-passes may be made of practicable utility by diverting water through old river channels across a delta, thereby relieving the present channel of part of the flood waters. New Orleans is protected from flood dangers in part by two by-passes to the Gulf of Mexico which take large quantities of the flood waters away from the river as it flows past the city—the Atchafalaya River, which takes to the Gulf up to 500,000 second-feet of the Mississippi flood waters, and the Bonnet Carre Spillway, which diverts up to 250,000 second-feet into Lake Pontchartrain, whence it passes to the Gulf.

Cutoffs across sharp bends in the river are resorted to for shortening the channel, thereby increasing surface slopes and resulting velocities, and decreasing stages in the river above the cutoffs.

The danger of flooding certain parts of the Mississippi valley is averted during floods which threaten to exceed the capacity of the leveed channel by building fuseplugs; that is, certain places in the levees are deliberately made weaker than the standard section, thereby predetermining that the breaks in the levees, should they occur, shall be so situated as to cause minimum damage.

Vegetation. Although vegetation promotes infiltration and therefore probably tends to decrease high flows and increase low flows of rivers, it cannot, even under the most favorable conditions, prevent floods.[6] Great floods occurred before man disturbed the forests or tilled the land, and great floods would recur even if the land were completely covered with forests and with other protective vegetation of the most effective types.

The major causes of fluctuations in rivers are the variations in precipitation and temperature, which forests do not affect sufficiently to have any bearing on the prevention of floods. Between the precipitation in the form of rain or the melting of snow and the appearance of

[6] Bibliog. 4·3, 5; 18·4.

the water in the rivers, there are interjected various and varying modifying influences, notably frozen or open ground, the texture of surface soils, slopes, stages of ground water, vegetation, and seasonal rates of transpiration. Among the many and diverse factors effective within the varied areas that constitute a river basin, vegetation probably plays a minor part as a modifying influence with respect to stream flow.

To be of value, any control of rivers for preventing floods or increasing utility must be effective at the particular times when floods occur or when water is needed for use, and, whatever other value vegetation may have, it does not afford that type of selective control. The effects of vegetation are not quickly changed, and they cannot be relied upon to bring about seasonal or other important control in the regimen of streams.

Since information relating to the quantitative effects of vegetation on river discharge is lacking, it is quite impossible to say by what amounts hydraulic works such as dams and levees for controlling river flow may be reduced in height because of improvements in regimen effected by changes in vegetation. There is thus no basis upon which to evaluate the results caused by changes in vegetation as an integral part of a program of river control.

Interbasin Diversions. Transmountain or interbasin diversions offer limited opportunities for a certain type of river control. They are seldom suggested for flood protection, although it has been proposed that the floods of Kootenai River above Kootenai Lake in the leveed agricultural valley in Idaho and British Columbia might be reduced by diverting a part of the flood waters of the upper Kootenai River through a dividing mountain range and causing such water to enter Kootenai Lake through another tributary. Opportunities for employing this type of flood protection, however, are seldom found.

The most common reason for interbasin diversions is the greater value of water for agricultural uses in one basin than in another. Several diversions have been made from the west slope to the east slope of the Rocky Mountains. These diversions are generally small, however, as they are made at high altitudes where the drainage basins are so small that relatively little water is available, the season of operation is short, and there are few opportunities for storage above the points of diversion. The largest diversion of this type yet to be undertaken is to be made through the Grand Lake-Big Thompson 17-mile tunnel under construction in 1942 by the Bureau of Reclamation, whereby about 300,000 acre-feet will be diverted annually through the Rockies, from Grand Lake in the headwaters of the

Colorado River to Big Thompson River, a tributary of the Mississippi through the Platte River. The water so diverted will be used for improving irrigation on a large tract of land north of Denver. Another important transmountain diversion for irrigation use is the Strawberry Valley Project constructed several years ago by the Bureau of Reclamation whereby water is diverted from Strawberry Creek in the headwaters of Duchesne River, a tributary of Green River (Colorado River basin), through the Wasatch Mountains into the valley of Great Salt Lake in Utah. Many other important diversions have been proposed in connection with irrigation, and some, perhaps several, relatively large projects of this type will be constructed when the values to be obtained shall justify the costs involved.

The largest interbasin diversion that has yet been made in this country is that through the Chicago Drainage Canal from Lake Michigan in the St. Lawrence River basin to the Illinois River, a tributary of the Mississippi, for the disposal of the sewage of Chicago and the protection of the purity of Chicago's water supply, which is taken from Lake Michigan. This diversion amounted at one time to about 7,500 second-feet (about 5,500,000 acre-feet annually), but under court decree the diversion has now been reduced to about one-fifth of that rate. This diversion tends to lower navigational stages and therefore to decrease harbor depths at all the Great Lake ports except those on Lake Superior, and to decrease by less than 1 per cent the discharges of the Niagara and St. Lawrence Rivers. Therefore, it has international aspects which may have some significance, as, for example, in the determination of the amount of water that may be used for the development of hydroelectric power at Niagara Falls in Canada and the United States. It is commonly understood, although not specifically set forth by the officers who negotiated the treaty, that this diversion was responsible for the greater amount of water allotted to Canada than to the United States for use at Niagara Falls.

An important interbasin diversion has recently been completed from the Colorado River to the Los Angeles region for the primary purpose of increasing the municipal water supplies of Los Angeles and nearby cities. The capacity of the diversion works and canal is 1,500 second-feet (about 1,000,000 acre-feet annually).

The oldest interbasin diversion in this country is probably that of Chamberlain Lake in Maine, from the headwaters of Allagash River, a tributary of St. John River, to the headwaters of Penobscot River. This diversion was constructed by lumbermen more than a century ago as a means for floating logs from the Allagash River basin into the Penobscot River basin, thence to the lumber market at Bangor.

Although international waters are involved, the diversion was effected at a time when no importance was attached to it and probably without the knowledge of anyone in governmental authority in the United States or Canada. The amount of water involved is never large.

Man-Made Changes in Regimen. In addition to the man-made changes in regimen caused by reservoirs, levees, interbasin diversions, vegetation, and the consumptive use of water in irrigation of which mention has been made, some miscellaneous changes should be noted. Drainage of lands with resultant lowering of the water table may affect rivers in at least two ways: first, by the construction of channels that expedite runoff, it may tend to increase flood discharges and to increase total runoff by decreasing evaporation losses through reduction in water surface area; and, second, it may retard runoff and so tend to decrease flood flows by creating available space for the ground storage of water above the water table, which, in the absence of the drainage works, might be filled with water to the ground surface.

The creation or improvement of a drainage channel for any purpose tends to promote rapid runoff and so, under some conditions of timing, to augment floods. Paved streets and hard-surfaced roads, with their attendant drainage channels, check and decrease infiltration and expedite runoff. Roofs, especially over large proportions of the area, as in cities, put water quickly into the drainage channels and so augment flood flows.

In recent years, increasing attention has been given to channel-improvement work and training, particularly in connection with small streams. Such operations may consist of straightening, the removal of obstructions like boulders and fallen trees, deepening, bank revetment work, and the like. Whether the principal objective of such work be flood control, sanitation, or landscaping, the net result will be a more rapid runoff which may be conducive to higher and sharper flood peaks than before such improvements were undertaken. It is quite probable that, subject to limitations of timing, the general result of such work will be to accentuate flood peaks while tending to shorten the duration of the flood period.

All these influences are generally minor, however, not only in comparison with the consumptive use of water in irrigation, but also in comparison with the artificial control of the regimen of rivers that may be brought about by reservoirs, which under the most favorable conditions may be used to convert the natural regimen into any artificial regimen desired.

Man's activities affect the regimen of rivers, therefore, in various ways, in part deliberate and in part incidental to other purposes. It would doubtless be impossible for modern civilized man to exist without changing the rates of flow of rivers, and some of the changing has deleterious effects that may be either widespread or local. Changes that benefit some individuals or localities may damage others. In connection with many of these changes and the determination of rights, benefits, and damages by administrative officials or the courts, sound hydrologic understanding and continuity of records of the quantity and quality of the water flowing in rivers are essential.

BIBLIOGRAPHY 4

1. Committee Report, Flood Control Methods: Their Physical and Economic Limitations, *Proc. Am. Soc. C. E.,* February 1940, pp. 265–282.
2. Symposium, Flood Control with Special Reference to the Mississippi River, *Trans. Am. Soc. C. E.,* Vol. 93, pp. 655–969.
3. E. A. SHERMAN, Relation of Forestry to the Control of Floods in the Mississippi Valley, H. D. 573, 70th Cong. 2nd Session.
4. KIRK BRYAN, Geology of Reservoir and Dam Sites, *U.S.G.S. Water Supply Paper 597-A.*
5. H. M. CHITTENDEN, Forests and Reservoirs in Their Relation to Stream Flow, with Particular Reference to Navigable Rivers, *Trans. Am. Soc. C. E.,* Vol. 62, pp. 245–546.
6. POSEY and I, Functional Design of Flood Control Reservoirs, *Trans. Am. Soc. C. E.,* Vol. 105, pp. 1638–1674.
7. G. R. CLEMENS, The Reservoir as a Flood-Control Structure, *Trans. Am. Soc. C. E.,* Vol. 100, pp. 879–927.
8. Symposium, National Aspects of Flood Control, *Trans. Am. Soc. C. E.,* Vol. 103, pp. 551–719.

CHAPTER 5

GOVERNMENTAL AND LEGAL CONTROL OF RIVERS

Public Interest in Rivers. Interest in rivers and their utilization is essentially universal because many rivers are used for several purposes which affect the general welfare and determine the nature, extent, and stability of local and regional development, all of which are dependent on the acreage of land that may be irrigated, the adequacy of municipal water supplies, the availability of cheap mechanical or electric energy, the practicability of water transportation, and the nature and limit of industrial growth.

In view of the general interest in the utilization of rivers, it is natural that such interest should extend to the degree of utilization that may be possible or practicable, complete economic utilization, of course, being the ultimate objective. This is not intended to imply that complete utilization may be expected at once or at any particular time, but rather that any use to be made of a river shall be in conformity with the best plan [1] for its ultimate complete utilization for valuable economic or recreational purposes. This ideal may seldom or never be realized, but nevertheless it should be the goal in connection with all plans. It may not be realized because of (a) lack of public interest and, therefore, of active public control, (b) lack of knowledge of potentialities or of vision as to possible future changes in uses and in methods of utilization, (c) errors of judgment with respect to relative values or in relation to the effects of any project or uses, or (d) failure to employ the best over-all plan of utilization. Although the difficulties involved in complete and perfect utilization are generally insurmountable, the ideal objective should be sought to the end that, so far as reasonably possible, incomplete or unwise use of a site shall not destroy or render impracticable the later complete or best utilization of the same site or of other sites in the river system.

Conflicts in Use. Some uses of water are consumptive; others are not.[2] Some impair the quality of water; others do not. Fortunately, many of the possible uses of a river are wholly compatible; that is,

[1] Bibliog. 5·3.
[2] Chapter 6.

a use for one purpose does not destroy or impair the utility for other purposes. Those uses which greatly deplete the flow or seriously impair the quality of the water, however, are not wholly compatible with other possible uses. Under these conditions, some compromise or adjustment must be made on the bases of relative human importance, economic values, priority of rights, or other considerations.

Because of differences in public values of the several uses of water, some are rated as higher than others. The order of rating is determined by the relation of the several possible uses to human life, in the following order: (a) domestic and municipal supplies, (b) irrigation, (c) power, (d) industrial processes, and (e) navigation. Although domestic, municipal, and, in arid and semiarid regions, irrigation uses are always rated higher than others, the order is otherwise not rigidly fixed but may vary with the relation of the various possible uses to the general development of the region.

Because of the constitutional provision that Congress shall have power "to regulate Commerce with foreign Nations, and among the several States, and with the Indian Tribes," navigation and the navigability of rivers have been given a legal importance that may be out of proportion to their economic or public values, and as a result navigational interests have been protected at times to the detriment of possible higher uses of water. This situation is now generally recognized, and there is a present tendency toward recognition of true relative values in spite of this general constitutional provision. If great public interests are at stake, such recognition of values must determine the ultimate solution of this problem—a problem that is related to possible conflicts in use and that is made more difficult by this constitutional provision. It is probable that this situation in relation to the utilization of rivers was never considered even in principle by the founders of our government.

Although relative ratings of the uses of water are generally recognized and condemnation procedure with respect to a lower use in favor of a higher one may be authorized in some states, the burden of the cost of the change, even if it be from lower to higher, must be borne by the use to which the change is made, because the state constitutions properly provide that private property shall not be taken for a public purpose without due process of law and payment of damages to be determined by commissioners or by a jury. Therefore, if such a change is justified, the value of the higher use must exceed the price paid for the lower use by an amount that is at least equal to all additional costs of making the change.

In states which do not provide for condemnation of a lower use in favor of a higher one, a change must await the voluntary sale of the lower use. Such a sale will come in time, of course, if the public interest is sufficiently great. The owner of the utility of lower rating, however, may be in a position to demand an exorbitant price and perhaps to delay for an indefinite time a change that is of great public importance. The principal value of the power of condemnation in such situations arises from the assurance of the ability to close the lower use at a fair price and without undue delay.

Aspects of Governmental Jurisdiction. It is obvious that water, a resource of vital public importance and significance, must not be owned or controlled in its utilization by individuals or private corporations without public restraint or regulation.

The Federal Government, under the Constitution, is limited in its jurisdiction with respect to rivers to problems related to: (*a*) utilization or control of rivers that cross or form international boundaries (international rivers), in so far as such utilization or control may affect citizens or property in an adjoining country; (*b*) utilization or control of rivers that cross or form state boundaries (interstate rivers), in so far as such utilization or control affects citizens or property in a neighboring state; (*c*) navigation in its relation to foreign or interstate commerce; and (*d*) utilization of streams on public lands. In general, other phases of river utilization and control appear to lie within the jurisdiction of the several states.

Quite properly, the Federal Government has gradually assumed the major responsibility for the construction and maintenance of levees for controlling floods in the Mississippi River basin because the menace of those floods extends through several states. Of late, however, there has been great pressure, with some degree of success, for the extension of such responsibility to the control of floods in other interstate and intrastate rivers. Such extensions of federal financing, construction, and operation of flood-control works, including both levees and reservoirs, added to the possibilities of a measure of control by the Federal Power Commission over the construction of reservoirs and water-power plants on navigable rivers and their tributaries that might be so operated as to affect adversely the navigational characteristics of those rivers, have apparently brought the Federal Government into wider relations with problems of river control and utilization than is indicated in the previous paragraph. How far these relations will extend and how they may finally be delimited are not yet evident.[3]

[3] Bibliog. 5·5.

Under these conditions, there are wide variations in the administration provided by the states to control or administer rivers and their utilization, and any statements herein with respect to state control or administration must necessarily be broad and general, because details vary among the states and among different sections of the country.

Water Rights. Water from whatever source is essential to many enterprises, and rights to its use must be established and maintained. Rights in water become the more important because they relate to a limited resource that may be insufficient to serve the needs of all, that varies greatly in quantity, and that is of such variable quality that its value for many purposes is seriously reduced. Rights in land are relatively simple, readily defined, and determinate. Land is fixed in position and may be accurately described; water, by contrast, is usually in motion and varies widely in quantity with respect to place and season. Obviously, it cannot be described or held in the same way as land, and, since it has great value, rights in it are fully as important as the rights in land.

In humid sections of the continental United States, rights in water are derived from the ownership of riparian lands; in arid and semiarid sections such rights are initiated by appropriation and perfected by beneficial use. As the boundaries between humid and arid sections do not follow state lines, there are a few states partly humid and partly arid in which the situation is mixed and where both kinds of rights are recognized.

The principle of riparian ownership of rights in water was brought to this country from England by the early settlers on the eastern seaboard as a part of the common or nonstatutory law. These settlers came from one humid country to another humid country, and the same rules with respect to rights in water were properly applicable. The doctrine has since been developed in this country by many court decisions. Under it, any owner of riparian lands is entitled to have the water of a stream that naturally flows through or contiguous to his land continue so to flow undiminished in quantity and unimpaired in quality. Obviously, such a doctrine must be administered in accordance with rules of reason because many necessary uses affect the quantity or quality to some extent.

Riparian rights in water are indefinite both as to amount and quality. They are inherent in the land and do not lapse by nonuse. The fact that they are undefined except by the general principle as stated does not diminish their validity. Infringements on such rights must relate either to unnatural low flows or to impaired quality of water, since claims for infringement damages must show actual damages of tangible value. Under these conditions, claims of invasion of rights cannot relate to such "acts of God" as great floods or even to medium flows unless it can be shown that such flows are habitually applied to valuable use. The doctrine does not set up the principle of ownership of water by the public, but rather the right of the owner of riparian land to the use of the water as it flows past or through such land.

The doctrine of appropriation, under which first in time is first in right and beneficial use is the basis, measure, and limit of the right, was developed and applied in arid regions through necessity. In those regions, there is insufficient water, and consequently some land must remain unirrigated. Since part of the water used in irrigation is consumed and the flow depleted, a riparian owner whose lands are situated below a point of diversion for irrigation must suffer a diminished flow past his land. An entirely different doctrine of rights is necessary if irrigation is to be practiced and regional development is to take place. Obviously, if an irrigation enterprise is to be stable, the rights in water must be established and maintained. Arid sections of the continental United States are developed, therefore, on the basis of public ownership and control of the water, which means that the division of the water among the various users must be administered by the public through some governmental agency.

States in arid and semiarid regions, therefore, declare by constitutional provision or by statutory law that the water in surface streams is owned by the public and provide for beneficial use by a prescribed procedure that varies somewhat in different states. The posting of a written notice of appropriation of a specified quantity of water to be diverted at a particular point and to be used for a specific purpose generally initiates the right. This right is thereafter perfected or made valid and effective only when the water has been diverted and used as indicated in the notice of appropriation. After the water has been put to beneficial use, the right may be adjudicated in an amount that does not exceed the amount actually so used and at a rate that conforms to good local practice. A protracted failure at any time to use the water for the purpose indicated in the notice of appropriation may constitute adequate justification for the legal abandonment of the right. This may be established by testimony and be made effective by a court of proper jurisdiction. The right in question then ceases, whereupon the use of the water reverts to the public and may be appropriated by another party who proposes to put it to beneficial use. Rights by appropriation differ from riparian rights in that they are definite and may be lost by nonuse, whereas riparian rights are indefinite as to amount and are always appurtenant to the riparian land whether used or not.

Rights by appropriation must be adjudicated in amount in order that the water may be properly divided among those who divert from the same supply. In theory, adjudications are made by a court, but in practice they are usually made by a state engineer or similar administrative officer with a right of appeal to the court. Nearly all adjudications are now so made, and the number of appeals is remarkably small. If no appeal is made within a specified time, such an adjudication is final and of full force and effect.

Certain states have constitutional provisions that the right to appropriate water shall neither be denied nor abridged, with the result that in such states the water of every stream is greatly over-appropriated, and the amount and priority of each appropriation must be adjudicated to provide a basis for the proper distribution of the water. Other states do not permit unlimited appropriation but instead provide for a determination by the state engineer of the availability of the water sought to be appropriated. In such states, an attempt is thus made to administer the acquisition of rights somewhat more rigorously, but each state makes provision for appeal to the courts with respect to any administrative action, thereby removing the possibility of injury due to the error or prejudice of one man.

Because of the importance of water in arid states and the widely variable supply, there has always been much litigation at great cost to the water user. In general, the owners of rights acquired by appropriation have suffered more in this respect than the owners of riparian rights. The newer arid states have attempted to profit by the experience of the older states and have generally provided for more rigid administration, with the result that there is less litigation. On the whole, the situation seems to be in better control, though with more litigation, under appropriation than under riparian rights. In Texas and California, the water rights conveyed by Spain and Mexico in connection with land grants further complicate the situation. These rights are recognized as valid with respect to the title to both land and water.

In Hawaii is found a third kind of water right [4] to which reference may be made, more as a matter of interest than because of any great general importance. Concerning the situation in this territory, F. H. Newell has reported as follows:

[4] Bibliog. 5·4.

In the Hawaiian Islands a system · · · has grown up, largely as the result of ancient usage. There water is considered as appurtenant to the land upon which it originates and as belonging to the owner of that piece of land. He may lease it or sell it separate from the land itself, and may convey it to distant tracts of land, subject, however, to any vested rights which may come down from ancient times or more recently have been acquired by prescriptive use, such, for example, as the rights of the natives to the use of the water on their small taro patches. Riparian rights do not appear to be recognized excepting for water for domestic purposes, nor does the theory of appropriation hold excepting in the cases above noted of ancient or prescriptive rights which have grown up through the needs of the people.

Much of the mountainous land in Hawaii on which water originates is the property of the territory, and to that extent the water belongs to the public and may be opened to appropriation as in the arid and semiarid states of the mainland. This water is frequently leased to sugar plantations for fixed terms of years and thus becomes a source of revenue. The Bishop Estate, also, owns large areas of mountainous lands and similarly rents the water originating on its lands for use elsewhere.

Intrastate Administration. Riparian rights need no current division or administration, and no administrative organization is provided. Disputes arising with respect to the rights or infringements on such rights are settled by arbitration or by court action.

Rights obtained by appropriation in arid and semiarid regions pertain to an inadequate and closely used supply, and the water must be continually divided among the users from the same sources of supply. Adjudications of rights must therefore be made by courts or by state administrative officials with right of appeal to the court, as a basis for the division. As a matter of experience, the actions of such administrative officials are seldom questioned even though the results may be tragic. For example, in times of shortage of water, certain fields having prior water rights may be given sufficient water to mature growing crops while nearby fields with inferior rights must go dry and the crops thereon fail. Under such conditions, the responsibilities of the man who apportions the water are great and the decrees of adjudication must be enforced without fear or favor.

The distribution of the surface waters within an arid or semiarid state is accomplished by state administrative officials, generally organized in each state under the state engineer. The work requires the services of many competent men, not only to distribute the water at a great number of points but also to obtain the records of stream flow [5] upon which such division of the water must be based.

[5] Chapter 20.

Interstate Treaties and Litigation in the United States Supreme Court. Rivers that form or cross state boundaries [6] cannot be administered without consideration of those boundaries and of the effects that activities or uses in one state will have on the uses of the river or on the riparian lands in another state. For example, the quality of the water may be impaired by sewage or industrial wastes discharged into the river in one state to the detriment of citizens of another state.

Such situations may be approached either by interstate treaty or by litigation in the Supreme Court of the United States. Each of these forms of procedure has been frequently followed, and doubtless each has advantageous aspects. In general, the Supreme Court seems to prefer the treaty approach, because that approach may afford greater opportunity for the consideration of equities and for the arrangement of details of utilization than is reasonably practicable by court action.

The Constitution of the United States provides in section 10 that "No State shall, without the Consent of Congress, · · · enter into Agreement or Compact with another State · · ·." Many treaties between states have been made, covering many different kinds of relations in which there was disagreement or divergence in interest, and some, perhaps many, of them have been negotiated without prior congressional authorization. Although prior congressional authorization to negotiate a treaty or compact does not appear actually to be required, such consent is generally first obtained from Congress. Before the resulting agreement is effective, however, it must be approved by the legislature of each state involved and by Congress.

Each interstate situation is different from every other, and each requires special consideration and treatment. It is not to be expected, therefore, that any two treaties or compacts will be alike. As an example, a recent treaty may be cited which was arranged between Colorado, New Mexico, and Texas providing for the equitable division of the water of the Rio Grande. This river, which has an insufficient supply of water for the irrigation of the arable land in its basin, is both an international and an interstate stream. The United States had entered into a treaty with Mexico providing that a certain amount of water would be made available at El Paso for diversion and use in Mexico, but it was apparently felt in some quarters that this treaty bore most heavily on one of the states. The Rio Grande furnished water for a development by the Bureau of Reclamation to irrigate lands in both New Mexico and Texas and for the irrigation of a large

[6] Bibliog. 5·1.

area in central New Mexico, which area included lands of Indians, who are the wards of the United States. The waters of the Rio Grande were also used to irrigate a large and highly productive area in the San Luis Valley in Colorado. In addition, there appeared to be resentment among citizens of the states because of a conviction in some sections that federal power had been unduly exercised in favor of one region and against another, and litigation was in progress in the United States Supreme Court to settle some of the issues involved. This litigation was delayed, however, in order to give full opportunity for the negotiation of a treaty. A treaty was finally agreed upon in spite of many difficulties and was approved by the legislatures of the three states and by Congress. Each state was allowed to use water as it saw fit and as water was available, subject to the requirement that Colorado allow water to pass into New Mexico in any year in accordance with a rule that took account of the total quantity available in the Rio Grande basin in Colorado during that year. Similarly, it was required that New Mexico allow water to pass into the Elephant Butte Reservoir, which controls the water supply for the lower New Mexico and Texas areas, in any year in accordance with a rule that took account of the total quantity of water available in that year in the Rio Grande basin in New Mexico above this reservoir. The treaty provided also for financing the administrative and engineering work needed for its enforcement and for its revision, if such should be found desirable after an experience of several years.

The La Plata River Compact between Colorado and New Mexico was brought before the Supreme Court of the United States by the State of Colorado through action to compel compliance with the terms of the compact by the La Plata and Cherry Creek Ditch Company. The twelve numbered paragraphs below indicate concisely the contentions of the Ditch Company and the decision of the United States Supreme Court with respect to each. The following syllabus of the decision, by which a decision of the Supreme Court of Colorado was reversed, is presented in full, not only because of the information it contains with respect to water rights on interstate streams but also because it clearly indicates the strong position of a properly made interstate treaty or compact:

OPINION DELIVERED BY JUSTICE BRANDEIS

Hinderlider, State Engineer, et al. *v.* La Plata River & Cherry Creek Ditch
Company 304 U. S. 92

Appeal from the Supreme Court of Colorado
No. 437.   Argued February 10, 11, 1938.—Decided April 25, 1938.

1. The water of an interstate stream, used beneficially in each of the two
States through which it flows, must be equitably apportioned between the
two.

The claim that on interstate streams the upper State has such ownership
or control of the whole stream as entitles it to divert all the water, regardless
of any injury or prejudice to the lower State, has been consistently denied by
this Court.

2. A decree of a state court can not confer a right in the water of an interstate stream in excess of the State's equitable portion of such water.

3. A decree of a state court adjudicating to a local user a right in the
water of an interstate stream in excess of the State's equitable portion thereof
is not *res judicata* as to another State and its citizens who claim the right
to divert water from the stream in such other State, and who were not
parties to the proceedings.

4. It is not essential to the validity of a compact between States for the
apportionment of the water of an interstate stream that there be judicial or
quasi-judicial decision in respect of existing rights.

5. Whether the apportionment of the water of an interstate stream be
made by compact between the upper and lower States with the consent of
Congress or by a decree of this Court, the apportionment is binding upon the
citizens of each State and all water claimants, including grantees whose rights
antedate the compact or decree.

6. A compact between two States for apportionment of the water of an
interstate stream may provide for division of the water at times, and at other
times for the use of the entire flow by one State or the other in alternating
periods; the authority may validly be delegated to the States' engineers to
determine when the use should be rotated.

So *held* where the evidence conclusively established that, at the times when
rotation was determined upon, the stream could in that way be more efficiently
used.

7. No vitiating infirmity being here shown in the proceedings preliminary
to the La Plata River Compact or in its application, the apportionment
made by it between Colorado and New Mexico of the water of the La Plata
River could not be held to deprive a Colorado appropriator of any vested
right, even though a right had previously been adjudicated to him in a water
proceeding in a court of that State.

8. The assent of Congress to the La Plata River Compact between Colorado and New Mexico does not make the compact a "treaty or statute of the
United States" within the meaning of §237 (a) of the Judicial Code, and a
decision of the state court against its validity is not appealable to this Court.

9. A claim based on the equitable interstate apportionment of water, like one based on the proper location of a state boundary, is not within the provisions of §237 (a) of the Judicial Code.

10. The decision of the Supreme Court of Colorado in this case, restraining the State Engineer from taking action required by the La Plata River Compact, denied an important claim under the Constitution and is reviewable by this Court on certiorari under §237 (b) of the Judicial Code.

11. Whether the water of a stream must be apportioned between the two States through which it flows is a federal question, upon which neither the statutes nor decision of either State can be conclusive.

12. That the States which are parties to a compact are not parties to the suit and can not be made so, does not deprive this Court of jurisdiction to determine the validity and effect of the compact.

101 Colo. 73; 70 P. 2d 849, reversed.

International Rivers and Treaties. The many international streams [7] along the northern and southern borders of the continental United States have already brought many important questions to the Department of State for negotiation with Great Britain and Mexico. These questions have been settled in part by general treaties, in part by special treaties, and are in part still pending.

On the Mexican border, the citizens of Texas, who are diverting water from the lower Rio Grande to irrigate about 500,000 acres of land in the Brownsville region, are urging a new treaty with Mexico which will protect and improve the water supply for this important agricultural development. The waters of the lower Rio Grande may be largely controlled by storage and use within Mexico because they come principally from the Mexican side of the boundary and there are no large Texas tributaries. The Mexicans wish to take advantage of their strategic position with respect to the waters of the lower Rio Grande to obtain concessions on the Colorado, where the United States is in position to control the supply of water and its utilization. The users of Colorado River water in the United States do not wish to relinquish any of their rights or interests in order to protect water users in Texas.

On the Canadian border, many difficult problems may be cited. Seattle proposes, in connection with an improved municipal water supply, to build a dam on the Skagit River which will back water into Canada. The Canadians, on the other hand, are endeavoring to obtain consent to raise the levels of Kootenai River in a highly developed agricultural valley in Idaho, in connection with the development of water power on the Kootenai River in Canada. Again, the waters of St. Mary and Milk Rivers are used for irrigation on both sides of the

[7] Chapter 6.

boundary, and conflicts of interests arise because of the insufficiency of the water supply. Other problems related to drainage on both sides of the boundary in the basin of the Red River of the North may be best worked out jointly between the two countries. In the Great Lakes and St. Lawrence River basins, the Chicago diversion from Lake Michigan to the Mississippi River affects, perhaps, the navigational stages of the Lakes and the discharges of the Detroit, Niagara, and St. Lawrence Rivers; the power development at Niagara Falls and navigation of the St. Lawrence River present problems; there are problems related to navigation and to the fluctuation of Lake Champlain in connection with Richelieu River, and problems related to water storage and power development in the basins of the St. John and St. Croix Rivers. All these situations and many others have been, are, or will be acute, and each requires special consideration and decisions by the treaty-making authorities of Mexico, Great Britain, and the United States.

Several international treaties relate to rivers, partly with respect to their functions as boundaries and partly with respect to the fluctuation of the stages and the utilization of the waters. Besides treating of the specific rivers in these respects, international commissions that have to do with the details of the administration of rivers have been created by treaty.

The International Boundary Commission, United States and Mexico, was created pursuant to the provisions of the treaty concluded March 1, 1889, with exclusive jurisdiction to examine and decide all differences or questions arising between the United States and Mexico along the 1,920 miles of the Rio Grande between El Paso and the Gulf of Mexico and along the 19 miles of Colorado River where it forms the boundary, growing out of changes in the beds or any causes affecting the boundary line. Questions for investigation and report touching control measures and other engineering problems may be submitted to the Commission upon concurrence between the governments through exchange of notes.

The International Boundary Commission, United States, Alaska, and Canada, defines, marks, and maintains the marking of the international boundary line between the United States and Canada and between Alaska and Canada.

The International Joint Commission was created by the treaty between the United States and Great Britain signed January 11, 1909, the object of which is "to prevent disputes regarding the use of boundary waters and to settle all questions which are now pending between the United States and the Dominion of Canada involving the rights, obligations, or interests of either in relation to the other or to the inhabitants of the other, along their common frontier, and to make provision for the adjustment and settlement of all such questions as may hereafter arise." The Commission has jurisdiction over all cases involving the use, obstruction, or diversion of boundary waters between the United States and Canada, of waters flowing from boundary waters, and of waters at a lower level than the boundary in rivers flowing across the boundary. It is charged with the measurement and apportionment from time to time of the waters of the St. Mary and Milk Rivers and their tributaries, which lie partly in Montana and partly in Alberta and Saskatchewan, and which are largely used for irrigation in both countries.

BIBLIOGRAPHY 5

1. Committee Report, Final Report of the Committee of the Irrigation Division on Interstate Water Rights, *Trans. Am. Soc. C. E.*, Vol. 104, pp. 1822–1866.
2. NATIONAL RESOURCES COMMITTEE, *Regional Planning*, Part V—Red River of the North, August 1937.
3. A. E. MORGAN, Planned Utilization of Water Resources, *Civil Engineering*, Vol. 7, No. 4, pp. 255–259 (April 1937).
4. F. H. NEWELL, Hawaii—Its Natural Resources and Opportunities for Home Making, 1909, Sen. Doc. 668, 60th Cong., 2nd Session, p. 25.
5. W. G. HOYT, Unusual Events and Their Relation to Federal Water Policies, *Proc. Am. Soc. C. E.*, February 1942, pp. 211–224.

CHAPTER 6

UTILIZATION OF RIVERS

Past, Present, and Future Uses. In the Biblical account of Creation, written probably nearly 3,500 years ago, the importance of a river was recognized and its utilization in man's service was recorded. From the earliest times, rivers have certainly occupied a prominent place in every stage of man's development because they have served as sources of his food and drink, of water for irrigation, and as routes of transportation and commerce. In more recent times, they have promoted industry by providing a source of cheap energy and by supplying water for use in industrial processes.

The ruins of irrigation canals, aqueducts, and wells built before written records were made provide mute evidence of the struggle for food and drink by early races of men. The Bible and other early writings contain many references to rivers in relation to human necessities and as symbols of well-being and plenty. Ruins, hieroglyphics, history, and literature all testify to the intimate relation of rivers to the activities and welfare of man.

Primitive man was a nomad who took up his temporary abode wherever he found the means for sustaining life. As food and drink were most easily obtained from rivers and from their valleys, he doubtless pitched his summer camp on a river bank. From the river, he obtained not only his drink but also a large part of his food, which was limited to that easily yielded to him by nature, and included fish from the rivers, game that ranged nearby, and the fruits, seeds, and roots of the plants that grew in the valley lands.

Throughout the ages, from the most primitive times until railroads and good highways largely eliminated the necessity for transportation on inland waterways, rivers have served as important routes of travel and commerce. Because of the interrelation of navigation and commerce, many large ancient cities grew up either on the seacoast or in river valleys, and the important activities of known ancient peoples were related largely to the navigable rivers of southern Asia, northern Africa, and southern Europe. With the development of agriculture through irrigation, which also antedated history, rivers served as the chief sources of water for the production of crops and were therefore responsible for the food so essential to the stabilization of residence and to community existence.

River valleys thus represented the strategic areas of national development and so became the battle grounds of the ages. In them, the assurance of ample supplies of food and drink made practicable the fixed habitation so essential to a sustained growth in culture and to the development of civilization. Since rivers were so all-important in the life of early man, the names, uses, and characteristics of rivers of southern Asia and the Mediterranean region, and the veneration of them, have been woven into the traditions and histories of the peoples who developed the earliest known civilizations.

Doubtless irrigation ranked with navigation as among the earliest of the extensive uses of rivers. The production of food and the exchange of commodities were dependent on them as the cheapest sources of water supply for agriculture and the safest and most comfortable routes of travel. The evidence of extensive irrigation is perhaps the most widespread among the many signs of the early use of rivers. In the valley of the Nile, to cite one example, there are intermittent, broken records of stage, the oldest of which date back about 5,000 years, and these records were primarily important because of their relation to irrigation. The Roda gage at Cairo, Egypt, with a written but broken record [1] extending back thirteen centuries, related to the natural irrigation by flooding of the delta of the Nile and to the lands which could be taxed each year because in any year only those lands that were situated below the flood level received the flood waters and produced crops.

There are many evidences of the early efforts to obtain supplies of water for community use. The growth of cities involved problems in making available satisfactory water supplies for household use, problems that led finally to the construction of long aqueducts, of which nine built to supply Rome with water were the most spectacular, one of them being 62 miles in length. The largest Roman aqueducts were built in the 400-year period from 300 B.C. to A.D. 100. At least three of these old aqueducts still bring water into Rome.

With the development of civilization, and especially with the building of cities, the demand for water for domestic and municipal uses increased, and the struggle to obtain adequate supplies for both large and small communities has continued to the present time. Increasing industrial activity has not only promoted the growth of cities and so

[1] Biblicg. 1·15.

increased the demands for municipal supplies of water but has also caused the erection of plants to furnish power, the profitable utilization of which has increased the needs for water for industrial processes. The uses of water related to power plants and factories, and the requirements for navigation, irrigation, and municipal systems for growing populations, have increased the demands for water that have in many sections reached or exceeded the limits of supply. To these increased demands, there has now been added the use of water for air conditioning. The extent of future requirements for this new use cannot yet be evaluated, but, whatever they may be, they will be added to those for other uses that have in many places already reached or are approaching the limits of availability of local supplies.

What the future demands for water will be cannot be predicted with accuracy. The gradual development of civilization has meant increased uses of water at every step forward. If this record of the past is a proper criterion for future prediction, it must be assumed that there will be a steady increase in the use of rivers and river waters if there is to be further progress in civilization. Certainly there has been a steady increase in the use of rivers for all purposes except navigation, which has declined in some regions during the last century because transportation by railroads, hard-surfaced highways, and, more recently, airplanes, is faster. The greatest future for river navigation will apparently be found in those tidal or canalized rivers that may be so improved as to permit ocean-going craft to enter inland ports, or that are situated contiguous to the routes of movement of sufficiently large quantities of nonperishable, low-priced freight that may be transported successfully at relatively slow rates of speed and thus at lower cost.

The intimate relation of rivers to man's welfare and development has thus been ever-present. The nature of the utilization of rivers in any period has been determined by the needs of the people of that period, and the extent of use has been limited only by the ability to adapt rivers to those needs. Man's success in using rivers has been, and is, based in large part on the experience gained in many trials that, by success or failure, has provided a background for use in subsequent trials. As the knowledge thus obtained has been supplemented by laboratory experimentation, by the development of theoretical hydraulics, and by improvements in the designs for and the materials and processes of construction, the uses of rivers have steadily increased.

Effects of Use on Regimen and Runoff. The use of rivers for many purposes affects both their regimen and their total runoff. The most potent factors are the storage and release of water, which, while decreasing the runoff to a small extent, may change the regimen greatly; the use of water for irrigation, which depletes the runoff by a large proportion of the amount so used; and interbasin diversions, which deplete the runoff of one basin and augment that of another.

It is commonly assumed that some uses of water deplete the supply and that others do not. Strictly speaking, practically any use depletes the supply to some extent, if in no other way than by affording a greater opportunity for evaporation. Except for a possible minor increase in evaporation, the use of water to develop hydraulic power does not deplete the supply. The water passes through the wheels and flows away without decrease in quantity. Such a use is "nonconsumptive." Water that is used for irrigation [2] is in part transpired by the growing vegetation to which it is diverted. The quantity of water returned from irrigation is much less than the amount which is diverted and applied to the land. Such a use is "consumptive." Water used in industrial processes may be consumed in those instances where evaporation is an essential part of the process or where chemical changes are involved; it is not consumed in other processes. It is consumed in steam boilers; it is not consumed in condensers, but it may be consumed in spray ponds. It is not consumed to any great extent in municipal supplies as it reappears as sewage without material diminution, although it is badly polluted and should be properly treated before being returned to the river.

Water diverted from one drainage basin to another is not thereby consumed, since it appears in the rivers of the basin to which it is diverted. However, the effect on the water supply of the drainage basin from which it is diverted is equivalent to full consumption.

Incompatibility of uses may result from (1) decrease in quantity, (2) impairment in quality,[3] or (3) change in elevation. The first and second conditions are obvious; the third results from a lowering of position as water is changed from a higher to a lower level, as, for example, in passing through the turbines of a water-power plant.

Effects of Use on Quality. Many uses of water do not change its chemical or bacterial quality. The floating of boats in navigation and the generation of water power do not in themselves affect the quality of river water. Irrigation, on the other hand, does affect the chemical quality of the water used because a portion of the water passes through the soil and underlying strata and removes soluble

[2] Bibliog. 6·1.
[3] Bibliog. 6·2, 3.

matter from them to the channels that receive the seepage or return water. The return water from irrigation is always of poorer quality than the water that is applied to the land, the degree of impairment varying with the amount and kind of soluble matter in the soil and in the deeper strata. The subsequent use for irrigation of the return water increases its chemical pollution with each use [4] until, in extreme instances, such as the water returned to the Rio Grande above Fort Quitman, Texas, it is at times so heavily loaded with salts that it will not promote plant growth.

The damaging effects on the quality of water in relation to its subsequent use are inherent in irrigation. The only remedy lies in dilution, by adding better water whenever and wherever practicable, and in flushing the lands with flood waters to wash out the salts, if such action is reasonably possible at any time. Continued, successful, and profitable agriculture by long-time irrigation is contingent upon keeping down the salt content of the land. Doubtless more irrigated lands have been abandoned through the ages because of increased salinity of the soils than because of failures in the quantities of water and the combination of all other possible causes. The more highly the water is mineralized at its source, the less the irrigated lands have been leached, and the poorer the drainage, both natural and artificial, the more pressing will be the problems related to the quality of the water and the greater will be the danger of short-lived irrigation.

Industrial pollution of rivers may be a very serious matter. Such pollution may destroy fish and plant life, impair the value of the water for other industrial uses, render it unfit for use in irrigation or for municipal supplies, and in some instances may make rivers so foul as to create a nuisance because of unsightly appearance or offensive odors. Industrial wastes may, however, be treated to reduce or modify their chemical content, the treatment varying with the nature of the industrial processes involved. In general, the value of any by-products that may be recovered will be insufficient to pay for more than a fraction of the cost of the treatment. The major part of the cost, therefore, must be met by the industry itself, and the amount involved may be so great as to cause an industrial plant to fail financially in competition with other plants so situated that the treatment of trade wastes is not required. An alternative to such financial failure may be the payment of part or all of the cost of treatment of industrial wastes by the public out of funds raised by taxation, thus subsidizing the plant to that extent.

[4] Bibliog. 3·4.

The problems of industrial pollution [5] are, therefore, of great economic importance and of broad significance because they may affect the stability of regional development and the lives and activities of many people who depend directly or indirectly on the industry or industries involved.   These problems, like all others affecting the general welfare, must be considered and finally solved in their relation to the public good, and the abandonment of a river to unrestricted industrial pollution should not be permitted unless the best interests of the people are thereby served.

Pollution by industry differs from pollution by irrigation in that the former may be prevented at some cost which may, it is true, be so great as to be prohibitive, whereas the latter can be prevented only by the abandonment of diversion for irrigation.

Pollution of rivers by municipal sewage presents problems that increase with the size of the contributing cities and decrease with the size of the rivers into which the sewage is discharged.   If cities are small and rivers are large, the dilution of the sewage is great and no nuisance may be created although the river water cannot thereafter be safely used for domestic supplies without chlorination or other treatment that will destroy pathogenic bacteria.   If cities are large and rivers are small, there is less dilution of the sewage and a nuisance may be created.

The water of sewage must reach river channels, lakes, or oceans, no other disposition being practicable. With an assumed consumption of 150 gallons of water per capita per day, a city of a million people will use water continuously at an average rate of 230 second-feet. Obviously, this large quantity of water must be discharged into natural bodies of water. If the sewage is discharged into a river, the quantity of sewage and the size of the river, or, in other words, the degree of dilution of the sewage, may determine the type of treatment necessary in order that the river may be kept reasonably clean. Absolute purity, of course, is impracticable, because the river water is not pure even before it receives the city pollution. The degree of purity to be sought is a matter of judgment or even of decree and may vary for different rivers and different conditions of utilization below the point or points of sewage discharge.

In recent years, sewage treatment has received a great impetus because the officials and inhabitants of cities, large and small, are feeling the necessity for treating sewage before discharging it into a river, whatever the size of that river may be.

[5] Bibliog. 6·2.

Interstate and International Considerations. The utilization of interstate rivers may involve rights and uses in more than one state and, therefore, may lead to conflicts of interest between residents of two or more states that can be settled only by interstate compacts or treaties, or by suits brought in federal courts, as indicated in Chapter 5. Interstate rivers may be used for several purposes; they form state boundaries in connection with which there may be boundary disputes and boundary determinations and markings; they may be navigable, and, so far as their navigability and use for navigation are involved, they come within the jurisdiction of the Federal Government under the interstate commerce clause of the Constitution. Interstate rivers may be used for the generation of power, for irrigation in agriculture, in connection with industrial processes, and for the disposal of sewage and industrial wastes. For all such uses interstate agreements or litigation in federal courts may be involved. The engineering and fiscal aspects related to the utilization of interstate rivers are not essentially different from those for other rivers, although each river and each site presents its own special problems.

There are many interstate rivers in the country, from the Androscoggin, Saco, and Salmon Falls Rivers on the Maine-New Hampshire boundary and the Okefenokee-Suwanee-St. Marys River systems on the Georgia-Florida boundary in the east to the Columbia River on the Washington-Oregon boundary and the Colorado River on the Arizona-Nevada-California boundaries in the west, including the Mississippi River system, which drains all or parts of twenty-seven states. In the Mississippi River system, the greatest on this continent, the most vital problems relate to navigation, a federal responsibility; to flood control, a mixed individual, state, and federal responsibility with many troublesome ramifications; and to pollution, especially of the Ohio River, which receives the drainage from the coal fields of West Virginia and from the highly industrialized regions of Pennsylvania and Ohio, a mixed state and corporate responsibility that involves interstate compacts for its successful handling. The interstate problems that arise in this great basin are legion, and many are of major importance. They include all of the many uses of water and affect the stability of development and industry and the prosperity of a vast region that constitutes the heart of the nation.

Similarly, international rivers may be used for developing water power, for navigation, drainage, flood control, irrigation, and municipal supplies. The problems not related to international aspects are similar to those in other rivers. All international questions related to their utilization, in their relations to the other country, are handled through the Department of State and are settled by negotiation and by international treaties.

There are three international rivers on the Mexican boundary, the Rio Grande, Colorado, and the Rio Tiajuana, and many on the Canadian boundary, from the Skagit in the extreme northwest to the St. John and the St. Croix in the extreme northeast. These rivers are largely utilized, the Rio Grande for irrigation, the Colorado and Columbia and their tributaries for irrigation and water power, the Missouri and its tributaries for irrigation, the Great Lakes-St. Lawrence River system for navigation and water power, and the St. John and St. Croix Rivers for lumbering operations and water power. The much discussed Passamaquoddy Bay tidal power project, situated in the tidal bay into which the St. Croix River discharges, although not strictly a river project, involves international navigable waters in which the normal tidal fluctuations would be modified, is international in its aspects, and cannot be carried to completion without a new treaty with Great Britain that will provide specifically for the conditions affecting the international features under which it may be constructed.

Public Welfare. "A river is more than an amenity, it is a treasure. It offers a necessity of life that must be rationed among those who have power over it." [6]

The utilization of rivers is intimately related to the public welfare. The size and type of a river may determine the nature and extent of development of a region—whether it shall be industrial because of the possibilities of generating cheap power, or agricultural either because of irrigation if the water supply is adequate, because of dry-farming if there is not sufficient water for irrigation and yet enough rainfall to produce certain kinds of crops, or because of grazing if there is inadequate rainfall or if the terrain is too rough for farming operations. Rivers may determine the limits of development not only in agriculture but also in industry and in the size of cities. The chemical quality of their waters affects the types of industrial development. The proper utilization of the rivers of a region may determine, therefore, the nature, limits, and stability of regional development, and these conditions will in turn determine the occupation, prosperity, and happiness of all the people who live near them or who are dependent, directly or indirectly, on the uses that may be made of them.

[6] Justice Oliver Wendell Holmes, U. S. Supreme Court decision in New Jersey *vs.* New York et al. re diverting water from the Delaware River. **283 US 336, 342.**

The public welfare is promoted by the highest and most complete use of rivers and by their proper governmental control, to the end that such use shall be attained and that the rights in the use of the water shall be secure in order that there shall be stable regional growth along the best practicable lines. Rights in the use of water are, therefore, established and maintained by law, by administrative officials, and by the courts, and procedures for taking private property for a public purpose are provided for. In 1915, the Supreme Court of the United States upheld the power of eminent domain in the following language: [7]

In the organic relations of modern society it may sometimes be hard to draw the line that is supposed to limit the authority of the legislature to exercise or delegate the power of eminent domain. But to gather the streams from waste and to draw from them energy, labor without brains, and so to save mankind from toil that it can be spared, is to supply what, next to intellect, is the very foundation of all our achievements and all our welfare. If that purpose is not public we should be at a loss to say what is.

In 1924, at the World Power Conference in London, England, Herbert Hoover, then Secretary of Commerce, made the following statement: [8] "To reduce human labour, to increase its productivity, is the most profound basis of social advancement."

The public is interested, therefore, that this great natural resource shall be controlled for the benefit of the many and not exploited for the profit of the few. The people in a region have a real and abiding right that a natural resource touching practically all human activities and therefore affecting their lives shall be properly utilized. The community must be assured that the use, control, or disposition of this resource shall not affect adversely the prosperity, comfort, or happiness of its people.

The proper purpose of law and of all government is to serve the public welfare by promoting comfort, prosperity, stability, and security. These objectives are attained in part by providing protecting agencies such as health officers, police and fire-fighting forces to serve locally, and military establishments and facilities to serve nationally; in part, by providing courts for the administration of justice and the protection of persons and property; and, in part, by promoting economic development and establishing social, fiscal, and economic relations within the nation and with other nations. These purposes are attained to some degree by the legal control of the rights to use the

[7] Justice Oliver Wendell Holmes, Mt. Vernon-Woodbury Cotton Duck Co. *vs.* Alabama Interstate Power Co. 240 US 30, 32.

[8] World Power Conference, IV, p. 1580.

rivers and by such administration of those rights as shall assure the
results that are sought.

Conservation. As indicated in Chapter 1, in the description of the
hydrologic cycle, the term "conservation" as commonly understood
cannot be applied to water because water moves continuously through
that cycle without the possibility of any considerable artificial change
in the time or rate of such motion. The storage of water in reservoirs does not constitute conservation because it is so limited in time
by surface evaporation as to produce little or no effect on the broad
phases of its natural circulation through the earth and air, even though
it may have great value in the seasonal regulation of the flow of
streams and thereby in increasing and improving their utility.

There are two phases of conservation in its broad sense that are
properly applied to water: first, the legal control of water in the
interest of the public with respect to the stability of rights in its use
for all purposes, to the termination of such rights in favor of higher
or public uses on payment of proper damages without "hold-up" in
time or price, to the protection from monopolistic utilization that may
not be of the highest value to the public, and, in general, to the promotion of full and proper utilization of the water supply for all purposes
in the public interest to the end that there shall be maximum orderly
regional development, so far as such development may be affected by
the limiting aspects of the supply of water; and, second, the preservation of the reasonable purity of the waters in order that they may have
maximum value for all purposes and that they shall not become
nuisances or constitute a menace to health.

As already stated, rivers are natural drains, and their waters become polluted regardless of man's activities. Such natural pollution,
however, is not generally offensive or dangerous to health. Sewage
and industrial and oil wastes may greatly impair the quality of the
water, and uncontrolled pollution by them should not be tolerated.
The control or abatement of such pollution may, however, be expensive
and may make manufacturing unprofitable in some regions. It may
be argued by some people that it is in the public interest to dedicate
selected rivers to extreme pollution and to allow them to become open
and offensive sewers, but it is very doubtful that such extreme action
would ever be taken or would be warranted. In any event, the public
should at all times and in all places control the limits of all pollution
and by so doing conserve the essential purity of this great natural
resource.

This important aspect of conservation is greatly complicated by the
facts that rivers cross state lines or form boundaries between states,

and that no state or group of states can dictate to another state what it shall do with its rivers. The citizens of one state may suffer, therefore, because of the lack of control of pollution in another state. The executive branch of the Federal Government is without jurisdiction in such a situation. The best remedy lies in mutual agreement through the consummation of compacts or interstate treaties looking to the preservation and conservation of the essential purity of interstate rivers, but failing such amicable adjustment, and as a last resort, recourse must be had to the federal courts.

BIBLIOGRAPHY 6

1. S. T. HARDING, Chairman, Consumptive Use of Water in Irrigation, *Trans. Am. Soc. C. E.,* Vol. 94, pp. 1349–1399.
2. A. F. DAPPERT, Progress in Control of Water Pollution in New York State, *Civil Engineering,* Vol. 8, No. 11, pp. 742–744 (November 1938).
3. Symposium, Stream Pollution, *Trans. Am. Soc. C. E.,* Vol. 89, pp. 1331–1401.
4. Committee Report, National Resources Committee, Water Pollution in the United States, H. D. 155, 76th Cong., 1st Session.

CHAPTER 7

RECORDS OF RIVER DISCHARGE AND THEIR UTILITY

Systematic Records. Records of the discharge of rivers must be collected systematically if they are to have any great value. Unless so collected, these records will not properly serve the uses to be made of them, for they will neither have the desired degree of accuracy nor show the maxima and minima of flow, and they will not contain sufficient information from which the total annual runoff or the average annual discharge can be computed. Systematic records must be obtained at gaging stations that have been established at carefully selected sites and that are operated continuously. There must be daily observations or continuous records of stage and such periodic measurements of discharge as will make possible the translation of records of stage into reliable records of discharge. Unless a gaging station is maintained continuously, the station equipment will be in no condition to record the extremes of flow when they occur nor will the operating engineers be prepared for such emergencies. Sporadic observations of stage and occasional measurements of discharge have relatively little value and fall far short of meeting modern requirements.

Although rivers have been used for domestic supplies, irrigation, and navigation throughout all history, systematic records of their discharge are of relatively recent origin. The need for such records has long been felt, and, as stated in Chapter 6, systematic records of the flood stages of the Nile have been kept at the Roda gage at Cairo, Egypt, for more than thirteen centuries. With the uses of many rivers increased nearly to the limits of their capacities, the need for information concerning daily quantities of water and the total annual or seasonal runoff has become increasingly urgent.

Development of Methods. The first attempts to obtain records of river discharge appear to have been made by the use of a slope formula, in which the relation of velocity to slope was based jointly on measurements of slope and observations of surface velocities by means of floats. This method was applied to the River Rhine at Basle, Switzerland, to obtain daily estimates for the years 1809 to 1826, which appear to be the earliest continuous records of river discharge obtained over a considerable period of time. In Italy, estimates of the discharge of the Tiber at Rome were computed in a similar manner for an eleven-year period prior to 1836, and the same method was followed in computations of the discharge of the Adda and Po Rivers for periods prior to 1844. Although the method of computing these early records of discharge was crude and inaccurate by present-day standards, nevertheless it represented an important beginning in the art of stream gaging.

In 1849, Charles Ellet, Jr., made measurements of the Ohio River near Wheeling, W. Va., using observations of velocities at various stages obtained by means of floats, from which to compute discharges and thus to derive an empirical formula showing the relation of discharge to depth of water on the bar which controlled the stage-discharge relation at the gage. Thus, Ellet recognized a section of the river that controlled and stabilized [1] the stage-discharge relation and on that basis rated a gaging station. From the formula thus derived, he computed a rating table which he applied to the daily record of depth of water on the bar to obtain daily records of discharge for the years 1844 to 1848.

The first current meter appears to have been made in Germany. It was used to some extent by T. G. Ellis in a survey of the Connecticut River but was found unsatisfactory, at least for the conditions under which he was working. About 1870, therefore, Ellis devised and built a cup-type current meter—probably the first instrument of that type, although a cup-type anemometer (Robinson) was already in use. He used this current meter, known as the Ellis meter, in making measurements of discharge of the Connecticut River near Thompsonville, Conn. From the results of these measurements he constructed a stage-discharge rating table for the station and applied it to a record of daily gage heights, thus obtaining a record of daily discharge for the years 1871 to 1874. About sixty years elapsed, therefore, between the first records obtained through the use of a slope formula on the River Rhine and the rating of a gaging station by a method which approximated present-day procedure.

In 1878 and 1881, respectively, the State Engineer of California and the State Engineer of Colorado began measuring and recording the flow of rivers in connection with the administrative problems related to water rights and the distribution of water for irrigation. In 1883 a "permanent" station was constructed on the Cache la Poudre River in Colorado and a water-stage recorder was installed in the following year.

[1] Chapter 11.

Stream gaging by the Federal Government had its inception in 1888, as an essential part of an irrigation survey of the arid sections of the country which was being made by the Geological Survey under congressional authorization. A school of investigation and instruction, at which instruments and methods were studied, was organized by the Geological Survey, with Frederick Haynes Newell in local charge, and was maintained from December 1888 to April 1889 at Embudo, N. Mex., on the Rio Grande. A current meter was devised by the adaptation of meters already available, and a procedure for obtaining daily records of river discharge was developed.

The first federal appropriation made specifically for stream gaging was enacted by Congress for the fiscal year 1895, and appropriations have been made annually since that time. A few gaging stations were operated during the period 1889 to 1894. Beginning when the appropriation for 1895 became available, the work was gradually extended in scope and improved in quality. The demand for records of river discharge has steadily increased as the uses for water have expanded and particularly as the limits of supply have been approached, first in arid states, with the use of water for irrigation, and later in humid states, with its use for municipal supplies, hydraulic power, industrial processes, and navigation. In response to this demand and with the availability of more adequate funds, the work of collecting systematic records of river discharge has expanded in scope and improved in quality to the present day.

Availability of Records. In 1942, there were available nearly or quite 70,000 station-years of records, generally well distributed throughout the country. Some sections are more adequately covered than others, and there is a conspicuous deficiency in records pertaining to small streams in humid sections of the country where the principal use of such streams relates to municipal supplies. Records of the flow of small streams, with respect to both quantity and concentration in point of time, are also playing an increasingly important role in hydrologic research. Of the 70,000 station-years of records published by the Geological Survey, about 50,000 which have been collected since 1915 are of higher accuracy and therefore more satisfactory for use than the earlier records. These records are now being augmented by the Geological Survey at a rate of more than 4,000 station-years annually.

Evaluating and Financing Projects. Sound and stable development of a site or of a region must rest on reliable evaluations of the elements which insure success. Among these elements are climate, soil, minerals, forests, water supply and other natural resources, raw materials, and transportation facilities. Since water in some amount is necessary for any development, knowledge of the availability of an adequate and satisfactory supply is essential to wise local or regional planning for whatever purpose. Without such knowledge, a project which involves the use of considerable quantities of water cannot be properly evaluated. Since such information, if adequate, must cover a sufficient period of time to show the approximate limits of high, low, and average flows, stream gaging on the proposed source or sources of water supply must have been under way continuously for several years before a project can be successfully and honestly promoted. Before it can be carried to the point of financing, reliable, systematic records that give assurance of an adequate supply of water at all seasons must be available.

Many developments which have been made for irrigation, water power, steam power, and even municipal supplies have failed in whole or in part as a result of inadequate water supplies and have led to loss and in some instances to regional instability because they were based upon hopes instead of upon records. Because of such past failures in water supply in connection with many enterprises, financiers now expect and properly demand assurances with respect to water supply based on governmental records as a prerequisite to the furnishing of money for development purposes. Reputable financiers will not participate in financing or otherwise assume responsibility with respect to procuring funds or marketing stocks or bonds unless Geological Survey records show that a satisfactory supply of water is available for the development.

Design and Construction of Hydraulic Works. Reliable information with respect to the water supply and its variations is indispensable for the proper design and construction of hydraulic works. The total quantity of water available annually will limit the output of the proposed plant, and the variations in supply will affect the nature and magnitude of the control works as well as the capacities of the plant and of the floodways and will influence the details of the design in many particulars.

Knowledge of the seasonal variations of stream flow and of the probabilities of floods in different seasons is very desirable in connection with the planning of a program involving the design and construction of cofferdams in a river channel in order to protect excavating and construction activities below flood stages. Current information with respect to the stages and quantities of water in the basin above the site of construction operations in a river channel may be of great value, especially if high floods which may overtop cofferdams are imminent. Timely warnings of the approach of such floods will make it possible to remove equipment and materials from parts of the river channel that may be flooded.

Operation of Hydraulic Works. The most efficient operation of hydraulic works, including storage reservoirs and plants that make extensive use of water, requires current knowledge of the quantities of water in the upstream sources of supply. Therefore, superintendents and operating engineers are demanding more and better information with respect to stream flow and its daily variations in the river basins above their plants. The problems of operation are among the most pressing reasons for the uninterrupted operation of gaging stations after the periods of promotion and construction have passed. Such problems lead not only to the continued operation of gaging stations but also to the continuation and expansion of cooperation with states and municipalities.[2]

Administration of Rights. In order to divide water among those who depend upon a common and inadequate source of supply, as particularly in the arid regions of the West where irrigation is practiced, there must be reliable information concerning amounts and priorities of rights and equally reliable records of the quantities of available water and of the quantities of water delivered to each user. Either state or federal governmental control of the division of the water and of the records of supplies and deliveries is essential, since there must be no thought or fear of favoritism in the division of an inadequate supply of water, which in low-water years may cause some of the users who have inferior rights to lose part or all of their crops. In accordance with the division of governmental authority in this country between the states and the nation, the distribution of the water is a function of state government, and the division of the water and the records of its distribution among the users are made by the state acting through its state engineer or an official of comparable authority. Records of the flow of water in the rivers are now generally collected under the direction and control of the Geological Survey, thus aiding the state and affording a measure of protection to the state officials by federal assurance of the integrity of the records. Such records might otherwise be collected by individuals who have also the more exacting, conspicuous, and vulnerable responsibility for the division of the water and for cutting off or reducing the supplies for some users during periods of deficiency.

Although the records collected by the Geological Survey are usually published within the year after their collection, the published reports

[2] Chapter 20.

will not serve the daily and hourly needs of the state's field engineers. Since these engineers must know at all times how much water is available for distribution by them, there must be close coordination of the work of the two field organizations and accurate ratings of the gaging stations in order that field observations of stage may be converted promptly into reliable records of discharge which shall be immediately available to those engineers who are actually dividing and delivering the water. Without reliable records of river discharge and public confidence in the integrity of the federal and state engineering forces by whom the water is measured and divided, there would be danger of serious disagreement between conflicting water users at any time of seriously deficient supply.

Litigation. Reliable and unbiased records of river discharge are essential to the determination and administration of justice among the many people who are affected by the control and utilization of rivers. The records collected by the Geological Survey are recognized as being wholly impartial and are commonly used in litigation. They are accepted by most courts as *prima-facie* evidence of the facts, and, unless successfully controverted, which can rarely be done, they serve as a basis for court action. In a suit, they are generally accepted by all parties without question.

Those Survey records which have been published are, of course, available for any use that may be desired of them. If unpublished, they are always furnished upon request and certified in manuscript form for court purposes, and if so furnished to one party of the litigation, they are also supplied to the other party in order that there may be no possibility of a feeling that favoritism has been shown or that partisan testimony has been given by the Survey, even in such an indirect way. The records of river discharge collected by the Geological Survey properly furnish, therefore, a basis of fact related to stages and discharges of rivers in those court proceedings in which such aspects are significant.

Hydrologic Studies. Hydrologic studies of all kinds are dependent on reliable, long-time, systematic records of water, including records of precipitation, evaporation, transpiration, infiltration, stream flow, water storage, ground-water stages and quantities, and water utilization collected at many places and in all seasons. The integrity of any conclusions that may be drawn or of any hydrologic laws that may be formulated will be no higher than the accuracy of the records upon which they are based. Students of hydrology in many fields of research, therefore, are seeking longer and better records related to the widespread and varied occurrence of water, its variations as a result of natural forces or human activities, and its utility for the many purposes of man.

Utilization of Records. Stream-flow records are largely used by engineers in both private practice and public service, in connection with evaluating, reporting, promoting, designing, constructing, and operating the varied projects and developments that depend upon water. The *Water Supply Papers* of the Geological Survey form an essential part of the working library of every engineer whose professional activities relate to any extent to hydraulics or hydrology. The records contained in *Water Supply Papers* are used also by superintendents of power plants, irrigation systems, and industrial developments as well as of other systems that use water in considerable quantities; by hydrologists working on many phases of water and its occurrence; by attorneys in their advice to clients and in preparing for and trying suits; and by all courts, including the United States Supreme Court, as a basis for decisions between individual, corporate, and state litigants and for the resulting awards. They are likewise used by municipal officials in connection with problems of water supply, industrial development, sewage disposal, and stability of growth; by state officials, including state courts, in the negotiation of interstate treaties, in the adjudication and administration of water rights, in the distribution of irrigation water among those entitled to it, and in the problems related to municipal and industrial pollution and its abatement. These records are consulted in the administration of the many federal laws relating to the disposition and utilization of public lands, by the General Land Office, Office of Indian Affairs, Bureau of Reclamation, Soil Conservation Service, and Forest Service. They are used also by the Corps of Engineers, United States Army, in connection with federal laws concerning the building, improving, and operating of navigational channels and relating to the construction and operation of flood-control and flood-protection works, and by the Department of State in negotiating interstate and international treaties.

The listing of the persons and of the corporate and governmental agencies that are interested in the varied purposes for which water is essential and that utilize records of rivers in their daily activities emphasizes the broad, continuing, and essential value of such records. It illustrates why the study of rivers and the collection of records of river discharge have increased steadily in public esteem and why states and municipalities [3] cooperate with federal agencies in financing

[3] Chapter 20.

liberally and on a continuing basis the field and office work related to the collection of these records.

Expansion and Progress in Stream-Gaging Activities. A comparatively recent use of stream-flow records is in connection with flood forecasting, particularly with respect to small, relatively short streams. In the past, flood forecasting was related principally to the larger streams, such as the Mississippi, Ohio, and Missouri, where the slow-moving flood crests made it easily possible, on the basis of gage-height records only, to issue accurate flood warnings long in advance. However, the increasing concentration of urban development within the flood plains of the shorter rivers, particularly in the East, has made necessary the inauguration of flood-forecasting services on many of these streams, with the result that discharges, as well as stages, are now being utilized.

It has been found in Pennsylvania, where an extensive flood-forecasting service is in operation, that the unit-graph [4] method may be advantageously utilized as a basis for forecasting. By this method, it is possible to follow an incipient flood through the whole period of precipitation and to have available good information with respect to a probable peak before it actually occurs. Pertinent information is obtained at gaging stations and from recording rain gages in each drainage basin. By following this procedure on the tributary streams and from relationships with the main stream which are established through experience, an integrated forecast may be obtained for the main stream, from source to mouth. In Pennsylvania, the use of the radio [5] has made possible the immediate transmission to the central office of information about current river stages, as well as about amounts and intensities of rainfall and depths and densities of snow.

There is a growing demand for more and better stream-flow records as the value of reliable records in relation to human activities has become more generally appreciated and as their use for many purposes has increased. There is a demand for more records of stage and discharge on more streams, since each record relates specifically to one stream and cannot be transferred with assurance to any other stream because of differences in precipitation, temperature, exposed water surfaces, geologic structure, topography, and vegetation. It is also a fact that utilization is never the same in any two drainage basins, more streams being utilized as more water is needed for varied purposes by the increasing population.

[4] Chapter 16.
[5] Chapter 8.

Records of higher and higher accuracy are in demand, especially in connection with the apportionment of inadequate supplies of water among several users, with litigation and the establishment of justice between conflicting users, with the problems of evaluation of projects and properties and of operation of plants and systems that require large quantities of water, and with the complete utilization of a river or of a site on a river, which necessarily involves complete control of the river flow. Hydrologists who coordinate the river records with records of other phases of the hydrologic cycle also need for such purposes records of the highest practicable accuracy.

To meet the demands for more gaging stations and continuing improvement in the quality of river records, additional funds are obviously needed, not only because more records cost more money but also because better records involve the greater costs of improved instruments, better equipment of gaging stations, and more intensive operation, both in field and office. The only element that may tend to decrease costs in connection with an expanded and improved stream-gaging program relates to possible decreases in operating costs as a result of such grouping of gaging stations as will tend relatively to decrease the expenses of travel by the engineers who visit the stations periodically. However, any such decreases will generally be far less than the increases caused by the improvements in instruments and equipment and the more intensive operation. The demand for an expanded and improved program is leading to more adequate financing, as described in Chapter 20, and to more and better records.

Length of Records. Systematic records must be continued indefinitely on many rivers, both large and small, because of their relation to the construction and operation of enterprises of many kinds, to the establishment, protection, and administration of water rights, to the distribution of water among many users, to the progressive and sudden changes in the regimen and runoff of rivers resulting from their physical control or from their utilization for consumptive purposes, to the changes in use that must be made from time to time, to the constantly diminishing unappropriated or unused supplies, to the administration of justice by the courts, and to the increasing importance of water in connection with the needs of modern civilization. Records of flow extending over a few years are not sufficient for the many important demands that are made or will be made on many rivers. Records that are long enough, say from ten to twenty years, to show approximate maxima, minima, and means of flow may be sufficient for some rivers that do not have and apparently will not have serious conflicts or problems in connection with the use of their waters. There is danger, however, that estimates of future needs for the records of such rivers may be erroneous because the needs of the future are most difficult to forecast. It seems certain that the number of gaging stations to be continued indefinitely will increase rather than diminish. In any event, such has been the tendency since the belief that a few years of records at any gaging station would serve all utilitarian needs was abandoned forty years ago.

BIBLIOGRAPHY 7

1. *U. S. Geological Survey Water Supply Papers,* Records of River Discharge, 15 volumes for each year.
2. ROBERT FOLLANSBEE, *A History of the Water Resources Branch of the U. S. Geological Survey to 1919,* published privately.

CHAPTER 8

METHODS AND INSTRUMENTS FOR MEASURING AND RECORDING STREAM FLOW

Units. The two principal groups of units concerned with the measuring and recording of stream flow are: (1) those related to discharge (rate of flow), and (2) those related to runoff (quantity of flow). Special attention is called to the distinction indicated above in the meanings of the words "discharge" and "runoff" that have been generally adopted by engineers and have been followed in this book.[1]

The basic units commonly used in connection with stream gaging in the United States are the "foot" for measurements of dimension and the "second" for measurements of time. From these units, there follow logically the "cubic foot" (c.f.) as the unit of quantity, and the "cubic foot per second" (c.f.s.) or "second-foot" (sec.-ft.) as the unit of rate.

Other units of discharge common in this country are "second-foot per square mile," for expressing the average rate of discharge from a basin, valuable for comparisons of discharge among rivers in the same region; "million gallons a day," used in connection with municipal water supplies and in Hawaii; and "miner's inch," employed in western mining states and defined as the quantity of water that will be discharged through a sharp-edged, 1-inch-square orifice under a fixed head which, however, varies among the states. A second-foot equals 38.4 miner's inches in Colorado, 40 miner's inches in California, and 50 miner's inches in Idaho; other western states use one or another of these three definitions. Because of the resulting lack of definiteness of this unit, it has been now largely displaced by the second-foot, but many old water rights that were acquired in connection with placer mining are defined in terms of the miner's inch, and in mining states it cannot be quickly or wholly eliminated in favor of the more definite unit.

Other units of runoff used in this country are the "gallon" (a cubic foot equals 7.48 United States gallons); the "acre-foot" (43,560 cubic feet), the quantity of water required to cover 1 acre to a depth of 1

[1] Bibliog. 8·12.

foot, used commonly in connection with irrigation; "inches in depth," the average depth in inches over the drainage basin represented by the runoff for the indicated time, generally a year, valuable for comparisons of runoff among rivers in the same region; "million cubic feet" (22.96 acre-feet), or "billion cubic feet," common in nonirrigating states in connection with reservoir capacities and quantities of stored water; and "million gallons," used in connection with municipal water supplies and in Hawaii.

In many countries and to a very limited extent in the United States, the "meter" (3.280833 feet) is the unit of dimension, leading to the "cubic meter" (35.3145 cubic feet) as the unit of volume, and the "cubic meter per second" (35.3145 second-feet) as the corresponding unit of rate. The "second" is the universal unit of time.

Recording Stream Flow Systematically. A systematic record of the flow of a surface stream is commonly made in the United States in terms of the mean daily discharge, expressed in second-feet. Such a record is ordinarily obtained by means of a record of stage at one of two general types of gaging stations, which is converted into a record of discharge by one or more of several methods. Since stage is converted into discharge by means of rating curves, tables, or formulas which express the relation of stage to discharge, it is essential that every record of stage which is to serve as the basis for a record of discharge shall be adequate and reliable and that its conversion to discharge shall be accurately made. Although generally only one rating curve or table is needed for such conversion, there are occasional exceptions. For example, a record of stage that is to be used in obtaining a record of discharge through necessity may be collected just upstream from a dam and power plant where at times part or all of the water passes through the turbines and openings of various kinds through and around the dam and, at other times, part passes over the spillway or crest of the dam. Under these conditions, the record of the stage above the dam will be needed for the computation of the partial discharge through each of the various openings and over the spillway or crest of the dam; a record of stage of the tailwater will also be needed since the discharge through the turbines will be a function of the vertical distance, or head, from headwater to tailwater; and several rating curves or tables will be required for the determination of the total discharge. In order that all conversions from stage to discharge may be reliable, the instruments, equipment, and methods must be adapted to the conditions, whether natural or man-made, pertaining to the site of the gaging station, and each installation must be adapted to meet varying local conditions, if satisfactory records of discharge are to be obtained at the least practicable cost.

The theory that underlies the collection of systematic records of discharge is simple and easily grasped; the difficulties that may confront the engineer in applying the theory are many and varied.[2] Because of the many variations in the conditions affecting the flow of water in natural channels and in the steps taken in collecting records of stage and discharge, constant expert attention is essential if reliable results are to be obtained.

The problems related to the collection of records of stage are essentially identical for all types of gaging stations, but the information needed for converting a record of stage into a record of discharge and the procedures to be followed in making the conversions vary widely with the type of station and the physical conditions affecting the flow at the site. A site for a gaging station involves more than the possibility either of collecting a good record of stage or of making accurate measurements of discharge. There are many sites where one but not both of these two purposes might be accomplished that would not serve satisfactorily as gaging stations because a gaging station must yield both accurate records of stage and reliable means for converting them into records of discharge. In many sections of the country, sites where both these purposes may be served satisfactorily [3] are not readily found, but they must be found and utilized if acceptable records of discharge are to be obtained at reasonable cost.

In addition to gages, there are various instruments, items of equipment, and devices used in connection with measuring or otherwise determining discharge, including (a) dams and other artificial means [4] for stabilizing the stage-discharge relation, (b) devices that will relieve the operating engineer of unnecessary effort or labor and that will provide for his use the best facilities that can be obtained within the limits of available funds, (c) means for maintaining the stability of the datum plane of the station gage to which all observations of elevation at the gaging station are referred, and (d) procedures for promoting the highest practicable reliability of observations and computations of the resulting daily records. The characteristics, equipment, and installation of gaging stations are described in Chapters 11, 12, and 13; methods and instruments are described in this chapter.

The instruments, equipment, and procedures now used in stream gaging have resulted from the experiences and ingenuity of many

[2] Chapter 14.   [4] Chapter 11.
[3] Chapter 10.

engineers working during a half century among the wide variety of conditions that pertain to a nationwide program. Perfection has not been and never can be attained. Continued improvement in instruments and equipment and greater refinement in field and office practices and procedures, therefore, are to be expected as long as the work

Fig. 6. Water-stage recorder installed in wooden shelter. Note double-topped boxed-in table.

of recording the flow of streams is actively prosecuted. The accepted methods and equipment of today will be replaced by the new and better methods and equipment of tomorrow.

Records of Stage. A record of stage that is essential to a systematic record of discharge may be obtained by means of either an instrument that records the stage mechanically (Fig. 6), or a staff gage, chain gage, or wire-weight gage (Figs. 7, 13, 14, 15) that is read by an observer at stated intervals of time, generally twice daily. The obtaining of a mechanical or "automatic" record of stage does not ordinarily offer unusual difficulties so far as instruments are concerned, since reliable water-stage recorders are obtainable that will yield records of stage having any degree of accuracy that may be desired or that is consistent with the other conditions affecting the accuracy of the records of discharge. However, troubles arise with respect

FIG. 7. Typical vertical staff gage with enameled sections on concrete pier.

to the operation of the water-stage recorder, to the instability of the stream's bed and banks at or in the vicinity of the gaging station, to impermanence of the datum plane, to excessive moisture in the recorder shelter, and to dust, sand, silt, snow, ice, and other local physical conditions, any of which may affect the continuity or accuracy of the record of stage. The nature and magnitude of the effects of these various sources of possible trouble vary widely with the climate, geology, topography, and vegetation of the region and with the local conditions at and near the gage site. Troubles arise also from human errors that affect the cost and reliability of the record of stage and, consequently, the duties of the stream-gaging engineer.

Conversion of Stage to Discharge. A record of stage is converted into a record of discharge through the application of some form of calibration or rating which expresses the relation of stage to discharge at the gaging-station site, and which may take the form of a rating curve or its equivalent expressed as a formula or table.[5] If there is a natural control, the site may be rated by measurements of discharge made preferably by means of current meters but also, if necessary, by means of Pitot tubes, Bentzel velocity tubes, floats, or slope formulas, or by volumetric methods. If there is an artificial control, the site may be rated in the same way as a natural control, or it may be rated in a hydraulic laboratory by calibrating a model or in the field by calibrating a similar structure, and by applying, perhaps inaccurately, the calibration thus made to the structure which functions as the control for the gaging station.

Types of Gaging Stations. The method of calibration or rating, whether by actual measurements of discharge or by the transfer of a calibration of a weir or other structure built in the stream channel, divides gaging stations into two general groups: (1) those rated directly by measurements of discharge made at or near the site, and (2) those calibrated indirectly by the transfer of ratings of similar structures made elsewhere. Any gaging station at which the rating is accomplished by means of discharge measurements made at or near the site is called a *velocity-area station* because each such measurement consists of measurements of the cross section and of the velocities of the water, the multiplying of the areas of the partial cross sections by the appropriate velocities to obtain partial discharges, and the summation of the partial discharges to obtain the total discharge. Gaging stations which are calibrated by the transfer of ratings made elsewhere include weirs, dams, Venturi flumes, and all other structures for which the discharge is computed from ratings of other structures, on the basis of the theory of similitude.

Each type of gaging station has valuable characteristics, and both types are used in every well-organized, broad, stream-gaging program in accordance with local situations and requirements. The weir or other comparable artificial device is utilized at existing dams and for measuring quantities of water that are too small for measurement by a current meter. In general, a weir is more practicable for small streams than for large rivers because of the great cost involved in

[5] Chapter 15.

constructing weirs and dams of considerable size. For this reason, a velocity-area station is the only kind that is practicable of installation on a large river in which no suitable dam exists and where a gaging station is needed.

Station Rating Curves. A gaging station situated in a reach of channel where velocity-area measurements of discharge are made, or at a weir or dam where all the water in the stream passes over the crest, will have a station rating curve that is of general parabolic shape, and its application to a record of stage will give the desired record of discharge. If, however, the station is situated at a dam that is used also for other purposes, there may be as many supplemental rating curves or rating tables as there are openings for the passage of water over, around, or through the dam. Each of these curves or tables must be applied separately because they may not apply concurrently and factors other than head may affect the magnitudes of discharge indicated by them. Such a gaging station is not rated until all the rating curves and rating tables for all the openings have been made.

Measurements of Discharge. The field and office processes and procedures involved in the determination of discharge vary widely. In making a current-meter measurement of discharge at a velocity-area station, velocities and depths must be measured at enough points in the cross section to disclose the essential shape and dimensions of the bed and the variations in velocity of current throughout the width of the stream. These measurements require that facilities be provided or available whereby the engineer can make observations of velocities and depths, measure the distances from an initial point on the bank to each point of observation, and place and support himself over any point where an observation is desired.[6] Measurements by the volumetric method at very low stages will ordinarily be employed only to supplement current-meter measurements of discharge at higher stages. At a weir, Venturi flume, contracted opening, or orifice of known calibration, the only field work needed for a determination of discharge is ordinarily the accurate observation of stage at one or more points above or within the structure.

VELOCITY-AREA METHOD. The field rating or calibration of a gaging station by means of the velocity-area method involves making discharge measurements by measuring the area of cross section and the velocity of the flowing water and multiplying these two quantities together. The area of cross section is determined by means of sound-

[6] Chapter 13.

ings and measurements of the distances across the stream from an initial point on the bank to the points of sounding; the velocities are determined by means of (a) current meter, (b) float, or (c) measurement of the surface slope of the flowing water. Although current-meter discharge measurements are all but universal, any one of these three devices may be employed at any gaging station as conditions or equipment require.

There are important differences in the accuracy of results that may be obtained by these methods. In using the current meter,[7] observations of the rates of revolution of the meter wheel are made within a selected cross section of a stream and are converted into velocities by means of a meter rating table (table showing velocities in feet per second corresponding to rates of revolution of the meter wheel) that has been prepared from observations made in a rating flume (Fig. 20). The accuracy attained depends on the integrity of the rating of the meter and on the sufficiency and competency of the observations of depth and velocity. In using a float, the timing of its passage over a measured course constitutes essentially a direct observation of the average velocity of that thread or filament of water in which the float has traveled over that course. The accuracy depends on the essential uniformity of the velocities throughout the length of the runs as well as on the sufficiency of the float runs and of the determinations of areas of cross section. Obviously, surface velocities based on the timing of floats must be adjusted, on the basis of vertical velocity curves or otherwise, to mean velocities. In a determination of velocity by a measurement of surface slope, the average slope over the reach of river in which the slope is measured is converted into an average velocity in that reach by means of a formula which expresses the relation of slope to velocity. The accuracy depends on the uniformity of slope throughout the reach in which the slope is measured, the sufficiency of the cross-sectional measurements within the reach, and the applicability of the coefficient or coefficients selected for use in the slope formula to the channel conditions where the slope is measured.

The current meter has a definite superiority over the other two devices for measuring discharge in that all observations of velocity and cross-sectional area pertain to a single section, whereas a float or slope-area measurement of discharge in a natural channel has at best only such accuracy as may be obtained where the observations are made in a reach of channel which is never uniform either in area of cross section or in the velocity of any thread of current throughout its

[7] Chapter 14.

length, and in which the average cross section can never be known accurately even though several or many cross sections may be measured, and in which the average velocity may not apply strictly to the average cross section thus determined. Although a current-meter measurement of discharge has the apparent advantage of higher accuracy, the float and slope-area methods have definite places in any broad stream-gaging program, and, because of the impracticability of making current-meter measurements of discharge at all times and places, recourse will continue to be had in some situations to these generally less accurate methods.

Current-meter gaging stations are generally accepted as the highest type of velocity-area stations; so far as it has been practicable to do so, float and, to a lesser extent, slope-area determinations have been largely abandoned except in the absence of a current meter or in the unusual circumstances that may pertain during floods. At such times, so much drift may be carried by the flowing water that a current meter cannot be submerged safely and recourse must be had to other methods for determining the velocity. Under these conditions, observations of the velocities of drift may be made in different parts of the channel or the slope of the water surface may be measured.

Slope-Area Method. Although, as suggested above, the slope-area method may be utilized in the determination of mean velocity and total discharge for any stages at which, for one reason or another, current-meter measurements are not possible or practicable, the greatest present value of this method in general stream gaging lies in the means it affords of ascertaining the magnitudes of peak flows, usually after such flows have passed. If correlated with a peak gage height at the station gage, such determinations are extremely valuable in helping to define extensions of rating curves above the highest available current-meter discharge measurements. The method is also very useful in determining peak discharges of streams on which no discharge records are being collected. Because of the wide use of the slope-area method in such situations, a typical procedure is briefly outlined.

A field investigation, preferably a detailed instrumental survey, is made, during which elevations and locations of high-water marks on both banks of the river are noted (for slope) and profiles of bed at several cross sections obtained (for area), all within a reach of river that is as nearly uniform in slope, cross section, and roughness as can be found. A reach in which the area decreases and the velocity increases progressively downstream is particularly desirable. Reaches are selected that are as long as possible without marked changes in channel conditions.

The discharge is computed by means of the Chezy formula

$$v = c\sqrt{rs}$$

and the Manning formula for c:

$$c = \left(\frac{1.486}{n}\right) r^{\frac{1}{6}}$$

The final formula is then

$$Q = A \left(\frac{1.486}{n}\right) r^{\frac{2}{3}} s^{\frac{1}{2}}$$

The value of n depends on the condition of the stream channel. If there are appreciable areas of overflow, the corresponding sections should be considered separately from the main channel and a different value of n selected for each. Values of n are available for a wide range of conditions as they have been determined by Manning, Horton, and others. The hydraulic radius r is determined directly for each cross section, and the slope s is the energy gradient or effective slope through the reach as defined below. A is the area of a cross section, and Q is the discharge in that cross section. The discharge for any reach will be the mean of the figures of discharge obtained in the cross sections at the ends of the reach, and the mean discharge will be the mean of the figures of discharge obtained for all reaches.

If possible, one cross section of a slope-area reach should be selected as the usual high-water measuring section at a gaging station. Then, if data to define the energy gradient are obtained, the results of recent high-stage current-meter measurements can be used to obtain by means of the Chezy-Manning formula a value of n which will be useful as a basis for the selection of a value of n properly applicable to the reach; otherwise, values of n must be selected on the basis of experience or from tables of such values.

The progressive cross-sectional areas of natural stream channels are constantly varying; therefore increasing and decreasing velocities cause the velocity head $v^2/2g$ to vary constantly. In a given reach, if the velocity in the downstream cross section is less than that in the upstream cross section, the energy slope or effective slope of the stream is the surface slope, plus the difference in velocity head

$$\frac{v_1^2}{2g} - \frac{v_2^2}{2g}$$

divided by the length of the reach. This would hold true if 100 per cent recovery of the velocity head could be assured. However, the consensus of opinion is that only 50 per cent of the velocity head is usually recovered and, therefore, that the energy slope is the surface slope plus

$$\frac{1}{2} \frac{\dfrac{v_1^2}{2g} - \dfrac{v_2^2}{2g}}{\text{Length of reach}}$$

If the velocity in the downstream cross section is greater than that in the upstream cross section and the velocity-head differential is negative, there is a loss, and the energy slope is therefore less than the surface slope by an amount equal to the velocity-head differential divided by the length of the reach.

If the stream channel is composed of areas with different values of n and r, the channel should be subdivided, for purposes of computation, into sections according to their respective characteristics. In such situations, a coefficient C_m must be applied to $v^2/2g$ as computed for the average velocity head of the channel to adjust it to the true velocity head.

$$C_m = \frac{\sum \dfrac{k^2}{a}}{\dfrac{K^2}{A}},$$

in which

$$k = a\left(\frac{1.486}{n}\right) r^{\frac{2}{3}}$$

for each section into which the stream channel has been subdivided, and K is the summation of the k's for the several sections.

WEIR METHOD. The weir method of collecting systematic records of discharge consists in obtaining a record of stage above a weir of known cross-sectional and longitudinal shape and dimensions and applying thereto the appropriate weir formula or weir table. Obviously, for the best results, the record of stage, and consequently of head on the weir crest, should be continuous, and the use of a water-stage recorder may therefore be indicated.

Weirs are much used for measuring discharge, with a high degree of accuracy under proper conditions. They vary widely in crest profile, in cross section, and in placement in the stream channel. If a weir measurement of discharge is to be reliable, the weir must have the following essential characteristics: (a) no appreciable leakage through or around it, since the only water measured is that which passes over the crest; (b) cross section of crest and of upstream and downstream faces identical with those of the weir for which terms and coefficients in the weir formula have been reliably determined; (c) profile of crest identical with that of a weir that has been previously rated; (d) placement in channel closely similar to that of a weir of the same kind that has been previously tested, thereby assuring the essential conditions of channel approach, velocity of approach, and end contractions that have been properly rated; and (e) steady discharge over the crest, that is, the surface slope of the pool above the weir should not be changing at the time of observation of head on the weir.

This method has the same basis of theory for all types of weirs, varying only in the terms, coefficients, and exponents used in the underlying weir formula. The simplest weir formula is $Q = clh^{3/2}$, for the discharge Q (in cubic feet per second) over a rectangular weir without end contractions, in which the velocity is expressed as $ch^{1/2}$ and the area of cross section as lh, c is a coefficient, h is the energy head (in feet), being the sum of the static head on the weir and the velocity head at the approach section, and l is the length (in feet) of the crest. The formula is varied [8] in terms, coefficients, and exponents for weirs of different crest profiles and cross sections, end contractions and channels of approach.

All other weir formulas are variations of this simple equation, with differences in the coefficient c and in the exponent of h, and, if appropriate, the addition of a term or terms to provide for the decrease in effective length due to end contractions and for departures from the simple rectangular weir. In connection with the use of a weir or dam, the formula and values of coefficients and exponents must be carefully studied in order that the formula adopted may be appropriate to the situation.

Weirs and dams are commonly unsatisfactory as gaging stations in connection with general stream gaging in several respects and in varying degrees, because (a) they are nonsensitive, especially at low stages and therefore are likely to yield inaccurate records at the most important periods of flow; (b) they have not been well calibrated for high heads and, therefore, yield unsatisfactory records of flood discharge; (c) they are liable to varying and unmeasurable changes in crest length due to the lodgment of drift on the crest at low stages; and (d) they are liable to unknowable changes in the coefficient c due to changes in the dimensions and shape of the channel of approach, especially on or near the upstream face.

[8] Bibliog. 8·1, 2, 13, 14, 15, 18, 20.

Many engineers believe that records of discharge are collected more cheaply at an existing dam than at a current-meter gaging station. Actually, such records are likely to be more expensive because of the greater costs involved in computations of partial flow through each of several water wheels and through sluice gates, fish ladders, and wasteways, whereas the records at current-meter gaging stations may be computed mechanically by means of a discharge integrator.[9] However, on rivers that are largely developed for production of hydraulic power, for navigation, or for other purposes, and in which backwater above dams extends over most of the reaches between them, there may be few or no good sites available as ordinary velocity-area stations. In such situations, recourse must be had to slope stations or to the use of dams as control sections, the selection of either of these two types of stations in preference to the other depending upon existing conditions.

Sharp-Crested Weirs. Sharp-crested weirs [10] are largely used for measuring relatively small quantities of water, especially in distributary systems for irrigation. For that purpose, standard sharp-crested weirs, such as V-notch weirs, trapezoidal weirs, and Cippoletti weirs, are common. Such weirs have been well calibrated, and their crest characteristics and their placements in the artificial channels of an irrigation system can be duplicated with considerable precision. Standard sharp-crested weirs also successfully record the flow of small streams under many conditions and in many regions, and they may be practicable in a few situations as gaging stations in small rivers. They are not common in systematic stream gaging, however, because of the high cost of construction of the stations if the weirs are built solely for that purpose, and such weirs are not common for any other purpose. Tables for standard sharp-crested weirs may be found in all hydraulic engineering handbooks and many collections of engineering tables. Experience has shown that sharp-crested weirs utilized as controls for gaging stations, if conditions permit, should be rated by current-meter measurements, supplemented perhaps by volumetric measurements, rather than to use weir formulas of frequently doubtful applicability. If such procedure is followed, the sharp-crested weirs function merely as artificial controls.

Dams. Broad- and round-crested dams or weirs not sharp-crested are utilized to some extent for stream-gaging purposes, but the cost of construction generally limits such use to existing dams that have been built to serve other purposes. Their employment for stream gag-

[9] Chapter 15.
[10] Chapter 11.

ing is, therefore, generally complicated by the diversion of part or all
of the water for irrigation, generation of power, municipal supplies, or
other purposes. The water so diverted must be measured in some
way and added to the quantity of water that passes over the crest of
the dam. The openings through and around dams may and probably will be of a variety of shapes, each of which will have its particular formula and coefficient which should be determined by test, if
practicable, or otherwise be estimated from the best available information.

Many determinations have been made of the discharge over dams
of various shapes of crest, and the results of these ratings are widely
scattered through engineering literature. The largest compilation is
contained in *Water Supply Paper* 200,[11] in which Robert E. Horton
brought together all records available to him in 1906 when the compilation was made. No comparable compilation has since been published. Contained in that report is a table of multipliers, computed
and arranged by E. C. Murphy, to be applied to the results obtained
by means of a Bazin formula for flow over sharp-crested weirs to
obtain the results shown by Horton for weirs of various shapes of
crest. The Bazin formula used as the basis of the comparisons made
by Murphy is

$$Q = \left(0.405 + \frac{0.0984}{h}\right)\left(1 + 0.55\,\frac{h^2}{(p+h)^2}\right)lh\,\sqrt{2gh}$$

in which p is the height of the weir and the other letters have the same
significance as in the simple weir formula cited above. For rectangular weirs, these multipliers range from 0.708 to 1.00, varying largely
with the shape and to a lesser extent with head on the dam and width
of crest; the range may be as much as 20 per cent for differences in
head of 10 feet or for differences in width of crest of 5 feet. These
ranges in multipliers illustrate the necessity for choosing with care the
coefficients to be used with respect to dams, and the possible inaccuracies that may result from the use of dams of shapes that have not been
carefully calibrated.

The complications pertaining to the computations, the lack of stand-
ardization of broad- and round-crested dams, and the resulting uncertainties, not only as to the proper coefficient to be used in a weir
formula in connection with each dam but also as to the variations in
such coefficients with varying heads, generally render such stations
unsatisfactory because the accuracy of the records obtained at them

[11] Bibliog. 8·2.

is, as a rule, inferior to that obtained at current-meter gaging stations, and because they are expensive to operate, especially with respect to the computation of the records. They are liable to the greatest errors at low stages for which variations in stage, shape of crest, and differences in nappe have the largest relative effects, and at high stages, for which coefficients to be used in a weir formula are least well known. Thus, the important stages of droughts and floods are, unfortunately, subject to maximum errors.

A dam is not commonly used as a gaging station, therefore, if a good site for a current-meter station can be found in the section of river where a record of flow is needed. However, in many rivers which have been extensively developed, the choice may have to be made between a gaging station located at a dam and a current-meter gaging station located within the fluctuating pool above a dam in which varying slopes of the water surface must be measured by means of two recording gages installed from 1,000 to 25,000 feet apart, the records from which will disclose the average slopes within the pool at all times. Such slope stations are expensive to operate; the computation of the discharge records is costly; and the accuracy of such records may not be of the highest order. If it is necessary that a dam be utilized as a control section, every effort should be made to establish the ratings applicable thereto by means of current-meter measurements rather than on the basis of theoretical or experimental coefficients.

VENTURI FLUMES. The use of a weir in measuring stream flow involves a considerable loss of head, since a definite drop in the surface of the water as it passes over the weir is necessary, even if the weir is submerged. In measurements made with sharp-crested weirs, there must be free fall over the weir and free entrance of air under the nappe. In many situations, such as in the canals and laterals of a large irrigation system, head must be conserved, and for this reason the use of weirs is frequently impracticable.

The Venturi flume,[12] which is based on the well-known Venturi principle, is essentially a structure of wood or concrete which provides a short constricted portion or "throat" for the passage of the water between an upstream contracting approach and a downstream diverging exit. The discharge may be computed by formula, the difference in head at the entrance and in the throat being utilized, among other factors, or the flume may be rated in the laboratory and reproduced in the field. An important advantage of the Venturi flume is its ability to function with a relatively small net loss of head.

[12] Bibliog. 8·4, 5.

The Parshall measuring flume, devised by Ralph L. Parshall, is an improved modification of the original Venturi flume. This flume utilizes a longer throat, which slopes downward instead of being level and requires not more than two stilling wells for water-level readings, whereas the older type of Venturi flume required four such wells in which simultaneous readings were made.

Since Venturi flumes are employed principally in connection with the distribution of irrigation water, their field of usefulness in systematic stream gaging is generally confined to those situations on small streams where the head which is available or can be made available is insufficient for the proper operation of a sharp-crested weir.

CONTRACTED OPENINGS. In the determination of flood discharges, recourse is had to every known device for obtaining estimates of quantities of flow. The contracted opening is a common device for that purpose. This method depends upon the same principle as the Venturi flume, and the basic formulas for the determination of discharge are identical. It may be used wherever a constriction of the river channel causes a sharp drop in the water surface, as, for example, between the abutments or piers of a bridge or between the walls of a narrow gorge. The drop in the water surface caused by the constriction, a measure of the velocity, and the cross-sectional areas of the contracted opening or openings and of the stream immediately above the drop provide the required observational data.[13]

ORIFICES. Orifices have long served as a means for measuring water in hydraulic laboratories. For such application sharp-edged orifices are common, and the coefficients for them have been well determined. Formulas for the flow through them, in terms of dimension and head, are contained in all handbooks on hydraulics.

Orifices as measuring devices enter to a considerable degree into the collection of river records because they are common in dams that serve as gaging stations, particularly in those dams at which no water is diverted for the production of electrical or mechanical energy. In such situations, the discharge through the dams is usually controlled by sluice gates which are in reality orifices. Such gates may be closed or opened full for indefinite periods, or opened by any fractional amount for any length of time. The outflow from storage reservoirs is frequently controlled for months and even years at a time by the operation of sluice gates alone, the water surface being held below spillway level by the manipulation of the gates. Sluice gates are

[13] Bibliog. 8·24; 18·10, 11.

usually either circular or rectangular in shape; they may be operated mechanically or manually; and they may discharge freely into the air or beneath the water surface.

Through necessity such dams are occasionally utilized as gaging stations, in which situations the discharge will be computed partly as flow over the spillways, if such flow occurs, and partly, generally to a greater extent, as flow through the sluice gates. The gates are rated by current-meter measurements, if possible, for various openings, usually expressed as fractions of full opening, and under different heads. The determination of gate ratings by theoretical means is beset by difficulties because of the wide range and variation in the values of the applicable coefficients. The gatekeeper's record of gate openings gives for each day the opening and time of run for each gate operated; these data, by means of the gate-rating tables and a ratio expressing the proportionate part of the day during which each gate is in operation, may be readily converted into mean discharge per twenty-four hours. The total discharge, of course, is the flow through the gates and the discharge, if any, over the main spillways and auxiliary spillways, if such are present. Experience has shown that, in situations where the discharge passes principally through sluice gates and where a reliable record of gate operation is available, the discharge may be determined with reasonable accuracy if the gates have been carefully rated by current-meter measurements and are kept free from drift and other obstructions. One of the principal sources of error may lie in careless operation of the gates, as a result of which the actual settings may differ by considerable amounts from the recorded positions, particularly with respect to manually operated gates.

TURBINES AS WATER METERS. In an increasing number of situations, it is necessary to operate gaging stations at dams that are used for the generation of hydraulic power and, therefore, to utilize turbines as water meters in connection with the recording of river discharge. Fortunately for the purposes of the stream-gaging engineer, a high degree of accuracy is demanded for the tests of turbines and power plants and the resulting ratings of turbines, because the value of a power plant depends on the continuing high efficiencies of its operation and because bonuses and penalties are involved in the efficiencies of the turbines.

RATING TURBINES AND POWER PLANTS. The testing of the efficiency of turbines and power plants involves the accurate measurement, under unusually difficult conditions, of the water passing through them. In many situations, it is not practicable to utilize for water-measuring purposes the head that would be required for the operation of a weir. Often, too, there are no opportunities to obtain accurate measurements by means of current meters because of the common use of penstocks to conduct water to the turbines and the generally turbulent conditions of flow in tailraces. To meet such situations, the Gibson method and the salt-velocity method, described below, have been devised and found successful. Since for their use, the water must flow through a conduit, they may not serve in measuring the flow at all power plants, especially at those where relatively low heads are utilized.

Gibson Method. The Gibson method appears to serve satisfactorily in the measurement of water passing through turbines if the water flows through a closed conduit that is at least 50 feet long and in which there is a valve or other device for controlling the flow. Gibson has described [14] the method and defined the conditions of its use in testing the efficiency of a turbine as follows:

The method makes use of two well-known principles, the first being Newton's second law of motion, sometimes referred to as the equation of impulse and momentum, and the second (attributed to Joukovsky) being a corollary of the first, namely, the relation between change of pressure and change of velocity of a column of water expressed in terms of the velocity of the pressure waves which are propagated during the change from one end of the column to the other.

Conditions of applicability:

1st. The water must flow through a pressure pipe or other closed conduit.
2nd. Means must be available for controlling the flow, such as a valve or turbine gage, at a point some distance from the intake. It makes no difference how large the conduit may be or whether the cross section is of uniform area or not. The accuracy of the measurement, however, depends to some extent on the length of the conduit, and it is desirable that this should be at least 50 feet, preferably not less than 100 feet. · · ·
The apparatus required for an efficiency test comprise the following:
(a) A headwater indicating and recording float gage that will give an accurate record of the headwater levels during a test. The instrument for this work must be specially designed to make one revolution of the drum in about four or five minutes so that it will show clearly, to relatively large scale, any surges that occur in the forebay during or immediately following the closing of the turbine gates.
(b) A tailwater float or staff gage for observing tailwater levels.
(c) The apparatus for obtaining pressure-time diagrams, which has been called the Gibson apparatus [15] and which is attached to the penstock at any convenient point by means of a ¼-inch connecting pipe.

[14] Bibliog. 8·25.
[15] Patented in Canada in 1919 and 1920 and in the United States in 1921.

(d) A pressure gage or piezometer for measuring the head acting on the turbine.

(e) Electrical equipment for measuring the output of the generator. It is assumed that the efficiency of the generator will have been previously determined.

(f) A signal system (usually electric bells) for communicating with the observers at the forebay, tailrace, pressure gage, Gibson apparatus, and electrical instruments and with the operator at the governor.

Also the equipment for measuring the power output of the turbine and for determining its efficiency.

Apparently, the equipment indicated in items (a), (b), (c), (d), and (f) are essential to the measurement of the water. In nearly twenty years since this description of the Gibson method was published, there has been no change in the underlying principles, but the procedure followed in testing the efficiency of turbines or plants has been improved and simplified. The current specifications for such testing are contained in paragraphs 117 to 133 of the *Test Code for Hydraulic Prime Movers*, American Society of Mechanical Engineers, 1938.

Salt-Velocity Method. The salt-velocity method, perfected by Professor Charles M. Allen, and first applied successfully in 1921, serves well in measuring the flow through water wheels under some conditions. It has been described by him as follows: [16]

The salt velocity method of water measurement is based on the fact that salt in solution increases the electric conductivity of water. Salt solution is introduced near the upper end of the conduit, and the passage of the solution by one or more pairs of electrodes, at other points in the conduit, is recorded graphically by electrical recording instruments. The passage of the salt solution between two points is accurately timed, and the volume of the penstock between the same points is accurately determined. The discharge in cubic feet per second equals the volume in cubic feet divided by the time in seconds.

It is evident that this description does not include the equipment needed for determining the power generated by or the efficiency of the turbine. Specifications for procedure in applying the salt-velocity method appear in full in paragraphs 88 to 96 of the *Test Code for Hydraulic Prime Movers*, American Society of Mechanical Engineers, 1938.

The salt-velocity method may be likened to the use of floats adequately distributed throughout the cross section of the conduit and each timed electrically in its passage from the point of introduction of the salt solution to a pair of electrodes.

[16] Bibliog. 8·26.

Groat [17] has successfully applied a chemical method, which he called chemihydrometry, to the measurement of water flowing through a power plant. His method appears not to have been developed, however, in such way as to meet competition with the Gibson and salt-velocity methods in those situations where either might be applied. No figures are at hand which would show relative accuracies and costs of the Gibson, salt-velocity, and Groat methods.

Instruments for Measuring and Recording Stream Flow. The principal instruments for measuring and recording the discharge of rivers at velocity-area stations are of two classes: (1) gages for indicating and recording stages, and (2) current meters for measuring velocity. Accessories include hand lines and reel lines for suspending weights and meters, weights for making soundings and holding meters in position, reels and cranes for handling heavy weights, tapes for measuring depths and distances, and stop watches for registering time as an element in the measurement of velocity. The major pieces of equipment of a gaging station include the supports and shelter for the gage or gages, and a bridge, cable, or boat to enable the engineer to make the requisite observations of depth and velocity at any part of the measuring section of the stream.

For float stations, in addition to gages, there must be surface and perhaps subsurface and tube or rod floats, and the equipment needed for releasing them at selected points in the current upstream from the selected course, for timing their passage over the course, and for measuring the length of the course and the areas of the cross sections of the stream at the ends of the course and at intermediate points.

For slope stations and for slope-area measurements, there must be available, in addition to the necessary gages, an engineer's level for measuring the slope of the water's surface at peak or other stage, and the instruments needed for measuring the distance along the river between the gages or between the ends of the reach and the cross sections of the stream at the ends and intermediate points of the reach.

For all types of stations, transits equipped with stadia wires for making necessary areal surveys and engineer's levels and leveling rods for setting gages and for referencing and checking their datums must be available.

The instruments needed in stream gaging, except water-stage recorders, gages, current meters, stop watches, and accessories for handling and placing the meters and for making soundings, are part

[17] Bibliog. 8·27.

of the equipment of every engineer who makes surveys, and their characteristics are described in textbooks on surveying.

WATER-STAGE RECORDERS. The essential characteristics of a water-stage recorder relate to reliability of performance with respect to both stage and time. The reliability of the time element relates to both the running and timekeeping qualities of the clock; the reliability of the stage element relates to the accuracy of transmission of the stage of the stream to the record sheet.

Recorders now standard for stream gaging are of the graph, rectangular-coordinate, float type. Recorders that make graph records with polar coordinates have been largely discontinued for general stream gaging for two reasons—the small scale of the graph, especially for low stages when accuracy may be of greatest importance, and the inability to compute the records mechanically by means of a discharge integrator.

Excellent recorders of the type that automatically prints the gage height in figures on a paper tape at regular intervals, such as 15 minutes, 1 hour, or 2 hours, have been made and used. They have largely been abandoned for general stream-gaging purposes because of the relatively high cost of the instruments themselves and of the computations necessary for converting records of stage made by them into records of discharge. Their records cannot be computed mechanically by means of a discharge integrator, as can a rectangular-coordinate graph record, and, further, a printed record affords little opportunity for visualizing the fluctuations in the stage of a stream, as may be readily done by casual inspection of a graph record. The record from a printing recorder may be of great value as an exhibit in court since it is practically impossible to change or alter it in any way. Such a record is also very convenient in situations involving the stages of lakes and reservoirs, which ordinarily are not subject to rapid or sudden fluctuations.

Pressure recorders have been tried and generally abandoned in connection with stream gaging because of their lack of reliability and precision in transmitting the stage of the water to the graph, as temperature and barometric pressure, as well as stage of water, affect the record. The use of polar coordinates by this type of recorder is a further drawback.

The rectangular-coordinate graph made by a water-stage recorder shows stage on one axis and the corresponding time on the other. The most common scale ratio for stage as relating to sizable rivers or those which have great ranges in stage is 1 : 12, that is, 1 inch on the graph represents 1 foot of river stage. Gage-height ratios of 1 : 6 are much used where the ranges in stage are moderate. The usual scale for time is 2.4 inches per day (0.1 inch per hour). Recorders are so constructed

Fig. 8. Au Drum water-stage recorder.

as to be easily convertible to other scales of both stage and time. The discharge integrator can be set for use on a rectangular-coordinate graph of any stage or time scale.

Water-stage recorders are of two forms: (1) weekly or 8-day recorders by which time is recorded usually, though not invariably, along the drum (across the record sheet) and stage is recorded around the drum, thus providing for an unlimited range of stage without reversals

FIG. 9. Stevens Type F water-level recorder.

in the graph; and (2) long-time (so-called continuous) recorders, in which time is recorded around the drum and stage is recorded along the drum and across the record sheet, thereby leading to the necessity for a mechanism which will cause reversals in the graph at the margins of the record sheet in order to record the full range of stage if the height of the graph without reversals would be greater than the width of the record sheet. Although these two forms of recorders are designed for and, therefore, adapted to use in different situations, the only important mechanical difference between them, to which there can be no exception, lies in the characteristics of the record sheets which are utilized. The record sheet or "chart" for a weekly recorder provides for a weekly record, but the paper supply for a long-time recorder feeds from a continuous roll and the record of stage may be removed at intervals of almost any desired length.

The weekly or 8-day recorder (Figs. 8 and 9) is suitable for stations that are easily reached by an engineer or observer, thus making practicable the changing of the record sheets or charts at relatively short intervals of time. An 8-day recorder is preferred to a 7-day recorder because of the 24-hour leeway afforded in the time of changing the record sheet. The records from such recorders are thus made available at weekly intervals, which is frequently a most important feature in situations where provisional records of discharge must be kept essentially current. Their clocks may be either spring-driven or weight-driven, preferably the latter, because of greater general reliability particularly under severe winter conditions. Some types of weekly recorders are provided with mechanisms which will produce reversals in the time element when the pen or pencil reaches the end of the record sheet, thus causing the graph to proceed in the reverse direction. The principal objection to this arrangement lies in the fact that the graph for the second week may be very difficult to distinguish from that for the first week if there is but little change in stage. In another type of weekly recorder, time is recorded around the drum rather than across it, thus providing an unlimited time capacity. The same objection as that mentioned above applies also to this situation in which the record for the second week may be partly superimposed on that for the first week. Both devices are of value, however, in insuring the continuity of records that might otherwise be broken, as for example through an observer's failure to reach the gaging station until several days after the time of his regular weekly visit.

Long-time recorders (Figs. 10 and 11) are suitable for gaging stations that are not easily reached. Therefore, they are much used in general stream gaging. They must always be equipped with weight-driven clocks which will run as long as the weight continues to fall except when a so-called fuzee recorder (a recorder in which the shaft over which the driving-weight cable operates is slightly conical and increases in diameter exactly as the paper-takeup roll increases in diameter) is used, in which situation the record must be removed and the driving weight rewound at intervals no longer than 60 days. If the well has not sufficient depth to provide for the needed length of time by a single fall of the clock weight, its capacity in that respect can be increased as desired by introducing a pulley or system of pulleys and adding appropriately to the driving weight. Many per-

FIG. 10. Stevens continuous water-level recorder.

fect records have been obtained from continuous recorders that have run for 100 days or more between times of visits by engineers or observers and, therefore, between rewindings of the driving weight. With such a recorder, however, it generally is desirable for an engineer to visit the station as often as convenient, in order to rewind the clock drive, remove the record, and perform all other duties essential to the operation of the station, because by more frequent visits the loss of record resulting from possible recorder or clock trouble will be minimized.

The availability of excellent long-time recorders has removed the absolute necessity for employing observers and has permitted the selection of the best sites for gaging stations without respect to the availability of local residents who might be hired to attend the gages, thereby greatly increasing the range of selection of gaging-station sites. Their availability has thus tended to improve the quality

FIG. 11.   Friez continuous water-level recorder.

and decrease the costs of the records, not only by the elimination of the cost of observers' services but also by decreasing operating costs, because the better the site for the station the more stable will be the stage-discharge relation and the fewer will be the number of discharge measurements needed for establishing and maintaining a reliable station rating.

In the early days of water-stage recorders, records were lost for an appreciable percentage of the time as a result of the stopping of the clocks. Because of this experience, excellent grades of clocks have now been adopted for recorders, and more attention is given to the testing, inspection, and adjustment of the water-stage recorders themselves before their installation. All modern first-class recorders are equipped with relatively expensive clocks that are reliable in action and are good timekeepers. As a result, there is now comparatively little loss of records because of clock troubles. Good water-stage recorders are not cheap; their clocks must be first class, the metals non-corrosive, and the workmanship excellent; otherwise, there will be failure in the continuity or accuracy of their operation.

As has been pointed out, continuous water-stage recorders must be provided with a mechanism which will make a reversal in the graph at the margins of the record sheet. In situations where there is a considerable range in stage, it is not uncommon for the graph to pass through two or more successive reversals before the peak is recorded. At gaging stations which are not visited weekly, there may be long periods of record during which no inspections will be made, thus affording no opportunity for checking the time or stage shown by the graph. Although the record paper for continuous recorders is apparently less subject to errors resulting from expansion and contraction than are weekly recorder charts, some variation in recorded time will usually occur in long records. In order that the proper divisions between days may be made on the record sheet, a midnight-marking device is a common accessory to a continuous recorder. This device makes a small mark in the margin of the paper at midnight, thus providing an excellent basis for the determination of time corrections when the record is computed.

LONG-DISTANCE STAGE TRANSMISSION. Gaging stations may be situated in places which are so difficult of access that under normal conditions of operation the charts or record sheets can be removed from the water-stage recorders only at relatively long intervals. Obviously, such records give little current information with respect to river stages; such information is often required in connection with the operation of hydroelectric systems and water-supply developments and is indispensable in flood forecasting. A field of usefulness exists, therefore, for a recording instrument which will furnish, at a point distant a few hundred feet or many miles from the gaging station, a concurrent indication of the river stage at the station. For this purpose, both long-distance water-stage recorders and long-distance water-stage indicators are available.

Long-Distance Water-Stage Recorders. The function of a long-distance water-stage recorder is to provide, in a power house or central office, a counterpart of the gage-height graph which is being, or might be, produced by an ordinary water-stage recorder at a distant gaging station. For this purpose, continuous electrical transmission is required. Long-distance water-stage recorders, which are of several types and kinds, depend for their operation on the transmission of electrical impulses which vary with fluctuations in stage at the gaging station as expressed generally in the rise and fall of a float in the well. Two separate instruments are always required, a sender or transmitter at the gaging station, and a receiver at the distant point where the record is desired. The receiver is connected by appropriate mechanism to a recorder on which gage heights, converted from electrical impulses, are recorded by a pen or stylus to produce a continuous graph. In some systems, identical gage-height records are produced at the transmitting and receiving stations; in others, a gage-height record is produced only by the recorder which operates in connection with the receiver.

Long-Distance Water-Stage Indicators. In many situations, the transmission of a continuous record of stage from a distant gaging station is not required; rather, some facility is needed whereby an instantaneous record of stage at the gaging station may be obtained at headquarters at any time. For this purpose, long-distance water-stage indicators utilizing either the telephone or the radio are satisfactory.

Transmission by telephone generally utilizes existing telephone facilities if available, the gaging station or transmitter being assigned a regular number. When this number is called or dialed from another telephone, a series of coded signals, which may be translated into a gage reading, is heard. The equipment for so converting water stages into intelligible sounds in code for transmission by telephone has been in successful operation for many years, although to a somewhat limited extent. The present trend is apparently toward the use of long-distance water-stage recorders because of the more satisfactory service generally so obtained.

During the past few years, the objectionable features of long-distance telephonic transmission have been overcome to some extent by the development of equipment to transmit river stages by radio. Transmission by radio involves the same basic principles as other types of transmission, that is, the conversion of river stages into electrical impulses. In radio transmission, the signals are radiated to collection centers through the medium of radio frequencies. Problems involved in using radio service of this kind include the type of equipment to be selected, the distances to be covered, and the locations of transmitter and receiver.

The installation of any radio equipment for the purpose of automatically transmitting river stages should not be undertaken prior to actual transmission tests from the gaging station to the collection center by competent radio engineers. This is necessary in order to determine the feasibility of the project and to decide upon the frequency and power to be employed. Ultra-high frequencies are practically always required in order to insure reliable communication, a fact which limits the range of the transmitter. This range may be somewhat extended by increasing the power at the transmitter. Since radio frequencies have not been specifically allocated for this use by private agencies, the principal use of this type of transmission will probably continue to be by various federal agencies, to whom regular frequencies have been assigned for such purposes.

NONRECORDING GAGES. Nonrecording gages are of two general types: (1) staff gages, on which readings of stage are made directly, and (2) chain, wire-weight, float-tape, and hook gages, in connection with which readings of stage are made indirectly by measurement to the water surface from fixed points. Float-tape gages and hook gages are used almost exclusively as auxiliary or reference gages in connection with the operation of water-stage recorders.

A staff gage may be either vertical or inclined. It must be securely attached to supports that should not change in elevation as the result of frost action, erosion, or fluctuations in river stages. Vertical staff gages may be graduated and painted by hand, but now they are generally constructed of enameled steel plates, accurately graduated by stencil and made in 3.4-foot sections which may be assembled to form gages of any desired lengths (Fig. 12). Such plates must be securely attached to heavy planking in order to assure rigidity, durability, and relative safety from destruction. They are particularly adapted to installation on bridge abutments and similar stable structures which provide protection from ice or drift. Inclined staff gages (Fig. 55) must generally be graduated in place with the aid of an engineer's level, in order to insure graduations that will show vertical elevations correctly.

A vertical gage may be difficult to read because of its distance from the bank of the river at times of high water. An inclined gage may obviously be closely read at any stage unless it is wholly submerged. Frequently, accurate staff-gage readings are difficult to make because of waves and surges, and *stilling wells* are sometimes utilized in situations where no great range in stage is involved. A stilling well may consist of a wooden or concrete well 3 feet or 4 feet square connected with the stream by an intake pipe 2 inches in diameter. Accurate readings may be made on a vertical gage attached to the inside of the well. Stilling wells are also utilized in connection with Venturi flumes and Parshall measuring flumes.

Because nonrecording gages are generally read no oftener than twice daily, the maximum stage occurring during a day or on a flood peak is seldom recorded as an actual observation of gage height. In some situations, where information is desired with respect to such

Fig. 12. Typical vertical staff gage with enameled sections on bridge abutment.

stages, *maximum-stage gages* may be desirable. The purpose of such a gage is to indicate by some mechanical means the maximum gage height which occurred since the last visit by the observer or engineer. Maximum-stage gages are of many types, some of which are ingenious and most of which are reasonably effective. As they give no indication as to the actual times of occurrence of maximum stages, their value is limited.

Staff gages, whether vertical or inclined, are liable to damage or destruction by floating ice, logs, and debris. They are liable also to changes in datum unless attached to ledge rock, masonry piers or abutments, or other equally substantial structures.

The chain gage (Fig. 13) was devised to take the place of the staff gage because of the danger of damage or destruction of the latter

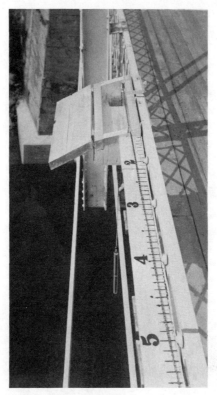

Fig. 13. Chain gage installed on highway bridge.

and to provide better accessibility at high stages. It must be placed on a bridge or other structure that spans or overhangs the stream whose flow is to be recorded. The stage is read on a long horizontal scale at the point where an index marker intersects the scale when the bottom of the weight is just at the water surface. The chain gage has the disadvantage of possible fluctuations in height of the bridge or structure to which it is attached, due to changing loads or temperature, and to changes in length of chain as a result of stretching and wearing of the links, and a further disadvantage that when readings are being made the extended chain offers considerable resistance to wind.

So-called weight gages and wire-weight gages are improved modifications of the chain gage. The weight gage (Fig. 14) utilizes, instead of a chain, a wire or cable which is wound on or unwound from a small

FIG. 14. Canfield weight gage installed on highway bridge.

reel and which is graduated in feet. Readings are made opposite the index graduations on a metal scale graduated in tenths and hundredths of a foot. The whole gage is housed in a small metal box attached to a bridge member or other support. The wire-weight gage (Fig. 15) utilizes an ungraduated wire wound on a horizontal drum 1 foot in circumference. Readings to the nearest foot are made on a counter and to tenths and hundredths of a foot on a calibrated disk on one end of the drum. Some types of wire-weight gages are provided with a "check bar" of known elevation. When the weight is placed on this bar, the readings on the counter and disk should agree with the check-bar elevation, thus affording a ready means of setting or checking the gage.

Obviously, nonrecording gages cost less than water-stage recorders, and the cost of their installation is much less. The records of stage obtained by their use consist of one or more readings daily which are inherently subject to human errors that generally cannot be checked or eliminated and to errors resulting from rough water and surges,

FIG. 15. U. S. G. S. Type A wire-weight gage installed on highway bridge.

which make the accurate reading of such gages next to impossible. Records of stage from nonrecording gages cannot be computed mechanically, and, of course, they are much less accurate than records from water-stage recorders. However, they serve satisfactorily in many situations, especially on streams that fluctuate slowly, and therefore they are better adapted to use on large rivers than on small ones. Satisfactory records of streams that fluctuate rapidly from either natural or artificial causes can be obtained only by means of water-stage recorders.

CURRENT METERS. Current meters are of two general types, differing essentially in the form of the meter wheel: (1) cup type, differential action, vertical axis of rotation; and (2) screw type, direct action, horizontal axis of rotation. With either type, the speed of rotation of the meter wheel varies with the velocity of the water that strikes it, and the rate of rotation is the measure of the velocity of the water in which it is placed. Either type gives reliable results when used in smooth-flowing, nonturbulent water. In turbulent water the cup type tends to over-register and the screw type to under-register. Both types are in common use, and each is better adapted than the other to certain conditions.[18]

The Small Price meter (Fig. 16) is the outstanding example of the cup-type current meter. It was originally designed by W. G. Price,

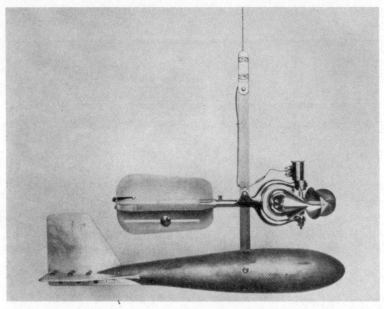

Fig. 16. Small Price current meter (cable suspension, Columbus-type weight).

in essentially the form now known as the Large Price meter, for use in the turbid waters of the Ohio River; it has been improved as the Small Price meter by engineers of the Geological Survey for country-wide use under the many and varying conditions of general stream gaging and may now be considered the standard instrument for such work. It may be used with confidence in measuring nonturbulent water as it flows in rivers that are clear or turbid, large or small, deep or shallow. It is made to indicate either every revolution or every fifth revolution of the meter wheel, and it is adapted for measuring velocities of current ranging between 0.25 foot or less and 20 feet per second. It may be operated from a bridge, cableway, or boat, or by wading, and may be suspended by cable or rod. Its rating is not liable to be changed

[18] Bibliog. 8·7, 8.

essentially by turbid water or by the rough treatment to which it may be subjected in measuring debris-laden flood waters. It may be operated by one man who also observes time and keeps notes. It is easily dismantled for cleaning and oiling and as easily reassembled. Because of these valuable qualities, possessed by no other one meter, the Small Price meter has come to be recognized as the only universal current meter yet developed that is reasonably well adapted to the many and varying conditions related to general stream gaging. However, when used in water that is highly turbulent or from a boat or cableway that has considerable vertical motion, it loses to a greater or less degree in accuracy of indication of horizontal velocity because of over-registration.

The vertical axis of this meter is supported on a pivot bearing set in a deep inverted cup in which air is entrapped, thereby preventing the entrance of water and silt that otherwise might cause a change in the rating of the meter by interference with the free motion of the meter wheel bearing on its pivot. The movement of the meter wheel on the pivot is nearly frictionless, and therefore the meter is sensitive to slight motion of the water even though it is of the differential type. Price regarded the setting of the pivot bearing in a deep inverted cup as an essential and characteristic feature of his meter.

The principal points of advantage of the Small Price meter are its usability and reliability of action under a wide range of conditions, its structural strength, its holding of accuracy of rating under the hard usage of field work, its sensitiveness, the interchangeability of parts, and the ease of dismantling and reassembling it. Its principal points of disadvantage are its over-registration under certain conditions which have already been mentioned and its recording of the maximum velocity of the water which strikes it without respect to the direction of motion, whether supported by cable and so left free to swing or by rod and so held in a fixed direction.

In recent years, in the "pygmy" current meter (Fig. 17), the Geological Survey has reproduced the Small Price meter at two-fifths size. The objective in developing this pygmy meter was to obtain a meter that would (1) operate reliably near the surface of the water and in shallow depths and (2) measure very low velocities reliably. The first objective was attained, and the pygmy meter has a definite field of usefulness in measuring shallow streams. The second objective was not attained because the weight, and therefore the friction between the pivot and its bearing, remain in the same relation to the driving force in the pygmy meter as in the Small Price meter.

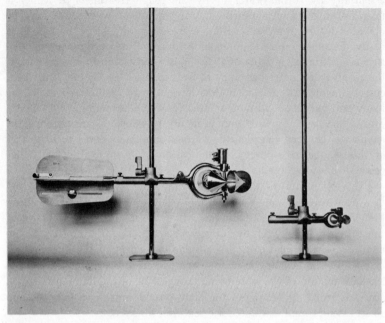

FIG. 17. Small Price current meter and pygmy current meter (round rod suspension).

FIG. 18. Haskell current meter.

The outstanding current meters of the screw type are the Haskell meter in this country (Fig. 18) and the Ott meters (Fig. 19) in Europe. The Haskell meter was developed by Dean E. E. Haskell for use in the Lake Survey, where river measurements are made in deep, strong-flowing, clear water. By utilizing different meter heads with different pitches of screw, it may be used in considerable ranges of velocity. Since its wheel rotates on a horizontal axis, it must either be overhung or have a part of the framework in front of the wheel, and it must have journal or ball bearings, into either of which the entrance of silt will cause changes in friction and, therefore, in rating.

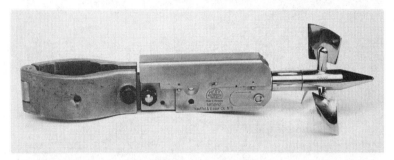

FIG. 19. Ott current meter.

As current meters must be used in this country in turbid rivers at depths ranging occasionally up to 100 feet or more and frequently up to 25 feet or 50 feet, it appears to be practically impossible to keep silt out of journal or ball bearings. No screw-type meter has been adapted to the wide range of conditions that occur in general stream gaging, although many attempts have been made to do so.

The Haskell meter is sturdy, and it is reliable for measuring velocities of water under the conditions for which it was developed. It under-registers the velocity of turbulent water. It measures reliably the velocity of smooth-flowing, clear water. Its points of advantage are its sturdiness and its reliability for use from a boat in large rivers of steady current, even though there may be moderate wave action. Its points of disadvantage are its lack of ready adaptability to the wide variety of conditions of general stream gaging, its under-registration in turbulent water, and its possible change of rating when used in deep, turbid streams as a result of the entrance of silt into the bearings.

The Ott meters, of which there are many variations, are not extensively used in this country because of their lack of universal adaptability and the danger of changes in their calibration when used in turbid water. They are excellent meters for special-purpose uses in clear water. Ott has met successfully the requirements of many conditions by means of a variety of forms of meter rather than by de-

FIG. 20. Current-meter rating station, Bureau of Standards, Washington, D. C. Note flume and electrically propelled car.

veloping a meter for universal use. Obviously, a variety of meters will not serve the needs of general stream gaging because of the great cost of the many meters that would be needed and the impracticability of transporting a variety of meters to each gaging station.

The screw-type Hoff meter has been extensively used in the investigational work of the Department of Agriculture, having been invented by E. J. Hoff of the Bureau of Agricultural Engineering. The meter wheel is light in weight, consisting of either three or four blades or vanes of hard rubber. Because of the lightness of the meter wheel, this meter is said to be particularly adapted to the measurement of low velocities, but because of its light construction, it is probably not suited for service under severe conditions.

CURRENT-METER RATING. The relation of the speed of rotation of the current-meter wheel to the velocity of the water which causes the rotation must be established, or, in other words, the current meter must be rated before it is ready for use. Thereafter, the meter should be rerated from time to time whenever it is repaired or modified in any way and, in any event, at least biennially. All federally owned current meters and many others are rated at the Bureau of Standards in its rating flume (Fig. 20) in Washington, D. C. If the results obtained by any current meter are to enter into official records or are to be used in court proceedings, rating by the Bureau of Standards is essential.

The rating of the meter is accomplished by propelling it over a measured course through still water in a rating flume. The flume at the Bureau of Standards is 400 feet long, 6 feet wide, and 6 feet deep, and the meter is moved through it at various uniform speeds ranging from the lowest speed that will cause the meter wheel to revolve to the highest that it is anticipated may be needed in the use of the particular meter being rated. The results of the various "runs" of the meter are plotted, with speed of travel on one axis and revolutions of the meter wheel on the other; a curve is adjusted to the points thus obtained (Fig. 21); and the curve is converted to tabular form for convenience in use (Fig. 22).

This method of rating assumes that the same rate of rotation of the meter wheel will occur when the meter is propelled through still water at a certain speed as when the meter is held at a fixed point in water flowing past it at that speed. It has not been, and perhaps cannot be, proved that this assumption is strictly correct. However, comparisons of current-meter measurements of discharge with measurements of the same water by weirs, calibrated tanks, and weighing tanks have demonstrated that there can be no appreciable error in the meter ratings thus made in still water.

The rating of current meters in rating flumes is often impracticable for extremely high velocities such as those in excess of 10 feet per second. In such situations, meter ratings for the higher velocities may be developed from studies of the performance of current meters in wind tunnels. The results obtained for the same current meter with respect to medium velocities in both air and water are compared, and on the basis of such comparison the meter rating may be extended

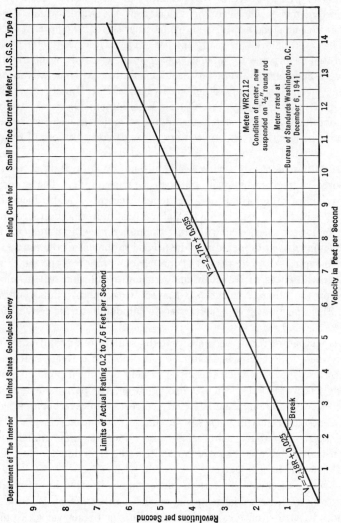

FIG. 21. Typical rating curve for Small Price current meter.

upward to the highest velocities desired by a consideration of the performance of the meter in the wind tunnel at such velocities.

Each individual current meter should be rated. No workmanship is perfect. Meters made in one lot, in the same plant, under the same conditions of manufacture, from the same materials, using the same templets, and with the finishing and adjusting as nearly the same throughout as it is humanly possible to have them will vary from each other appreciably with respect to their ratings, apparently because of slight and undiscovered differences. These differences in ratings are a constant source of surprise and wonder as to both their magnitudes and the varying shapes of the rating curves. A so-called standard rating curve or rating table for meters of a certain make, size, or kind should not, therefore, be used if the measurements of discharge made by them are intended for record or court purposes.

It is important that a current meter which is in constant use be at all times in proper working condition, in other words, in as nearly as possible the same condition as when it was rated. In order that the field engineer may be assured concerning the mechanical condition of his meter, the so-called spin test is applied, generally before and after each discharge measurement. The test consists merely in placing the meter, with its shaft in a vertical position, on a level floor or table, starting it spinning by a quick movement of the hand, and noting the time until it comes to complete rest. Of course, the meter must be so placed that no air currents can reach it. With a Small Price meter, a "spin" of two minutes or longer is considered to be evidence that the instrument is in good operating condition.

STOP WATCHES. A stop watch is needed for observations of time as an element in the measurement of velocity. If, for example, the revolutions of the meter wheel are counted, as is usual, for a period of about 50 seconds, an error of 1 second in the observed time causes an error of 2 per cent in the velocity. Such an error, or a greater one, might readily be made with an ordinary watch. Although such errors would generally be compensating, they might not be so for particular individuals, and, in any event, they should be avoided by the use of a stop watch.

The stop watches generally used in stream gaging measure time to the fifth of a second. As they are likely to receive rough usage, especially in working around steel bridge members, they should be inexpensive but at the same time sturdily made. As each observation of time in a discharge measurement requires generally less than a minute, a stop watch need not be as accurate a time keeper as an ordinary watch. Commonly, a satisfactory stop watch for this work will

DEPARTMENT OF INTERIOR - GEOLOGICAL SURVEY
Water Resources Branch
RATING TABLE FOR TYPE.. *A*...CURRENT METER NO... *2112*....
SUSPENSION   *RoD*   RATED   *Dec. 6, 1941*

| Time in Seconds | VELOCITY IN FEET PER SECOND | | | | | | | | | Time in Seconds |
| | Revolutions | | | | | | | | | |
	3	5	7	10	15	20	25	30	40	
40	.188	.298	.406	.570	.842	1.12	1.39	1.66	2.20	40
41	.185	.291	.397	.557	.823	1.09	1.35	1.62	2.15	41
42	.181	.285	.388	.544	.804	1.06	1.32	1.58	2.10	42
43	.177	.278	.380	.532	.785	1.04	1.29	1.55	2.05	43
44	.174	.273	.372	.520	.768	1.02	1.26	1.51	2.01	44
45	.170	.267	.364	.509	.752	.994	1.24	1.48	1.96	45
46	.167	.262	.357	.499	.736	.973	1.21	1.45	1.92	46
47	.164	.257	.350	.489	.721	.953	1.18	1.42	1.88	47
48	.161	.252	.343	.479	.706	.933	1.16	1.39	1.84	48
49	.158	.247	.336	.470	.692	.915	1.14	1.36	1.80	49
50	.156	.243	.330	.461	.679	.897	1.12	1.33	1.77	50
51	.153	.239	.324	.452	.666	.880	1.09	1.31	1.73	51
52	.151	.235	.318	.444	.654	.863	1.07	1.28	1.70	52
53	.148	.231	.313	.436	.642	.848	1.05	1.26	1.67	53
54	.146	.227	.308	.429	.631	.832	1.03	1.24	1.64	54
55	.144	.223	.302	.421	.620	.818	1.02	1.21	1.61	55
56	.142	.220	.298	.414	.609	.804	.998	1.19	1.58	56
57	.140	.216	.293	.407	.599	.790	.981	1.17	1.55	57
58	.138	.213	.288	.401	.589	.777	.965	1.15	1.53	58
59	.136	.210	.284	.394	.579	.764	.949	1.13	1.50	59
60	.134	.207	.279	.388	.570	.752	.933	1.12	1.48	60
61	.132	.204	.275	.382	.561	.740	.918	1.10	1.45	61
62	.130	.201	.271	.377	.552	.728	.904	1.08	1.43	62
63	.129	.198	.267	.371	.544	.717	.890	1.06	1.41	63
64	.127	.195	.263	.366	.536	.706	.877	1.05	1.39	64
65	.126	.193	.260	.360	.528	.696	.863	1.03	1.37	65
66	.124	.190	.256	.355	.520	.686	.851	1.02	1.35	66
67	.123	.188	.253	.350	.513	.676	.838	1.00	1.33	67
68	.121	.185	.249	.346	.506	.666	.826	.987	1.31	68
69	.120	.183	.246	.341	.499	.657	.815	.973	1.29	69
70	.118	.181	.243	.336	.492	.648	.804	.959	1.27	70
	3	5	7	10	15	20	25	30	40	

FIG. 22. Typical rating table for Small Price current meter. (See Fig. 21.)

INDEX................*228 - 227*...................... NO...*2112*....
EQUATIONS.. *V = 2.18.R + 0.025*... *V = 2.17.R + 0.035*..... *Dec. 6, 1941*..
Limits of Actual Rating.. *2.2*. to .*7.6*... feet per sec *Rod*
at Bureau of Standards, Wash., D.C. Condition of Meter *NEW*

Time in Seconds	VELOCITY IN FEET PER SECOND									Time in Seconds
	Revolutions									
	50	60	80	100	150	200	250	300	350	
40	2.75	3.29	4.37	5.46	8.17	10.89	13.60	16.31	19.03	40
41	2.68	3.21	4.27	5.33	7.97	10.62	13.27	15.91	18.56	41
42	2.62	3.13	4.17	5.20	7.79	10.37	12.95	15.53	18.12	42
43	2.56	3.06	4.07	5.08	7.61	10.13	12.65	15.17	17.70	43
44	2.50	2.99	3.98	4.97	7.43	9.90	12.37	14.83	17.30	44
45	2.45	2.93	3.89	4.86	7.27	9.68	12.09	14.50	16.91	45
46	2.39	2.87	3.81	4.75	7.11	9.47	11.83	14.19	16.55	46
47	2.34	2.81	3.73	4.65	6.96	9.27	11.58	13.89	16.19	47
48	2.30	2.75	3.65	4.56	6.82	9.08	11.34	13.60	15.86	48
49	2.25	2.69	3.58	4.46	6.68	8.89	11.11	13.32	15.53	49
50	2.20	2.64	3.51	4.37	6.55	8.72	10.89	13.05	15.23	50
51	2.16	2.59	3.44	4.29	6.42	8.55	10.67	12.80	14.93	51
52	2.12	2.54	3.37	4.21	6.29	8.38	10.47	12.55	14.64	52
53	2.08	2.49	3.31	4.13	6.18	8.22	10.27	12.32	14.37	53
54	2.04	2.45	3.25	4.05	6.06	8.07	10.08	12.09	14.10	54
55	2.01	2.40	3.19	3.98	5.95	7.93	9.90	11.87	13.84	55
56	1.97	2.36	3.13	3.91	5.85	7.79	9.72	11.66	13.60	56
57	1.94	2.32	3.08	3.84	5.75	7.65	9.55	11.46	13.36	57
58	1.90	2.28	3.03	3.78	5.65	7.52	9.39	11.26	13.13	58
59	1.87	2.24	2.98	3.71	5.55	7.39	9.23	11.07	12.91	59
60	1.84	2.20	2.93	3.65	5.46	7.27	9.08	10.89	12.69	60
61	1.81	2.17	2.88	3.59	5.37	7.15	8.93	10.71	12.49	61
62	1.78	2.13	2.83	3.53	5.29	7.03	8.79	10.53	12.29	62
63	1.76	2.10	2.79	3.48	5.20	6.92	8.65	10.37	12.09	63
64	1.73	2.07	2.75	3.43	5.12	6.82	8.51	10.21	11.90	64
65	1.70	2.04	2.71	3.37	5.04	6.71	8.38	10.05	11.72	65
66	1.68	2.01	2.67	3.32	4.97	6.61	8.25	9.90	11.54	66
67	1.65	1.98	2.63	3.27	4.89	6.51	8.13	9.75	11.37	67
68	1.63	1.95	2.59	3.23	4.82	6.42	8.01	9.61	11.20	68
69	1.60	1.92	2.55	3.18	4.75	6.33	7.90	9.47	11.04	69
70	1.58	1.89	2.51	3.13	4.69	6.23	7.79	9.33	10.89	70
	50	60	80	100	150	200	250	300	350	

Fɪɢ. 22. Typical rating table for Small Price current meter. (See Fig. 21.)

cost between \$10 and \$20; although they are less complicated, they are not, even at that price, of as good quality as an ordinary watch costing the same amount because of the much more limited market for stop watches. It is not advisable to use high-grade watches with stop attachments, not only because of the high first cost, but also because of the high cost of maintaining such watches in running order under the conditions of their use.

WEIGHTS FOR SOUNDING AND PLACEMENT OF METERS. The same weight is used both for determining the depth as a necessary element of the cross-sectional area of the stream and for placing and holding the meter in position in the current while observations of velocity are being made. To serve these purposes satisfactorily, it is essential that the weight shall be heavy enough not only to sink to the bed of the stream without swinging far downstream from the vertical, thereby insuring that the measurement of depth shall be reliable, but also to hold the meter so that it shall be nearly vertically under the point of support while the observation of velocity is being made, thereby insuring that the meter is held steadily at a proper depth.

In order that the weight shall be as light as practicable and yet properly serve the two purposes, it is necessary that its shape shall be such as to offer a minimum resistance to the force of the current. The weight should also afford as much protection to the current meter as is reasonably practicable while the observations of depth and velocity are being made. The first trend of development in weights was to seek less resistance; to that end, the flatiron shape was discarded when the torpedo and elliptical shapes were developed. However, these shapes were too short to afford adequate protection for the meter. To provide better protection for the meter the C-type (Columbus type) (Fig. 23) was evolved, with sufficient length to extend beyond the meter wheel and so to take the force of blows against drift, snags, rocks, and other obstructions. The lengthening of the front part of the weight made necessary a corresponding lengthening of the back part and steering vane to retain balance. Better directional and stabilizing characteristics were also obtained by the lengthening. The C-type weight has sufficient length, even in the 15-pound size, to afford the desired protection to the Small Price meter without any serious reduction in efficiency. The longer C-type weight offers greater resistance to the force of the current than the elliptical weight, which is shorter and approaches more nearly the teardrop shape. This weight represents, therefore, a compromise between the primary purposes of a weight for making soundings and placing the meter in position and in affording protection to the current meter while it is used in swift water.

C-type weights are now obtainable from stock in six sizes, ranging from 15 pounds to 150 pounds, and heavier weights are made on order.

STAY-LINE CABLES. The handling and placement of heavy weights in swift water, particularly when suspended on hand lines, are frequently facilitated by the use of *stay-line cables*. A stay-line wire

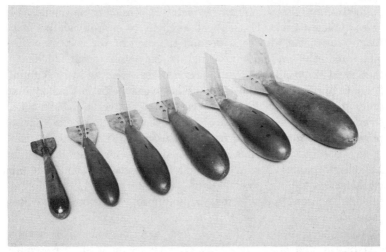

FIG. 23. Columbus-type sounding weights (15-, 30-, 50-, 75-, 100-, and 150-pound sizes).

or cable is a heavy wire or light cable (rarely more than $\frac{1}{4}$ inch in diameter) stretched across a stream above the measuring section and approximately parallel to it, at an elevation high enough to clear flood stages. It may be attached to trees, if available, or to artificial anchorages. A specially designed sheave rides on the stay-line wire and carries a pulley, through which passes the *stay line*. One end of this line is attached to the meter hanger above the meter; the other leads to the cable car or bridge. By taking up on the stay line, the engineer may move the meter and weight upstream to a position vertically below the point of observation. By this means, the effect of the current in carrying the meter and weight downstream is overcome, soundings will represent true vertical depths, and the meter may be placed and held in the proper positions for velocity observations. Ordinarily, the part of the stay line that is in the water is wire of small diameter, and the part that passes through the pulley and is handled by the engineer is ordinary sash cord or manila rope. By slacking off on the stay line, the sheave may be moved along the stay-line cable or wire until it is directly upstream from the next point of observation. In order that the stay line shall not raise the meter from its correct position, the cable should be placed far enough upstream from the measuring section so that the part of the line from the meter to the pulley will make an angle no greater than 30 degrees with the horizontal.

METER-SUSPENSION CABLES. A meter-suspension cable should have two characteristics: (1) sufficient strength to sustain not only the weights used, but also to withstand the drag of the current on the meter and cable and on any debris that may strike them or lodge on them; and (2) small diameter to prevent excessive drag by the current. Most engineers demand also an insulated conductor in the core. In order to obtain these features, special cables have been built up of strands of steel wire. They are now made for the Geological Survey in two types, the Kinnison and the Ellsworth. Each type is made in two sizes, and each has an insulated conductor core. Each type has characteristics that make it preferable for use under certain conditions.

The Kinnison-type, direct-lay, preformed, galvanized plow-steel cable has a breaking strength of not less than 500 pounds for a cable 0.09 inch in diameter, and of not less than 950 pounds for a cable 0.11 inch in diameter. Both sizes of cable are made up of 6 strands, each strand consisting of 7 wires of 0.009-inch diameter in the 0.09-inch cable and 0.013-inch diameter in the 0.11-inch cable. The insulated core consists of 15 No. 36 copper wires covered with insulating wrappings. This type of cable is relatively rough and is, therefore, preferred for use in hand lines.

The Ellsworth-type, reverse-lay, lay-set, galvanized plow-steel cable has a breaking strength of not less than 800 pounds for a cable 0.10 inch in diameter, and of not less than 1,500 pounds for a cable 0.125 inch in diameter. Both sizes of cable consist of 18 wires wrapped about the insulated core in one direction and 15 similar wires wrapped in the reverse direction, the two wrappings thus covering the core. These wires are 0.012 inch and 0.015 inch in diameter, respectively, for the two sizes of cable. The insulated core consists, for the respective sizes of cable, of 6 or 8 stainless-steel wires, No. 36 Brown and Sharpe gage, and 6 or 8 bare copper wires, all bunched, not twisted together, and covered with insulating wrappings. This type of cable is relatively smooth and is preferred for use on reels.

It is essential that the steel wires used in the Kinnison and Ellsworth types of cable or their equivalent, shall be preformed or lay-set or similarly treated to insure that the cable shall be usable for stream-gaging purposes. Without such treatment, the cable would ravel when cut, it could not be threaded through small openings, and the core could not be easily and safely exposed for making electrical connections.

When hand lines are used, that part of the line which is ordinarily above the surface of the water is composed of a "hand cable." This cable generally consists of two No. 16 insulated copper conductors encased in a ⅜-inch rubber covering. The principal purpose of the hand cable is to facilitate manipulation by hand from cableways or bridges. The diameter of the Kinnison cable is so small that, even when a weight of only 15 pounds is attached to the line, its handling in making soundings is extremely difficult.

Since depths of water will vary, as will distances from bridges and cableways to the water surface, the lengths of underwater cable required will vary correspondingly at different gaging stations. Ordinarily, no more steel (Kinnison) cable will be needed than an amount equal to the greatest depth of water in the section, and the remainder of the hand line may consist of hand cable. In order that the respective lengths of hand and steel cables may be adjusted to suit varying conditions, the surplus steel cable is wound on a small reel at the point of attachment to the hand cable. This reel permits the use of any length of steel cable desired, up to the total length available. Various types and forms of connectors are used at the reel, at the meter and hanger, and at the head set worn by the engineer.

Although the double-wire system is generally used in discharge measurements to provide an electrical circuit, a single-wire system with return through ground is sometimes employed, especially with reel suspension. In such situations, a single-conductor cable, which is much stronger, for the same diameter, than a cable which carries two conductors, may be utilized. Such a cable may consist merely of 6 or 7 strands of 7 galvanized steel wires each and is obtainable from stock in ⅟₁₆-inch or ⅟₃₂-inch diameters.

REELS AND CRANES. With the increase in size of weights for sounding and for holding the current meter in position in the flowing water, reels and cranes have been devised for the efficient handling of such weights on bridges, cableways, ice cover, and boats. Reels came first, and booms, now more properly called "cranes," soon followed. The reel is practically a necessity for use with weights of 50 pounds or more, and saves much human energy in the handling of smaller weights.

A reel, or sounding reel as it is sometimes called, consists essentially of a drum varying in circumference from 1.0 foot to 2.5 feet and in length from a capacity of 80 feet of 0.10-inch Ellsworth-type cable

Fig. 24. Automotive equipment used in measuring Mississippi River, showing special-type crane. Reel for handling meter and weight powered by motor of automobile.

to 175 feet of 0.125-inch cable; a crank and ratchet assembly for raising or lowering the weight or holding it in any desired position; a brake, in some instances; and a counter or indicator on which depths may be read directly. Reels of these types may generally be utilized in handling weights up to 175 pounds; greater weights must ordinarily be handled by mechanical power, as is done at certain gaging stations on the Mississippi River (Fig. 24).

The reels may be essentially the same for the several kinds of supporting structures used by the engineer in making measurements of discharge, but the methods of attaching the reels to the supports necessarily vary. For use on a cableway, the reel is attached securely to the cable car (Fig. 25) and is placed in position over the stream by moving the car on the cable; for use on a boat, the reel is rigidly attached to the boat (Fig. 69) and put in position by moving the boat; for use on ice cover, the reel is supported by a simple, light, portable

FIG. 25. Canfield gaging reel mounted in cable car.

frame (Fig. 26) which may be mounted on skis or carried by the engineer with the meter and weight from hole to hole in the ice as he progresses across the river in making the observations of depth and velocity; for use on a bridge, the reel is attached to a metal crane mounted on some form of truck (Fig. 27) that can be rolled along the bridge from measuring point to measuring point as the measurement progresses. The crane is more necessary on a bridge than on a cableway, boat, or portable frame because the meter and weight must commonly be raised to the level of the bridge handrail at the completion of the observations at each measuring point, brought through the frame of the bridge, moved to the next measuring point, put through the frame of the bridge, and lowered to the bed of the river

Fig. 26. Portable support for reel. May be used on ice or on railroad bridges. Courtesy of M. R. Stackpole.

Fig. 27. Reel attached to crane for discharge measurement from bridge.

again. The device for supporting and moving the reel and meter equipment on a bridge is likely to be much more complicated, therefore, than it is on a cableway, boat, or ice cover. As bridges vary widely in framing as well as in driveways and footwalks, there are

Fig. 28. Improvised wooden crane, with reel, for discharge measurements from bridge.

corresponding variations in the truck and framework that support the reel and crane. Although cranes made of metal can be obtained commercially in a variety of types which are adapted to different conditions of use and to the handling of heavier or lighter weights, frequently "home-made" cranes may be devised and constructed (Fig. 28) of wood or other material at relatively small cost. Such cranes will often be found satisfactory for the handling of weights not exceeding 100 pounds.

BIBLIOGRAPHY 8

1. SCHODER and TURNER, Precise Weir Measurements, *Trans. Am. Soc. C. E.*, Vol. 93, pp. 999–1190.

2. R. E. HORTON, Weir Experiments, Coefficients and Formulas, *U.S.G.S. Water Supply Paper* 200.

3. R. E. HORTON, Turbine Water-Wheel Tests and Power Tables, *U.S.G.S. Water Supply Paper* 180.

4. R. L. PARSHALL, The Improved Venturi Flume, *Trans. Am. Soc. C. E.*, Vol. 89, pp. 841–880.

5. PALMER and BOWLUS, Adaptation of Venturi Flumes to Flow Measurements in Conduits, *Trans. Am. Soc. C. E.*, Vol. 101, pp. 1195–1239.

6. C. H. PIERCE, Equipment for River Measurements, Parshall Flume Type of Artificial Control, *U.S.G.S. Mimeographed Circular,* 1934.

7. B. F. GROAT, Characteristics of Cup and Screw Current Meters, *Trans. Am. Soc. C. E.*, Vol. 76, pp. 819–870.

8. YARNELL and NAGLER, Effect of Turbulence on Registration of Current Meters, *Trans. Am. Soc. C. E.*, Vol. 95, pp. 766–860.

9. LASLEY LEE, Equipment for River Measurements, Structures from Which Discharge Measurements are Made, *U.S.G.S. Mimeographed Circular,* 1933.

10. C. H. PIERCE, Performance of Current Meters in Water of Shallow Depth, *U.S.G.S. Water Supply Paper* 868-A.

11. E. G. HOPSON, The Automatic Volumeter, *Trans. Am. Soc. C. E.*, Vol. 80, pp. 572–593.

12. Am. Soc. C. E., *Manual of Engineering Practice,* No. 11, Letter Symbols and Glossary for Hydraulics, with Special Reference to Irrigation.

13. C. G. CLINE, Discharge Formula and Tables for Sharp-Crested Suppressed Weirs, *Trans. Am. Soc. C. E.*, Vol. 100, pp. 396–423.

14. R. R. LYMAN, Measurement of the Flow of Streams by Approved Forms of Weirs with New Formulas and Diagrams, *Trans. Am. Soc. C. E.*, Vol. 77, pp. 1189–1337.

15. J. G. WOODBURN, Tests of Broad-Crested Weirs, *Trans. Am. Soc. C. E.*, Vol. 96, pp. 387–453.

16. W. R. HUTTON, On the Determination of Flood Discharge of Rivers and of the Backwater Caused by Contractions, *Trans. Am. Soc. C. E.*, Vol. 11, pp. 211–227.

17. NAGLER and DAVIS, Experiments on Discharge over Spillways and Models, Keokuk Dam, *Trans. Am. Soc. C. E.*, Vol. 94, pp. 777–844.

18. F. W. GREVE, Parabolic Weirs, *Trans. Am. Soc. C. E.*, Vol. 84, pp. 486–515.

19. L. G. PULS, Spillway Discharge Capacity of Wilson Dam, *Trans. Am. Soc. C. E.*, Vol. 95, pp. 316–333.

20. A. R. WEBB, Supplemental Tests—Weirs with Aprons Inclined Up Stream and Down Stream, *Trans. Am. Soc. C. E.*, Vol. 96, pp. 408–416.

21. E. C. MURPHY, Current Meter and Weir Discharge Comparisons, *Trans. Am. Soc. C. E.*, Vol. 47, pp. 370–391.

22. J. W. LEDOUX, A Mechanism for Metering and Recording the Flow of Fluids through Venturi Tubes, Orifices, or Conduits, by Integrating the Velocity Head, *Trans. Am. Soc. C. E.*, Vol. 76, pp. 1148–1171.

23. G. S. WILLIAMS, Description of Pitot Tubes and Their Use, *Trans. Am. Soc. C. E.*, Vol. 47, pp. 6–14.

24. E. W. LANE, Experiments on the Flow of Water through Contractions in an Open Channel, *Trans. Am. Soc. C. E.*, Vol. 83, pp. 1149–1219.
25. N. R. GIBSON, The Gibson Method and Apparatus for Measuring the Flow of Water in Closed Conduits, *Mechanical Engineering*, Vol. 45, pp. 679–684.
26. ALLEN and TAYLOR, The Salt-Velocity Method of Water Measurement, *Mechanical Engineering*, Vol. 46, pp. 13–16.
27. B. F. GROAT, Chemi-hydrometry and Its Application to the Precise Testing of Hydroelectric Generators, *Trans. Am. Soc. C. E.*, Vol. 80, pp. 951–1305.
28. WILM, COTTON, and STOREY, Measurement of Debris-Laden Stream Flow with Critical-Depth Flumes, *Trans. Am. Soc. C. E.*, Vol. 103, pp. 1237–1278.
29. K. R. KENNISON, Design of an Open-Channel Control Section, *Trans. Am. Soc. C. E.*, Vol. 105, pp. 744–764.

CHAPTER 9

FUNCTIONS AND CHARACTERISTICS OF GAGING STATIONS

Gaging Station Defined. A gaging station, as its name implies, is a selected site on a stream equipped and operated to furnish basic data from which systematic records of discharge may be derived. The proper selection of the site [1] is of major importance in relation to the accuracy and cost of the records to be collected. The equipment consists essentially of a gage [2] by or from which a record of stage is made, the structures, if any, built for the purpose of stabilizing the relation of stage to discharge,[3] and the facilities used by the engineer [4] in making discharge measurements, such as bridges, boats, or cableways. The systematic operation of a gaging station [5] varies not only with its equipment but also with the characteristics of the site.

Since a discharge measurement involves both the velocity and the cross-sectional area of the flowing water, means must be provided whereby the engineer may measure distances normal to the stream and may ascertain depths and velocities of the water at as many points as may be needed to obtain not only the accurate dimensions of the cross section but also a representative distribution of velocities therein. If a bridge or cable provides the necessary support for the engineer while making these measurements, it may be graduated by permanent markings at regular 5-foot or other intervals to afford the means for measuring such horizontal distances; if a boat or a wading section is used, a temporary tag line or tape must be stretched across and over the stream at the measuring section when each discharge measurement is made.

With the passage of time, gages may be displaced or destroyed or they may be changed in elevation as the result of erosion of beds and banks or by the lifting action of ice. In order that the records of stage may assuredly refer to the same datum [6] throughout the period of record, the datum of each gage must be referred to and occasionally checked with at least one and preferably two or more bench marks

---

[1] Chapter 10.　　　　[3] Chapter 11.　　　　[5] Chapter 14.
[2] Chapter 8.　　　　[4] Chapter 13.　　　　[6] Chapter 12.

that are entirely detached from the gage, its supports or shelter, and that are not liable to destruction or to change in elevation. Practically none of the records of stage in this or any other country that extend back more than half a century relates with certainty to a fixed datum, and all are, therefore, of greatly reduced value for many engineering, statistical, and hydrologic purposes. As an example of such unreliability, the classic Nile records [7] may be cited.

Characteristics of Stage-Discharge Relation. The particular characteristics of each gaging station determine how efficiently it can perform the functions for which all gaging stations are established. The most important characteristics are those which affect the stability of the relationship of stage to discharge. The conversion of a record of stage into a record of discharge is predicated on that relationship, which is called the *stage-discharge relation.* Unfortunately for the accuracy and cost of stream gaging, that relationship varies in stability from essential permanence to constant change. It is by means of that relationship, however, unstable though it may often be, that a continuous or intermittent record of stage is converted into a record of discharge, which, of course, is the ultimate purpose of a gaging station. The degree of instability of that relationship, that is, the amounts, rates, and frequencies of shifts or changes in the stage-discharge relation at any gaging station, affects not only the amount of work required to establish and adequately to revise that relationship and, therefore, the cost of operating the station, but also, and more important, the accuracy and reliability of the resulting records of discharge. Since the stability or instability of the stage-discharge relation is determined primarily by the nature of the station site, the finding and selection [8] of that site which will afford the highest degree of stability in that relationship are of prime importance, and the ability to select such a site is a fundamental qualification of a successful stream-gaging engineer.

The principal physical characteristics which determine the stability or lack of stability of the stage-discharge relation at the site of a gage relate to the nature, configuration, and vegetal cover of the river's bed and banks and of the overflow area at and downstream from the gage. These characteristics collectively constitute the factors which determine the stage-discharge relation and are known as the *control* [9] of the station.

The graph showing the stage-discharge relation, called the *station rating curve,* is commonly parabolic in form (Fig. 29), but under

[7] Bibliog. 1·15.   [9] Chapter 11.
[8] Chapter 10.

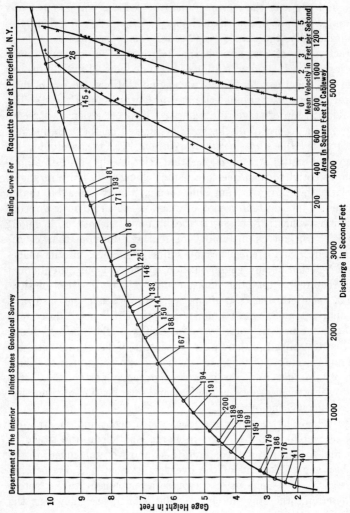

FIG. 29. Typical station rating curve. Note area and mean velocity curves and results of discharge measurements. (See Fig. 77.)

some conditions may depart from that form because of combinations of parabolic curves of widely variable characteristics resulting from the successive effects at different stages of essentially diverse controls. No two sites have the same rating curve. Each site must, therefore, have its stage-discharge relation established by discharge measurements sufficient in number and so spaced with respect to stage as to define the stage-discharge graph throughout the river's range of stage. Extrapolation of the graph far beyond the discharge measurements is dangerous,[10] whether the extrapolation be made to lower or to higher stages than those for which discharge measurements are available.

If the stage-discharge relation is stable, the same rating curve will apply year after year, and, after the relationship has been established, only occasional discharge measurements will be needed to verify the permanency of the rating curve. If, however, the stage-discharge relation is unstable, many discharge measurements will be required in order to show at all times the changed position of the stage-discharge graph. If the shifts are large and are related to considerable changes in stage, such for example as may occur during floods, the delineation of each shift in the stage-discharge relation should be made promptly after the stage which produced it; if the shifts occur gradually and continuously, discharge measurements must be made frequently, and in rivers of rapidly changing bed (the Colorado River, for example) discharge measurements must be made as often as three or four times a week. A day's record of the discharge of any river will never be more accurate than the precision with which the rating curve used represents the true stage-discharge relation on that day.

In addition to the stability of the stage-discharge relation, the "sensitiveness" of that relation should be carefully considered. It is common practice to plot the rating curve on rectangular-coordinate paper with stage (gage height) on the vertical axis and discharge on the horizontal axis, choosing scales of plotting that are appropriate to the whole range of the graph and that will cause the curve to fall as nearly as may be in the general direction of the diagonal of the sheet. The steepness of the resulting curve at any point will be a measure of the "sensitiveness" of the record of stage at that point, since the steepness indicates the rate of change in stage for a given change in discharge and so determines the accuracy with which the stage must be observed in order to obtain any required degree of ac-

[10] Chapter 15.

curacy in discharge. If the change in stage is small for a large change in discharge, the record is said to be "nonsensitive" at that stage; and, conversely, if the change in stage is large with respect to the change in discharge, the record is said to be "sensitive" at that stage. Obviously, a sensitive record of stage may be more accurately converted into a record of discharge than a nonsensitive one. The two extremes of sensitiveness may be illustrated by reference, on the one hand, to a V-shaped control section which will yield a record of stage in which large changes will correspond to only small changes in discharge, and, on the other hand, to the control section formed by a long dam of horizontal crest on which large changes in discharge, especially in times of low water, will cause only small changes in stage. In the wide range of gaging stations operated in connection with a broad stream-gaging program, there is every variation in sensitiveness between the two extremes cited. In the selection of sites for gaging stations, the probable sensitiveness of each possible site as well as the probable stability of the stage-discharge relation should, therefore, be carefully considered as important elements in the final choice of sites.

Significance of Stage-Discharge Relation. The characteristics of the stage-discharge relation and the establishment and revision of the station rating curve are of basic importance in connection with systematic stream gaging. For any gaging station, the characteristics of the stage-discharge relation are obviously of far greater significance, over a period of years, than the location of the station with respect to transportation facilities, the availability of local residents, or the cost of installation and equipment. If the stage-discharge relation is essentially stable, the cost of operation will be moderate and, other things being equal, the accuracy of the records will be high; if it is essentially unstable, the cost of operation will tend to be high and will increase with the degree of instability, while the accuracy of the records will tend to be low and to decrease as the instability increases.

The stage-discharge relation must apply to the record of stage that is collected and used as the basis of the discharge record and, therefore, to the section of the river in which the gage is placed. It generally has no essential significance with respect to the exact place where a discharge measurement is made, which may be at a section that is near to or at a considerable distance from that in which the stages are observed. It is necessary, of course, that the quantity of water measured shall be substantially the same as that which flows past the gage and that the stage at the gage shall be observed and carefully coordinated with the discharge measurement. The section

or sections in which discharge measurements are made will be so
selected as to obtain the greatest accuracy for such measurements and
may be different for different stages of the river, especially for low
stages when wading measurements may be made, or for high stages
when a bridge in the vicinity may afford the only practicable support for the engineer and his gaging equipment.

Establishment of Stage-Discharge Relation. The stage-discharge
relation is established by means of measurements of discharge and coincident observations of stage made under normal river conditions;
that is, when no backwater from any cause is present. Each such
discharge measurement is plotted, usually on rectangular-coordinate
paper, with stage (gage height) on the vertical axis and discharge on
the horizontal, thus defining the position of the station rating curve
at the point so plotted. As opportunities are afforded, a sufficient
number of discharge measurements must be made, well distributed
through the range of stage, to define the position of the rating curve
through that range. Subsequently, enough discharge measurements
must be made to extend the curve to new ranges of stage as needed, to
modify the curve if changes in the stage-discharge relation occur, and,
in short, to insure the applicability of the curve at all times and for
the full range of stage. Unless the stage-discharge relation at a station
is properly established and maintained, the record of stage for that
station cannot be converted into a reliable record of discharge.

The station rating curve is developed as rapidly as practicable after
the establishment of a gaging station. The rapidity of its development will be determined largely by the availability of stages over a
considerable range and, therefore, by such fluctuations in stage and
discharge of the stream as will permit the making of discharge measurements over such a range of stage.

Stage-Discharge Relation and Equipment. Since the stage-discharge relation for a first-class gaging station is either essentially
permanent or changes only occasionally and then within narrow
limits, and since for all gaging stations the cost of operation generally
increases as the frequency and magnitude of shifts in the stage-discharge relation increase, it follows that those physical characteristics
of a river which largely control and determine this relation must be
relatively permanent if the operation of the gaging station is to yield
accurate records at low cost. Since the establishment of the stage-
discharge relation is a fundamental requirement in the operation of a
gaging station, it follows that the equipment used in obtaining the
gage-height record and in making the discharge measurements must
be so selected and installed as best to suit the particular character-

istics of the individual stations. As each gaging station has its own stage-discharge relation and its own particular problems with respect to recording stage and measuring discharge, careful consideration of the most effective and most appropriate equipment to be used at that station will always be needed. Deep and swift rivers, for example, will require the 100-pound, 200-pound, or even heavier sounding weights and heavy cranes and reels (in some cases power-driven) for handling them, whereas shallow, sluggish streams may be measured adequately with hand lines and 15-pound weights, or by wading. Nonsensitive stations, where small increments of gage height correspond to relatively large increments of discharge, will require gage-height scale ratios of 1 : 2 or even 1 : 1 on the water-stage recorders; sensitive stations, on the other hand, may produce discharge records of equivalent accuracy through the use of gage-height scale ratios as small as 1 : 24. Stations situated below water-power plants or on streams that fluctuate often or rapidly will almost invariably require water-stage recorders, whereas at stations on large rivers that fluctuate very slowly gage-height records of comparable accuracy may be obtained from two reliable staff-gage readings daily. It is not enough, therefore, that every gaging station be provided with good equipment, because the proper operation of that station requires that the equipment be not only good but at the same time suited to the particular problems existing at that station.

Stage-Discharge Relation and Operation. After the site for the gaging station has been carefully selected and adequately equipped in conformity with its physical characteristics, the subsequent successful operation of the station and the best determination of the stage-discharge relation depend upon the proper and most advantageous utilization of the equipment thus provided. As is pointed out in Chapter 14, the proper operation of a gaging station involves four principal objectives. All these objectives have a definite and intimate bearing on the establishment of the stage-discharge relation as well as on the continued proper maintenance of that relationship as it may vary at irregular intervals through the years as the result of physical changes in channel and control or for other reasons. All these objectives must be recognized and observed if acceptable results are to be obtained, and this in spite of the fact that the funds available for the operation of a gaging station are all too frequently inadequate for the amount of field work that is needed to obtain a satisfactory record of discharge.

Stage-Discharge Relation and Accuracy. The ideal situation in the successful operation of a gaging station involves a first-class gage-

height record and a permanent stage-discharge relation expressed as a
well-defined rating curve that is not subject to material shift or change.
It involves also freedom or relative freedom from various disturbing
effects, whether natural or artificial, as, for example, backwater from
ice, aquatic vegetation, and log jams. However, such ideal conditions
are rarely found, and the records of gage height at most gaging stations are complicated by one or more disturbing elements which tend
to impair the accuracy of the final records of discharge. Obviously,
a stage-discharge relation that is subject to sudden and frequent
changes or shifts is not conducive to an accurate discharge record, no
matter how excellent the gage-height record may be, and, under such
conditions, records of discharge of even ordinary accuracy involve
greatly increased field work in the form of additional discharge measurements, properly timed with respect to season as well as to stage,
in order that these disturbing elements may be disclosed and properly
evaluated. Backwater from ice is present in most northern streams
more or less continuously during the winter. The amount of backwater may fluctuate constantly or it may remain steady for periods of
several days. The accuracy and value of the winter records depend
very largely upon the extent and accuracy of the field information
that may be obtained concerning the amount and occurrence of such
backwater. Similarly, there may be backwater from aquatic vegetation in streams in all sections of the country. As has been pointed
out elsewhere, however, such backwater is easier to define and evaluate
than the more erratic backwater caused by ice. Accuracy in the
stage-discharge relation will be attained, therefore, only as a result
of constant vigilance and efficient effort to the end that the effect
of disturbing elements may be minimized to the greatest possible
degree.

Stage-Discharge Relation and Cost. It is futile to expect that
uniform accuracy of discharge records will be obtained by the expendi-
ture of a certain fixed sum of money, for instance at the rate of $500
or $600 per station per year for the operation and maintenance of a
group of gaging stations and the computation of the final records of
discharge, since the relative permanence of the stage-discharge relation will never be the same for the individual stations of the group.
It will be recognized, therefore, that systematic stream gaging involves
several variables, including among others the degree of permanence
of the stage-discharge relation and the cost and accuracy of the
records, and that these variables are interdependent. After the gaging station is established and placed in operation, except for those sites
on relatively small streams that may be improved by means of arti-

ficial controls,[11] the engineer has little or no control over the permanence of the stage-discharge relation, and frequently such relation does not prove to be nearly as permanent as was originally expected. The selection of the site for the gaging station which will have the best and most nearly permanent stage-discharge relation is, therefore, of great importance with respect to the cost of the final records of discharge.

It is evident that, because of the varying permanence of the stage-discharge relation at different gaging stations, a fixed and predetermined cost of operation of individual stations will necessarily involve a variable accuracy in the final records. On the other hand, if a definite standard of accuracy is fixed and decided upon, there will of necessity be great and perhaps unexpected variations in the costs of the records obtained from individual stations. The engineer is properly concerned with the balancing of these factors, one against the other, to the end that the best possible records of discharge at the lowest reasonable cost may be obtained.

[11] Chapter 11.

CHAPTER 10

ESTABLISHMENT OF GAGING STATIONS

Controlling Characteristics of Gaging Stations. The physical characteristics of the river channel [1] should be studied most carefully before the selection of a gaging-station site because they will determine the relative stability of the stage-discharge relation and, therefore, will control very largely both the accuracy with which a record of stage may be converted into a record of discharge and the cost of that record of discharge. There is complete stability of the stage-discharge relation only when any one stage corresponds at all times to one definite discharge. Because of shifting beds and banks, the seasonal occurrence of ice or aquatic vegetation, or other reasons, such complete stability is seldom found in nature, but a place in which it obtains in the highest practicable degree should be carefully sought in every reconnaissance for a gaging-station site. Channel characteristics may not be correctly evaluated even in a short-time study; in a cursory reconnaissance they may not even be accurately observed. Nevertheless, on an early evaluation of them, correct or otherwise, rest the future cost of equipment and operation, the accuracy of the records that will be obtained, and, therefore, the degree of success which the site may have as a gaging station.

Although other attributes of the gaging-station site may be considered relatively minor in comparison with the channel characteristics, they are sometimes sufficiently important to warrant an adverse decision relative to a site which apparently has satisfactory physical characteristics but is seriously defective with respect to one or more of these minor attributes. Since the satisfactory establishment of the stage-discharge relation requires that discharge measurements be made throughout the whole range of stage, an important attribute of the site is the availability either of suitable existing facilities for making discharge measurements, such as a bridge, good wading sections, or reaches of river suitable for boat measurements, or of natural conditions that are favorable to the erection of a cableway. Another important attribute is the assured accessibility of the gaging station

[1] Chapter 11.

at all seasons of the year and at all stages of the river, and this obviously applies also to all flood plains that must be traversed and all bridges that must be crossed in order to reach the station. Still another attribute is the nature of the route for transportation. This is especially important in connection with the establishment of the station, since there may be great differences between several possible sites in respect to the cost of transporting the heavy materials and equipment needed in the construction of the well and shelter, the cableway, its supports and anchorages, and perhaps an artificial control. Under extreme conditions, the difficulty and cost of transportation might even be the deciding factors in determining the type of installation, whether recording or nonrecording, to be adopted. Still another attribute, also related to the cost of construction, is the availability of local labor, since obviously in construction work labor available at or near the site is greatly to be preferred to labor transported from a distance, involving the cost of either daily transportation to and fro or the maintenance of a camp for the workmen. The availability, particularly in remote regions, of a competent local observer is an important factor in connection with the operation of a gaging station, and this attribute, also, may affect the determination of the type of installation to be adopted, since if no local resident is available to make daily staff-gage readings a water-stage recorder must be installed, and if one is not available even to change weekly record charts a continuous water-stage recorder must be installed and relied upon to operate without attention during the periods between engineers' visits, which may sometimes be made at intervals of several weeks. Although the accuracy of records and the cost of installation are primarily dependent on the characteristics of the gaging-station site, they may thus be affected by combinations of all the factors mentioned above and probably by others. The controlling characteristics of the site are, therefore, interdependent; they are regional as well as local; and all of them must be carefully considered before the establishment of a gaging station.

Selection of Site. The selection of a satisfactory site for a gaging station involves far more than the discovery of a place where a gage may be installed cheaply and securely. It involves the finding of that site which will yield the best record at the lowest reasonable cost in the stretch of river, whether it be a few rods or many miles in length, where a record of discharge is needed. In a compromise between quality of record and cost, that site should be selected which will apparently give the better record in preference to a site where a station could be installed and operated more cheaply but would probably yield a record of lesser accuracy.

A site should not be adopted on the excuse that, although poor, it will be cheap to develop and operate, and that a better and more expensive site will be used later when more funds are available, since both the earlier and later records will be less valuable because of their lack of continuity at the same site. There are likely to be so many unavoidable and unforeseen reasons for changing the location of a station, such as the construction of dams and the resulting pooling of water, the diversion of water for one of several possible purposes, or the canalization of the river channel, that the deliberate selection of a site which is later to be changed should be avoided whenever possible. Also, a site should not be adopted on the theory that it will yield records which will satisfy the immediate requirements of that portion of the river, if another site that will yield better records is available. Conditions frequently change rapidly and unexpectedly, and any record may eventually become valuable for purposes that were not obvious when the station was established. Therefore, in considering possible sites for a gaging station only the best that is available should be selected. Rather than choose an inferior site because of its low first cost when a better site can be made available, it is generally far more desirable to economize in initial equipment and early operation, since, as funds permit, improvements can be made in both these respects without attendant loss of continuity in the records or impairment of their quality.

In connection with the selection of a site, if possible, sufficient time should be allowed in which to study and evaluate the controlling characteristics at all seasons of the year and at all stages of the river. To this end, observations should extend through periods of high and low water and of such disturbing conditions as aquatic vegetation, operation of fish traps, ice cover, ice jams, placer mining, and log driving, because any of these conditions may be damaging or even disastrous to the stability of the stage-discharge relation.[2] In order to obtain full preliminary information, the establishment and operation of a temporary gaging station or of several such gaging stations for a year or more may even be warranted before decision is reached as to what site should be chosen for the permanent gaging station. If such careful preliminary studies are made, later relocations of gaging stations will be avoided, funds will be saved, and accuracy and continuity of records will be enhanced. Unfortunately, however, de-

[2] Chapter 9.

mands for the immediate establishment of a gaging station are generally so insistent that little or no opportunity is afforded to carry on such preliminarly investigations. Usually, a detailed reconnaissance by an experienced engineer must be relied upon to determine the best site for the proposed station. In this reconnaissance the engineer, in order to make the best possible selection under the circumstances, will evaluate and give proper weight to each of the many controlling characteristics of channel and site, reference to which has already been made. Most of the gaging stations now in operation in this country have been established as the result of such reconnaissances, and it may properly be stated that, in general, these stations are functioning satisfactorily and yielding acceptable records.

Selection of Equipment. The equipment of a gaging station should be decided upon after careful consideration of the physical conditions at the site, the degree of accuracy needed in the records, the amount of money available for construction and operation, the probable degree of stability of the stage-discharge relation, which may relate to the feasibility of building an artificial control, the availability of a bridge, and the practicability of obtaining the services of a satisfactory local observer. Whether a water-stage recorder should be used instead of a staff or other nonrecording gage depends ordinarily both on the various controlling characteristics of channel and site and on the sufficiency of available funds. In theory, if the records of all streams were of equal importance, the criteria for consideration in choosing between the two types of installations should be the frequency and rates of fluctuations in stage and the availability of a competent observer and the cost of his services. In general, the larger the river, the less will be the need for a water-stage recorder, because the fluctuations in stage on a large river will be less rapid and less frequent than those on a small stream, and consequently the inaccuracies in the discharge record resulting from the lack of a continuous record of stage will generally tend to be less as the size of the river increases. This statement, however, does not apply to any station situated below a hydroelectric plant or other water-power development which usually carries a fluctuating power load. Such a station cannot generally be successfully operated without a recording instrument. Gaging stations on important rivers that are extensively utilized and that have conflicts of interest in their waters, especially where some uses may be adverse to others, should always be equipped with water-stage recorders in order to obtain continuous records which are not subject to the human errors that are always present to some extent in records from nonrecording gages, because, eventually, the records will be used in court proceedings to establish justice among different users of the river and so, quite properly, may be subjected to the most searching examination and to criticism that may or may not be warranted. It is even conceivable that errors and inaccuracies in records so used may lead to miscarriages of justice.

As stated in Chapter 8, there are now on the market two or more reliable water-stage recorders of both the weekly, or 8-day, type and the long-time or so-called continuous type. As between the two types, weekly recorders will generally serve best at stations that are easily accessible and especially at stations from which records are required at frequent intervals because of their relation to the routine operation of hydraulic works; continuous recorders will serve best at less accessible stations and wherever it may not be practicable or necessary to change the record each week. In the nationwide stream-gaging program of the Geological Survey, the two types are divided about equally in numbers. In a small program and whenever the conditions warrant, there are definite advantages in using only one type and make of recorder, thereby avoiding the disadvantages that arise in operation and especially in familiarizing each observer or engineer who may be employed with the peculiarities of several different instruments. It is desirable to avoid the danger of loss of records that may arise at any time from failure to appreciate those peculiarities and also to avoid the probable added investment in spare recorder clocks which will be required if there is not complete interchangeability among the recorders. Such interchangeability is desirable because each clock must be removed periodically for cleaning, oiling, and repair by a competent jeweler and must be replaced meanwhile by another clock. In a large program, on the other hand, in which both types of instruments must be used and in which there will be frequent interdistrict changes in assignments of the younger engineers, there are definite advantages in having each field man familiar with both types of recorders of several different makes. A field man must be familiar with the causes of clock troubles and mechanical difficulties related to recorder operation, as well as with the remedies therefor, and such familiarity can be acquired only through actual experience with a wide variety of instrumental equipment.

Nonrecording gages are used at all gaging stations. At stations where recording instruments are installed, nonrecording gages are used to check the operation of the water-stage recorders and also to serve in filling in the gaps in gage-height records during periods when the recorders fail to operate. At stations where water-stage recorders are not used, nonrecording gages provide the records of stage which are later converted into records of discharge. At each gaging station, the record of stage must relate to only one gage, and measurements of discharge must be referred to that gage in order that the station rating curve may be consistent with the record of stage. Thus, there must be only one "station gage," although another gage or several of them may be needed for certain specific purposes.

Among nonrecording gages, staff gages, either vertical or inclined, are the simplest and therefore most easily understood by observers. The use of vertical staff gages (Figs. 7 and 12) depends ordinarily on the availability of, or on the possibility of constructing, suitable supports which will not be subject to the danger of damage or destruction by ice or drift. Frequently the downstream faces of bridge abutments offer such protection, and vertical staff gages are often attached to them. Sometimes vertical staff gages are installed in progressive sections, being attached to concrete posts or vertical timbers set securely into the ground. Such an arrangement will generally be satisfactory on rivers which are not subject to the action of ice or which carry little drift. In exposed situations, inclined staff gages (Fig. 55) are generally used because they offer less opportunity for damage by ice or drift. They are usually built to follow the profile of the river bank and so are less subject to damage than exposed vertical staff gages.

Because of the vulnerability of staff gages, the chain gage (Fig. 13) was developed for use at gaging stations where the danger of damage to a staff gage was great, where a staff gage could not be readily installed, or where a structure was available or could be built to support the chain gage above the stream. Although strong sash chain serves best in this kind of gage, the length of any chain is likely to change with use because of its many wearing surfaces. Wire-weight gages (Fig. 15) have, therefore, largely superseded chain gages because of their reliability as to length and for other reasons set forth in Chapter 12.

Observers. The employment and supervision of observers present various problems which should be considered before the gaging station is established. If a water-stage recorder is installed and regular personnel is available for visiting the station, at weekly intervals where a 7-day or 8-day instrument is used, or at longer intervals up to 30 days or more where a continuous recorder is utilized, the services of a local observer may be dispensed with, thus saving perhaps $5 or $6 a month, which are average salaries for this work. When practicable, however, if a station cannot be visited by an engineer at least once a week, it is generally advisable to employ an observer in order to insure that any failure of the recorder to function properly or any change in conditions affecting the stage-discharge relation shall be known promptly, to the end that any break in the records may be short and any other change corrected or reliably recorded.

The observer [3] should understand the operation of the recorder and be able to change weekly record sheets or charts, to check the functioning of the intake pipe by comparing inside and outside gage readings, to operate the float-tape gage if one is installed in the gage well, to observe and record any conditions at the well or in the river which might affect the record of stage, and to make such notes concerning river conditions as will assist the engineer in interpreting the record of stage and converting it into a record of discharge.

Probable Accuracy of Records. The accuracy of the records of discharge will be governed in the first instance by the accuracy of the record of stage, which will depend principally upon whether or not a water-stage recorder is used. It will be governed very largely by the reliability of the conversion of the record of stage into the record of discharge, which conversion is affected by the stability of the stage-discharge relation, by the extent to which the station rating curve is well defined by discharge measurements, by the magnitude and duration of backwater, by the rapidity and frequency of fluctuations in stage and discharge, and by the method and accuracy of the application of the station rating to the record of stage,[4] whether by integration or by a computer using various appropriate methods. The average anticipated annual variations in accuracy in records of daily discharge obtained by stream gaging range from less than 1 per cent for the best stations with stable controls and continuous records of stage to 5 per cent (or even 10 per cent for the poorest) for nonrecording stations with shifting controls, rapid and frequent fluctuations in stage and discharge, and inadequate information in the form of discharge measurements for properly delineating the stage-discharge relation. For stations with badly shifting controls, the relative accuracy of the records of discharge generally varies directly with the amount of effort put forth in obtaining frequent well-spaced discharge measurements, particularly at times of critical stages. The definition of the stage-discharge relation is based on discharge measurements, and, the more variable this relation may be, the greater will be the number of discharge measurements needed to define properly the magnitude and duration of the changes therein. In general, increases in available funds, at least up to the amount needed for obtaining first-

[3] Chapter 14.
[4] Chapter 15.

class records, should lead to corresponding improvements in the quality of the records.

Costs of Installation. The costs of installation of a gaging station include the cost of the gage or gages; of the structures that must be built to support the gage or to house the recorder; of the cableway, if one is needed, or of a boat and equipment, if a boat is to be used; of an artificial control, if one is installed; of labor and the services and expenses of engineers engaged in the construction work; and of bench marks and miscellaneous materials. The costs of installation of a station in a remote region may even include the expense of a camp or shelter or under unusual conditions of a cabin for living quarters.

Although costs may have little relation to the size of the river, they vary with the range of fluctuations in stage, with the nature of the bed and banks, with the distances from the sources of supply of materials, with the availability of labor, with transportation facilities, especially the condition of the highway leading to the vicinity of the site, with the weather as it may affect working conditions for the men, and with the stages of the river and fluctuations therein. The installation will not be complete until construction, grading, and painting are finished, bench marks set, and the gage or gages referred to the bench marks. The station will not be in operation until a water-stage recorder has been placed in service or until an observer is making regular and periodic observations of stage on a nonrecording gage.

The cost of installation of a gaging station may range from about $100, under favorable channel conditions, if a nonrecording gage is used and a bridge is available for the making of discharge measurements, to as much as $10,000 (or even $25,000, for the station on the Colorado River at Lees Ferry, Ariz.) for a first-class station on a large river with shifting bed and great fluctuations in stage. Commonly, the total cost of installation of a recorder station on a river of moderate size with reasonably stable bed ranges between $500 and $2,500, exclusive of the cost of the water-stage recorder. A fair average cost under such conditions would be about $1,200.

Costs of Operation. The field costs of operation of a gaging station are affected largely by the relative stability of the stage-discharge relation because that condition determines the number of discharge measurements needed yearly to define the shape and periods of use of the one or more station rating curves which will be employed in converting the record of stage into the record of discharge. These costs are affected also to some extent by the type of the equipment, whether a bridge, cableway, or boat is used in making the discharge measurements, by the relative accessibility of the site, by the salary of the observer, and by other factors. The office costs of operation relate to a variety of activities which supplement the work carried on in the field and which include such work as the checking and analysis of basic data, preparation of rating curves and tables, computation of records of discharge, and general administration. Field costs of operation bear little or no definite relation to office costs since each depends upon a variety of factors, many of which are unrelated. Perhaps under average conditions field costs and office costs related to the maintenance of a gaging station will be about equal, but wide departures may be expected with respect to different stations or groups of stations. The total costs in field and office generally range from $300 to $800 per station-year, but may be as much as $5,000 per year or even more, for a station at which frequent discharge measurements are required and where a resident engineer is stationed, with perhaps an assistant during flood periods. The average cost in an extensive stream-gaging program is about $500 per station-year.

CHAPTER 11

CONTROL SECTIONS

Definition and Significance.   In Chapter 9, the control of a gaging station was defined as that combination of the physical characteristics at, and more especially downstream from, the station site, such as the nature, configuration, and vegetal cover of the river's bed and banks and of the overflow area within the range of possible effect, which determines the stage-discharge relation at the gage site.   As related to the simplest types of controls, the *control section* is that cross section of the river which functions at ordinary stages as the primary control for the gaging station.   Since the control determines the stage-discharge relation at any gaging-station site and since the computation of records of stream flow is predicated on that relationship, the vital importance of controls in the procedure of collecting records of stream flow is obvious.

Controls may be either *natural* or *artificial*, depending upon whether they are of natural origin or have been constructed either for the specific purpose of stabilizing the stage-discharge relation or for some other reason, and obviously they vary widely not only in stability and permanence but also in nature and profile.   Some controls are formed by single topographic features, such as reefs of bed rock extending across the stream (primary controls); some are made up of two or more features so situated that they combine to determine the stage-discharge relation at all stages; some consist of two or more features (primary and secondary controls, or multiple controls) which come into action at different stages of the river and so serve consecutively in controlling the stage-discharge relation; some are V-shaped and consequently sensitive to small changes in discharge; some are relatively flat like a horizontal rock ledge or the crest of a dam and so are nonsensitive; and some consist of long stretches of river channel of essentially uniform section and characteristics which combine to control the stage-discharge relation at the gage (channel controls).

The simplest and most satisfactory type of natural control consists of a rock reef (Fig. 30) situated either at the head of a series of rapids or at the crest of a waterfall, creating a pool of appreciable extent, of which a record of stage may be obtained by the installation of a gage. However, such favorable natural controls are rarely found in many sections of the country where the river beds shift either intermittently or constantly; in those sections, controls vary widely in type, shape, and stability.

Stable natural controls of such shape and profile that they will produce rating curves of reasonable sensitivity should always be utilized if practicable. They are preferable to artificial controls because they

Fig. 30. Natural control, West Branch of Ausable River near Newman, N. Y.

are integral parts of river channels that have been stabilized by the river itself and so are less likely to be changed by hydraulic forces or by the destructive action of ice. Artificial controls, on the other hand, disturb the natural conditions of flow and, therefore, are subject to constant attack by natural forces and, unless well designed and maintained, are liable to change and possible destruction.

Natural Controls. Unless an artificial control is available or is to be built, the engineer must accept and utilize natural control conditions essentially as he finds them. Without building an artificial structure, he cannot change in any appreciable permanent degree the sensitiveness of the control features or the stability of the stage-discharge relation, and, if the stream is relatively large, the construction of an artificial control solely for stream-gaging purposes is generally impracticable for reasons of cost. Gaging stations on all rivers except those of small size, therefore, must generally be established and operated without modification of the natural conditions that determine the stage-discharge relationship. Careful study should therefore be made of each possible site for a gaging station in order that the location having the most favorable natural conditions may be selected.

Unless the control features are so conspicuous that their characteristics can be readily and reliably evaluated, it may be impossible to predict their sensitiveness or permanence by inspection or even by detailed surveys. Under such conditions, it is highly desirable, although not ordinarily possible, that several sites be studied by the in-

FIG. 31. Natural control, Delaware River at Port Jervis, N. Y.

stallation and operation of temporary gages, simultaneously or consecutively, for sufficiently long periods to disclose their respective characteristics at different stages and in different seasons, before selection is finally made of that site which apparently will yield the best records of discharge at the lowest cost.

Since such studies can rarely be made, a careful reconnaissance is usually relied upon to disclose the best available site for a gaging station. Such a reconnaissance is much more likely to be successful in regions where the slopes of the streams are relatively steep and ledges or other firm reefs extend across the channels than in regions of shifting stream beds and banks. A site for a gage in the pool above a firm reef or rock ledge (Fig. 31) with rapids below is generally reasonably safe from the standpoint of essential stability of the stage-discharge relation. If the reef is nearly level across the stream, the control so formed may be nonsensitive, and if there are alternative sites, preference should be given to that one at which the profile of the control departs farthest from the horizontal, other conditions being reasonably comparable.

Gaging stations that have multiple control sections of different characteristics may have rating curves of unusual shapes, sometimes containing reversals. A *reversal* is said to occur when the slope of the usual parabolic rating curve, which normally decreases with increasing stage and discharge, changes direction by increasing through a certain range, called the *range of reversal*, and then decreasing normally again. Such a rating curve may be the result of a contracted section or other feature situated below the low-water control, which becomes effective as a control at a medium or high stage and which produces a steeper rating curve than that induced by the low-water control. The situation may be illustrated by assuming that two weirs have been placed in a stream channel below a gage, the weir of shorter crest being installed downstream from the weir of longer crest. At low water stages, the longer weir forms the control for the gage; as the stage increases, the pooling of water caused by the restriction in cross-sectional area at the lower and shorter weir may submerge the upper weir, and the lower weir thereupon becomes the control throughout the higher stages. The resulting rating curve (Fig. 32) is a combination of the individual rating curves of the two weirs with a short transition curve between them.

Although perhaps the majority of station rating curves are the resultants of the effects of two or more controls that come into action consecutively, there are only a few combinations of natural controls that cause actual reversals. In general, the routine plotting of a station rating curve on rectangular cross-section paper will not disclose to the eye any ordinary departure from a single parabolic curve. If, however, there is a combination of two or more well-defined parabolic curves that are not sufficiently diverse in characteristics to cause a reversal, the different curves may be disclosed by plotting the station rating curve on logarithmic cross-section paper on which, if the scales have been properly selected, a single parabolic curve will appear substantially as a straight line and a combination of such curves will appear as a succession of approximately straight lines (Fig. 33), each having a different slope from the others. A study of compound rating curves by means of such plotting will emphasize the dangers involved in the extrapolation of such curves far beyond the stages of available discharge measurements.

An engineer must have had experience in constructing and analyzing rating curves and tables and in studying the relation of rating curves of diverse kinds and shapes to the physical channel conditions that

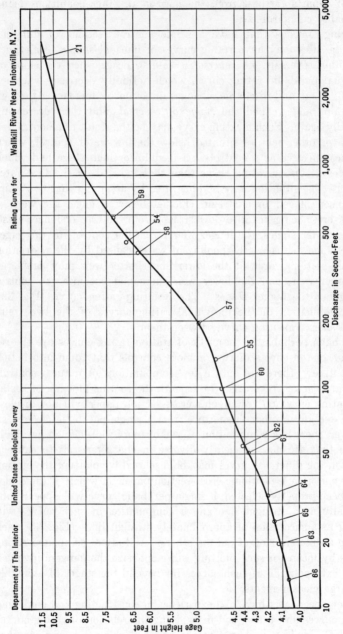

FIG. 32. Station rating curve containing reversal (logarithmic-scale plotting).

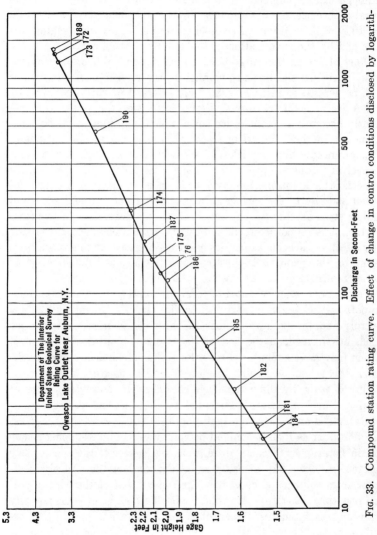

FIG. 33. Compound station rating curve. Effect of change in control conditions disclosed by logarithmic-scale plotting.

form controls before he can have any basis for judgment as to the kind of rating curve that would be obtained at any particular site for a gage, and therefore as to the general suitability of that site. Although expert judgment in such matters can be acquired only from actual experience, the development of such judgment may be aided by the study of descriptions of channel conditions at different gaging stations and by the examination of the resulting rating curves.

Effect of Ice on the Stage-Discharge Relation. When air temperatures fall below the freezing point, ice may appear in flowing water in three general forms: (1) solid ice, (2) frazil or slush ice, and (3) anchor ice.[1] Solid ice forms on the surface of the water and frequently becomes a complete ice cover which is ordinarily in flotation but not in motion. *Frazil* or slush ice is an accumulation in masses of small needle-like particles of ice which form during very cold weather in turbulent open water. *Anchor ice* consists of masses of ice particles which, forming on river beds on cold, clear nights, are detached and rise to the surface through the influence of sunlight or, in shallow streams, through the action of wind. Regardless of the form in which it is found, ice tends to obstruct stream channels, decreasing their effective carrying capacities and consequently tending to increase the stage, thus causing backwater and the continued modification of the stage-discharge relation while such obstruction persists.

Frazil and anchor ice, in the form of floating masses, may cause temporary backwater in early winter by their lodgment on shallow controls and in shallow portions of the river channel. Anchor ice which has formed on the bed of the stream at or near the control section may have a similar effect prior to its detachment. Such backwater effects can generally be detected without great difficulty on the graph made by the water-stage recorder. If, however, masses of frazil and anchor ice are intercepted by shore ice or become permanently lodged on the control, they tend to produce constantly increasing backwater as their accumulation continues. Solid ice, being generally in flotation, will cause little or no backwater if the control section remains open, but this situation rarely occurs and ordinarily backwater from solid ice is caused by the constriction of the control section resulting either from the solid ice itself which is, of course, nearly seven-eighths submerged, where it is in full flotation, and to that extent decreases the water-carrying capacity of the channel, or from the collection and subsequent freezing into solid ice on or near the control of masses of frazil or anchor ice. Periods of alternate freezing

[1] Bibliog. 14·1.

and thawing often result in the formation of several layers of solid ice, sometimes with slush ice, anchor ice, or flowing water between the layers. Such a condition is not only frequently productive of heavy backwater but also adds greatly to the difficulty of making discharge measurements through the ice. In addition to the "breakup" of the ice which occurs every spring, occasional breakups may occur during the winter. If such breakups come at periods of comparatively low discharge, the streams will frequently have insufficient carrying capacity to remove all the broken floating ice and jams will be formed. Ice jams may produce heavy and variable backwater, and the determination of the proper corrections to be applied to the gage-height record under these conditions is most difficult.

Unless a proposed gaging-station site may be kept under observation for several winters, the relative effect on the stage-discharge relation of backwater from ice is largely unpredictable in advance. Gaging stations situated short distances below sizable lakes or reservoirs will generally be relatively free from ice and consequent backwater because of the slightly higher temperatures that obtain in such bodies of water. In some instances, the selection of a site for a gaging station at a deep pool above the head of a series of rapids may be an insurance against serious backwater troubles. On the other hand, the establishment of a gaging station immediately above or within a stretch of shallow rapid water is almost certain to lead to serious backwater troubles resulting from the deposition and subsequent freezing of frazil and anchor ice in the shallow channel.

Small streams are generally less subject to backwater from floating ice than streams of larger size. Sometimes a small stream will acquire a complete ice cover when the stage is fairly high. With continued cold weather, the flow of the stream decreases and the ice cover does not continue in flotation but remains essentially in the place where it was formed, supported partly by arch action and partly by large stones in the stream bed, thus allowing the diminished flow of water to pass beneath the ice without backwater effect. Under certain conditions, the effect of backwater from ice can be reduced, if not eliminated, by the construction of an artificial control. If the solid ice is kept cut back from the crest of the control for a distance of several feet, the control will remain open without backwater, provided that free fall over the control is maintained. No remedy is available when backwater builds up below the artificial control and eventually submerges it.

Occasionally, when the pool above an artificial control is completely frozen over and the solid ice extends to the control, the pressure in the air space between the under surface of the ice and the water surface just upstream from the crest of the control will be alternately reduced below and equalized with atmospheric pressure, causing a continuous pulsation in stage at the gage. This pulsation usually shows a very short periodicity and an amplitude depending upon the amount of departure from atmospheric pressure under the ice sheet. Amplitudes of a foot or more are not uncommon. This phenomenon is referred to, perhaps somewhat incorrectly, as "siphonic action." In rare instances, it may also appear, to a limited extent, in connection with natural controls. Siphonic action, obviously, may be eliminated by keeping the pool free from ice for several feet above the control. In small stream channels, heavy falls of snow may actually produce backwater, especially if the snow is drifted into the stream in large amounts by high winds. Though this is an unusual situation, it is cited to indicate how diverse and varied may be the causes of backwater during the winter.

As indicated above, it is seldom possible to determine in advance, unless the gaging station can be located in a stretch of river known to be open at all times, just how extensive the backwater effect of ice will be. A site for a gaging station having been selected and the station placed in operation, conditions must be met as they are found. Since little can be done in the way of relieving serious backwater conditions, the best procedure to follow will be to obtain well-distributed discharge measurements, at strategic times if possible, throughout the winter, to the end that the effect of backwater from ice on the stage-discharge relation may be evaluated and the record of stage corrected in such a manner that the resulting records of discharge may be of reasonable accuracy.

Effect of Aquatic Vegetation on the Stage-Discharge Relation. Aquatic vegetation is one of the common causes of instability in the stage-discharge relation. Its effect in this respect is seasonal and recurrent. In northern latitudes, aquatic plants start growing in late spring or early summer, reach maturity in late summer, and disappear rather rapidly in the autumn as the water becomes cold and fall floods occur. In the South, their occurrence is less seasonal. These plants decrease the hydraulic capacity of the channel and so produce backwater because progressively higher stages are needed to obtain the greater channel depths required for the passage of any given quantity of water. If, therefore, aquatic vegetation is present within the control section of any gage, the stage-discharge relation pertaining to that gage may vary appreciably during the growing season and the effective control will thus be unstable to a greater or less degree. In general, instability in the stage-discharge relation caused by aquatic plants is probably more difficult to anticipate in the selection of a gaging-station site than the instability caused by a shifting stream bed.

It may be difficult and even impossible to find in a particular stretch of stream a site for a gage where at times there will not be backwater caused by aquatic vegetation. Since, however, the backwater effects of plant growth are generally seasonal, increase gradually, reach a peak at a more or less determinable time, and disappear as regularly, though more rapidly, the amount of such backwater effect at any time can readily be ascertained from the results of discharge measurements and proper allowances therefor made when the record of stage is converted into the record of discharge.[2]

There appears to be no practicable means for preventing such growths, since chemicals put into the water for this purpose would probably have toxic effects on fish and other animal life and so cannot safely be used. As the range of stage within which backwater from aquatic vegetation is of consequence is generally small, it may be practicable at some gage sites to avoid or decrease its effects by the construction of artificial controls. Whether the difficulty is so eliminated or whether the gage-height records are corrected for backwater before conversion into discharge records, the effects of aquatic growth, though always troublesome, are, among the various effects arising from the many causes of instability of control, probably the least difficult to evaluate and allow for.

Artificial Controls. An *artificial control* consists generally of a low dam or weir constructed across a stream channel below a station gage for the purpose of stabilizing the stage-discharge relation. It must, of course, be stable in itself and must supplant, partially at least, the unstable natural control at the gaging station. In order to accomplish this result effectively, the height of the structure must be sufficient to control the stage-discharge relation through a considerable range of stage. Theoretically, the steeper the general slope of the stream, the smaller and less costly will be the structure needed to accomplish the stabilization of the stage-discharge relation through any given range of stage. In theory, therefore, artificial controls are more practicable and more effective on streams of steep slopes than on those of flat slopes. Actually, however, artificial controls on streams of steep slopes are difficult to operate because they create relatively small and shallow pools which offer little protection for the intake pipes in winter and also because the pools are often rapidly filled from up-

[2] Chapter 15.

stream with gravel and rocks which cover the intake pipes and frequently render the controls ineffective. On any stream, artificial controls of average height will usually be effective through only the lower part of the range of stage, as they may be partially or completely submerged by backwater from a secondary downstream control and so become ineffective at high or even medium stages. Although, for a given height of structure, such ineffectiveness will be reached at a lower stage on a stream of flat slope than on a stream of steep slope, other considerations will generally govern in the location and design of an artificial control, particularly since many such controls are constructed for the prime purpose of stabilizing the stage-discharge relation only at low stages.

An artificial control should be adapted to the shape of the natural channel and to the slope and other hydraulic conditions of the stream, the extent of its departure from natural channel conditions being a direct measure of the magnitude of the natural forces that will operate to cause its destruction. Flowing water erodes the materials with which it comes into contact, and, it should be borne in mind, such erosive effects will increase at least with the square of its velocity. Any artificial control of ordinary type tends to decrease velocities of the flowing water immediately above it and to increase such velocities immediately below. Therefore precaution must be taken to prevent erosion immediately below an artificial control by providing a downstream "apron" and, of course, by so bonding the control structure with the bed and banks of the stream as to prevent underflow or side-cutting. There is danger that too little thought may be given to the design and construction of an artificial control simply because it is small and relatively cheap, just as too little attention is sometimes given by highway and railroad officials to the water-carrying capacities of small bridges and culverts. The occasional accidents caused by the failures of such apparently unimportant structures could have been avoided easily and at little cost in time and money if adequate thought had been given to their design.

There are wide variations in the conditions of channel and flow at the control sections for gaging stations, and probably such diverse conditions can best be met by varying the designs of artificial controls. As those variations have not been and apparently cannot well be so classified as to be of much aid in the preparation of designs, it seems impossible to attempt to standardize artificial controls by adopting one or more types or forms. Each artificial control should be built to suit the conditions at its site, following such general principles and methods as have been found by experiment and experience to be most advantageous. These principles and methods will be discussed below.

Height of Structure and Extent of Stabilization to Be Sought. The range of stage within which stabilization of the stage-discharge relation is to be attempted will largely determine the height and cost of the structure. The decision regarding this range should be based on considerations not only of cost but also of the gradient of the

FIG. 34. Low concrete artificial control, Cayuga Inlet near Ithaca, N. Y. Designed to stabilize stage-discharge relation for low flows.

stream, of the range of stage within which instability of the stage-discharge relation is a serious detriment to obtaining reliable records of discharge, and of the causes of the instability, whether shifting bed and banks or backwater caused by aquatic vegetation or by ice.

The difficulties which attend the functioning of artificial controls in swift streams have already been pointed out. Frequently, since instability in the stage-discharge relations of such streams relates principally to low stages, it is possible to attain essential stability by a concrete artificial control of rectangular cross section, the crest profile of which follows closely the profile of the stream bed and only a few inches above it (Fig. 34). Although such a control provides little water cover for the intake pipe, it permits the passage of rocks and debris and will more effectively stabilize the control at low stages than a higher structure built under the same channel conditions. It is relatively cheap because it is low and also because, since it induces little or no disturbance of the natural flow, the downstream apron may frequently be omitted entirely.

In situations on rapid streams where such a simple stabilization of the stream bed provides insufficient water cover to prevent occasional freezing of the intake pipe, a higher structure may be built. In

Fig. 35. Modified Columbus-type control, Platte Kill at Dunraven, N. Y. Note catenary crest profile and upstream apron.

order to prevent the eventual filling of the pool, a sloping upstream apron is added (Fig. 35). This upstream apron is generally about 5 feet wide, smooth, and with a slope of 5 : 1 from crest line to upstream edge, extending the entire length of the control. It is highly effective in streams carrying heavy bed loads since the increasing velocity from the edge of the apron to the crest of the control is sufficient to carry all semisuspended or rolling material over the crest. The intake pipe leading to the gage well is so placed as to be near the upstream edge of the apron with the invert of the pipe at about the same elevation. Upstream aprons may be adapted to almost all shapes and types of controls.

The construction of check dams has been advocated as a means of arresting and retaining during flood periods the bed loads of small streams of steep gradient which might otherwise be deposited in the pools above artificial controls. Such dams may consist of horizontal stop logs or planks supported either by timber cribs weighted with rock or by concrete piers. Sufficiently large openings are left between successive stop logs to pass ordinary flows. Check dams perform efficiently enough their function of stopping and holding heavy bed loads, but their effectiveness is lost as soon as the pools above them are filled, after which the accumulated deposits of gravel and rock must be removed, often at considerable expense. Experience has shown that devices such as upstream aprons, which permit the free passage of the bed load over artificial controls, are greatly to be preferred to check dams because of their greater effectiveness and a much lower cost of maintenance.

In situations where it is desired to stabilize the stage-discharge relation not only for low stages but also for medium and high stages, higher artificial controls must, of course, be built and because of their greater height elaborate protection in the way of downstream aprons must be provided to prevent excessive erosion below the structure that might eventually lead to its collapse. Such structures are not practicable on rapid streams which carry heavy bed loads of silt and heavier material, since because of their height no means is available to provide for the passage of such material over the control and because the use of one or more check dams upstream from the artificial control for the purpose of intercepting the moving bed load has not proved satisfactory by reason of the cost of frequent removal of the deposits which have accumulated above them. Such controls will be effective in streams of low gradient or in streams of steeper gradient that do not carry heavy silt or bed loads. It must be recognized, however, that since an artificial control 2 or 3 feet in height may affect the water level for a considerable distance upstream, depending, of course, on the gradient, precautions must be taken to guard against the possibility of subsequent claims for real or fancied damage resulting from this artificial raising of the water level.

If the purpose of the artificial control is to avoid backwater from ice, the control must be of sufficient height to create a pool of relatively quiet water above it. This pool will frequently freeze over solidly, but, if the ice is kept cut back from the crest of the control, all or nearly all backwater will be eliminated, provided, of course, that the artificial control is not rendered ineffective by backwater from ice in the channel below. The greater the sensitiveness of the control the greater, in general, will be the relative freedom from backwater. Controls provided with V-notches will usually eliminate all ice effect at very low stages. Obviously, an artificial control designed to eliminate the effect of backwater from aquatic vegetation must be of sufficient height to raise the water at the gage by an amount greater than the maximum amount of backwater produced by such vegetation. Often such a structure will defeat its own purpose, to some extent, since the creation of a pool of relatively quiet water above the control will provide added opportunity for weed growth therein. Furthermore, algae and similar vegetal growths frequently flourish on the crest of the artificial control itself, causing appreciable backwater and requiring periodic cleaning of the control for their elimination. In general, therefore, it may be stated that the economic practicability of attempting to eliminate backwater from ice or aquatic vegetation by the construction of artificial controls exclusively for such purposes has not been demonstrated. The incidental value in these respects of an artificial control constructed for the usual purpose of stabilizing the open water stage-discharge relation, however, cannot be questioned.

Sensitiveness of Stage-Discharge Relation. Although the sensitiveness of the stage-discharge relation pertaining to an artificial control, as to a natural control, is important at all stages, it is generally of particular importance at low stages. At many gaging stations one of the principal reasons for the construction of artificial controls is the desirability of improving the sensitiveness of the stage-discharge relation at such low stages. By means of a suitably designed artificial control it is possible so to concentrate the lower flows in a restricted width of the control section that small increments of discharge will correspond to such large increments in stage that discharge quantities may be determined with reasonable accuracy from the record of stage. In order that the profile of the crest of the artificial control may be designed to produce a reasonably sensitive stage-discharge relation, some knowledge is necessary concerning both the amount and duration of the maximum and minimum flows to be expected as well as concerning the degree of accuracy which will be required in the computed daily discharge records during such periods. Furthermore, the crest profile should be so designed as to be self-cleaning, at least to the extent that small pieces of drift will not lodge thereon and cause backwater at the gage.

If extremely low flows, less than 1 second-foot, for example, are to be accurately measured, either a 90-degree V-notch or a notch such as is incorporated in the Columbus-type control (Figs. 36 and 37) must be provided as part of the artificial control. A 90-degree steel V-notch plate with beveled edges bolted to the concrete of the control structure will provide a good degree of sensitivity for flows up to about 3 second-feet, the capacity of the particular notch shown in Figs. 38 and 39. In connection with an extensive program involving the gaging of many small streams, it would be possible to develop a

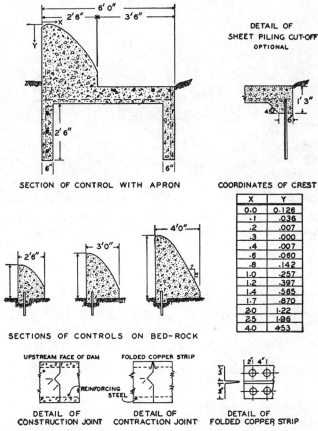

SECTION OF CONTROL WITH APRON

DETAIL OF SHEET PILING CUT-OFF OPTIONAL

SECTIONS OF CONTROLS ON BED-ROCK

COORDINATES OF CREST

X	Y
0.0	0.126
.1	.036
.2	.007
.3	.000
.4	.007
.6	.060
.8	.142
1.0	.257
1.2	.397
1.4	.565
1.7	.870
2.0	1.22
2.5	1.96
4.0	453

UPSTREAM FACE OF DAM
DETAIL OF CONSTRUCTION JOINT

FOLDED COPPER STRIP
REINFORCING STEEL
DETAIL OF CONTRACTION JOINT

DETAIL OF FOLDED COPPER STRIP

Fig. 36. Plans for Columbus-type artificial controls. (From Equipment for River Measurements, Preliminary Report on Studies of Artificial Controls, *U. S. Geological Survey Mimeographed Circular*, 1935.)

laboratory rating which could be employed at all the stations at which V-notch plates of a standard size were used. Experience, however, has shown that even plates of identical dimensions will have slightly different ratings at different installations, owing presumably to variations in the approach conditions. The Columbus-type controls or V-notches in controls of other types are objectionable to the extent

Fig. 37. Columbus-type control, Home Creek near New Philadelphia, Ohio. Note reinforced-concrete shelter, inclined staff gage, and footbridge.

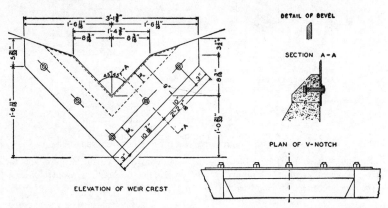

Fig. 38. Plans for 90-degree V-notch plate. (From Equipment for River Measurements, Structures for Artificial Controls, *U. S. Geological Survey Mimeographed Circular,* 1933.)

that their use requires structures of appreciably greater height and consequently greater cost than controls of ordinary parabolic or catenary profile. In spite of these drawbacks, V-notches or trapezoidal notches will be necessary at many stations in order to provide the required degree of sensitivity at low stages.

Except under very special conditions, when the discharge of a stream is so regulated that low flows do not occur, artificial controls of horizontal crest generally will not be sufficiently sensitive, and for this rea-

Fig. 39. Ninety-degree V-notch plate (Fig. 38) in concrete artificial control.

son they are now seldom built. For the same reason, controls having a main horizontal crest and a long rectangular notch are now little used because the notch, though providing some increase in sensitiveness, still does not furnish the necessary sensitivity for low stages, and furthermore there is an undesirable break in the rating curve for stages at which the water is just beginning to flow over the main crest. A design that has been found effective for average conditions consists of a crest with a catenary or near-parabolic profile which can be easily laid out during construction by hanging a rope loosely from the two ends of the control. This type of crest (Fig. 35) provides for a good concentration of the low water flow in the center of the control and is self-cleaning to a reasonable degree; since its profile is continuous there will be no break in the rating curve.

Cross Section of Artificial Control. Experience has tended to show that, except in special situations, broad-crested controls (Fig. 40) generally give more consistent results than sharp-crested ones. It also appears that the best results are obtained if the *nappe,* or body of water passing over the crest, is not affected by air entrapped behind it. In other words, the downstream face of the control should, if possible, be so designed that the nappe will cling to it at all stages of flow. This is not particularly difficult except where sharp-crested V-notches or other devices to provide for low flows are involved. For such controls, even though great care in design may have been used, the nappe

Fig. 40. Trenton-type artificial control, Pequest River at Huntsville, N. J. Photograph by W. S. Eisenlohr, Jr.

may alternate in certain ranges of stage between aerated and non-aerated, or adhering, conditions, each condition of nappe having its peculiar stage-discharge relation with respect to the gage. Figure 41 shows such a change in nappe as recorded on the chart of a water-stage recorder. Although such a situation may not be conducive to any particular error in the figures of daily discharge, two separate ratings must be developed and much greater care is therefore needed in the computation of the record of discharge than would be required if the nappe were nonaerated at all times and at all stages of flow. Figure 42 shows several typical cross sections of artificial controls, all of which are in general use.

Even though, as mentioned above, it may be possible to develop laboratory ratings for V-notch or trapezoidal notch plates, it will be

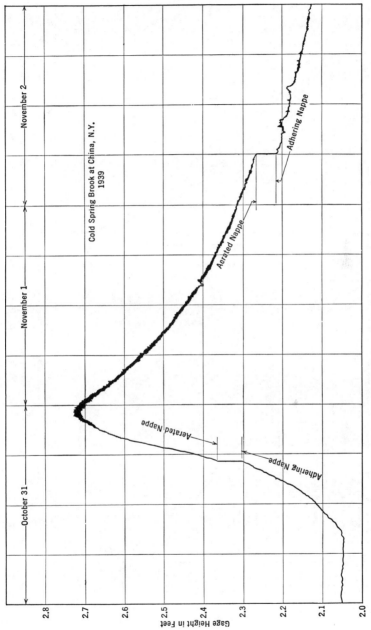

Fig. 41. Graph from water-stage recorder, showing varying conditions of nappe.

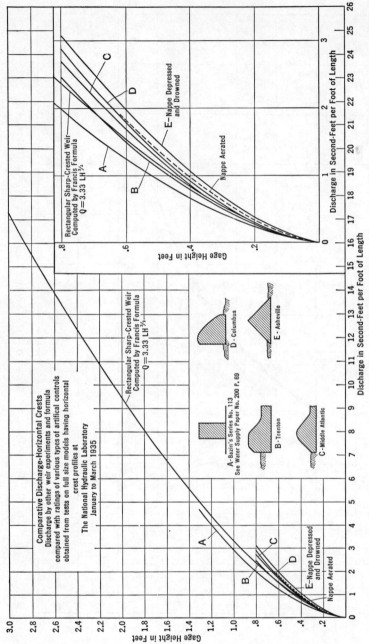

FIG. 42. Typical cross sections and data on performance of various types of concrete artificial controls. (From Equipment for River Measurements, Preliminary Report on Studies of Artificial Controls, *U. S. Geological Survey Mimeographed Circular*, 1935.)

found much more desirable to rate the entire control from zero flow to the highest flood stages. The current meter is generally used for this purpose, but for very low discharges the volumetric method may be employed. In this method, the entire flow may be piped from the V-notch into a measuring box and the time of filling obtained with a stop watch. This method of measurement for very low flows is highly accurate and provides an acceptable means of determining the stage-discharge relation for such flows.

Precautions to Be Observed. Turbulent flow below the artificial control causes excessive erosion, and therefore every effort should be made to reduce turbulence by proper expedients in design. This may be accomplished in part by so designing the crest and the downstream face of the control that the direction of the water will have a large horizontal component. The greater that horizontal component, the less will be the tendency to turbulent flow. No general rule can be given for the design of a downstream apron. A control built on a ledge of bare rock will require no apron, whereas one in gravel will require most elaborate protection to prevent undercutting from below. Under difficult conditions, the toe of the apron must be provided with a deep cutoff wall, and in many instances rough paving of the stream bed even below the cutoff wall will be advisable. Experience has shown that a raised lip 3 inches high and 6 inches wide at the toe of the downstream apron will so dissipate the velocity of the water as to reduce materially the danger of erosion beneath the apron.

The matter of leakage through or around a control structure is important, not only because of the amount of water, perhaps small, that fails to pass over the crest and so is not reflected in the stage-discharge relation, but also because such water may tend eventually to weaken, if not destroy, the structure. In porous material, the artificial control should be built on a cutoff wall sufficiently deep to eliminate any possibility of leakage underneath, although under these conditions there will always be a small amount of ground-water seepage. Similarly, the ends of the structure should be extended far enough into the banks to insure against the danger of sidecutting during high stages. It may frequently be necessary to protect the banks against erosion near the ends of the artificial control by riprapping or other means. As most artificial controls are comparatively low and relatively wide in proportion to height, there is little danger of overturning, because the criteria applicable to dams of larger size are usually well satisfied. This, however, does not mean that in critical cases the same considerations which obtain in the design of dams of larger size should not, if required, be applied in connection with the design of artificial controls.

Cost. A control structure built in porous material with a specially designed profile to provide for extremely low stages will obviously involve a much higher cost than a simple structure of rectangular section extending but little above the natural bed of the stream and designed only to stabilize the stage-discharge relation for low flows. However, artificial controls are built to accomplish certain purposes and if in order to attain such objectives expensive structures are required they must be built regardless of cost. Since stream gaging is ordinarily a long-term undertaking, the cost of an artificial control should properly be considered a capital expense distributed over a period of years. On this basis, the investment involved in even an expensive artificial control will be fully justified if it leads to the accomplishment of the purposes for which the station was established. Nothing, therefore, can be saved by building makeshift structures if records of a high degree of accuracy are required, and such records are in constantly increasing demand, especially in connection with low flows. If an artificial control is properly designed and constructed, its annual maintenance cost should be very small. Controls should be inspected frequently, of course, to guard against unforeseen contingencies, but in general the length of life of a well-designed structure should be comparable with that of the other appurtenances of a modern gaging station.

Construction Materials. Although undoubtedly plain or reinforced concrete is the most desirable material for the construction of artificial controls, other materials have been and will on occasion continue to be used. In some situations, a row of interlocking steel piling across the stream has been successfully utilized as a control and especially if the piling can be so driven as to simulate a curved profile of crest (Fig. 43). Such a control may have the disadvantage of a rather jagged crest which tends to collect floating debris. Naturally, this type of construction would be deliberately used only in special cases, usually where very deep water and difficult foundations would make the construction of a concrete artificial control both costly and difficult. On small streams, timber controls were formerly used to a considerable extent, usually with a horizontal main crest and a small rectangular notch. Such controls were not satisfactory, because of excessive leakage, their inability to resist the action of ice, and the necessity for continual replacement and repair. Timber may be considered a generally undesirable material for this purpose. Where rock or boulders of suitable size are available, dams of rough rubble masonry have sometimes been built to serve as artificial controls. In remote regions where the transportation of materials for concrete constitutes a problem, this type of construction, if well executed, may serve satisfactorily. It can hardly be recommended, however, unless problems of transportation costs or inaccessibility of site must be reckoned with. In some situations, mountain streams with beds of boulders can be provided with makeshift artificial controls, which nevertheless serve reasonably well, by utilizing large boulders in place as integral parts of a continuous rough masonry wall. Such a rough

Fig. 43. Station control adapted from existing interlocking steel piling, Onondaga Creek at Syracuse, N. Y.

control is frequently a great improvement over natural conditions and may serve adequately under the circumstances.

Dams as Control Sections. Dams that have been built for other purposes are sometimes utilized as control sections for gaging stations. Although, when used in this manner, they serve essentially as artificial controls, they have many disadvantages and few advantages. They are nonsensitive because large changes in discharge will correspond to only small changes in stage, especially at low stages; their crest lengths and shapes may be altered by the use and changes in use of flashboards, and their effective crest lengths may be decreased in unmeasured amounts by the lodgment of drift. Very often perhaps only a minor part of the flow passes over the spillway of the dam, and the remainder must be measured by means other than ordinary stream-gaging methods. The openings through a dam may be of many kinds and shapes—water-wheel penstocks, wasteways, and sluiceways of various kinds and dimensions, including, for example, navigation locks, fish ladders, and logways, the reliable rating of the water-carrying capacity of each such opening being most difficult to obtain, and the computation of the probable flow through all of them complicated and onerous. On the other hand, dams as control sections for gaging stations may give reliable records of flood flows because of the permanence of their stage-discharge relations at flood stages and because of the reasonable assurance with which upward extensions of the rating curves can be made. Even though no definite stage-discharge relationships have previously been established, dams may frequently be utilized as a means of obtaining records of flood flows which, though recognized as subject to error, may have a very definite value during periods when, for any reason, current-meter gaging stations located elsewhere on the river are inoperative or when, in the absence of gaging stations, no other records of flood discharges are available.

Since the crests of dams vary greatly as to shapes and dimensions, no one formula or coefficient in a formula can be used in computing the flow over them. In some situations, the spillways may be rated by current-meter measurements of discharge throughout the range of stage in the same way that other control sections are rated; in others, they may be rated by means of laboratory studies of models; and, finally, the rating may be assumed by comparison with the results of laboratory studies of models of several shapes that resemble as closely as possible the shape of the dam which is to be used. Of these methods, that of establishing the stage-discharge relation of the dam by means of current-meter measurements is the surest to yield reasonably reliable results. If that course is followed, the gaging station will have the characteristics of the ordinary stream-gaging station so far as the measurement of the water that passes over the spillway is concerned, but with all the complications and uncertainties that pertain to the measurement of the diversions, the variations in the quantities of water which pass through and around the dam, and the changes in the control section caused by variations in the elevation and shape of the crest resulting from the use of flashboards and the lodgment of debris.

If dams are used as control sections for gaging stations and cannot be rated by means of current-meter measurements, records of both laboratory studies and field tests of dams with respect to the stage-discharge relation should be fully utilized. Such records are distributed rather widely through engineering literature. It is probable that the largest single compilation of these records is contained in

Water Supply Paper 200.[3]   Records of this kind are deficient in several ways and especially so with respect to the great heads that are utilized as bases for estimates of flood discharges.   They are deficient also with respect to the many variations in crest shapes.   These uncertainties, added to those resulting from the nonsensitiveness of this kind of control and the many uncertainties connected with determinations of low flows over the spillway and the calculation of discharge through openings, make the use of dams as control sections for gaging stations generally unsatisfactory from both the standpoint of cost and that of accuracy of records.   However, with the increased utilization of rivers and the resulting increase in the number of dams, the location of sites for gaging stations that are not situated within the backwater of dams is becoming increasingly difficult in many sections of the country. Engineers are thus forced in many instances either to use dams as control sections, or to establish gaging stations within a backwater pool, installing two water-stage recorders therein in order to obtain a continuous record of the slopes of the surface of the pool and utilizing the record of slopes thus obtained in computations of discharge.[4]   In such situations, the choice should probably be made on the basis of the probable accuracy of the records, since either type of station will be relatively unsatisfactory and expensive to operate.

At many gaging stations which utilize dams as control sections a portion of the total flow passes through water wheels to produce power.   The shafts of the water wheels or turbines may be directly connected to machinery, as in many small industrial plants, or they may be connected to generators for the production of electricity. Computations of the discharge through the wheels of mechanical power plants must be based exclusively on water-wheel data; computations of flow through hydroelectric plants may be based on either water-wheel data, electrical output, or both.

Water wheels in modern installations, whether they be of the reaction or impulse type, are provided with manufacturers' ratings or tables which are based on the results of experimental tests.   From these tables the flow utilized by the wheels may be calculated with reasonable accuracy.   Experience has shown, however, that as a result of mechanical wear and cavitation there is a tendency, increasing with the length of service of the water wheels, to require progressively more and more water for the production of a given unit of energy. For this reason, water-wheel ratings should be checked or revised occasionally.   Various methods may be chosen for this purpose, depending

[3] Bibliog. 8·2.
[4] Chapters 8 and 15; Bibliog. 11·3.

upon the facilities afforded for the measurement of flow, such as current-meter measurements, the Gibson method, salt-velocity method, and others. If opportunity exists in the tailrace for the proper use of the current meter, the performance of water wheels may be checked more easily and more cheaply in this manner than by any other method.

In modern hydroelectric plants, a daily record of flow is usually kept. This record may be computed in part from the kilowatt-hour output of the plant, the plant efficiencies, heads, percentage of gate openings, and other data being taken into account, and in part from a record of the heads on the spillway crest, a rating table based on theoretical considerations for the conversion to discharge being used. A few hydroelectric plants have Venturi meters installed in the penstocks for the purpose of measuring directly either the amounts of water used by individual units or the total amount used by all the units of the plant.

Under the best conditions at modern plants, the flow utilized in the production of energy may be determined with a degree of precision fully comparable with that of the best gaging stations. Under other and less favorable conditions, however, the determination of the amounts of water so used may be little more than a crude approximation.

In the computation of flow through sluice gates, submerged orifices, fish ladders, logways, and navigation locks, each situation must be treated as a separate problem. For instance, the amount of water used by a navigation lock may be determined from the cubical contents of the lock and the daily record of lockages, with an allowance for leakage and, if greater precision is sought, a further allowance for the varying displacements of the vessels using the lock, all these factors being expressed in terms of average cubic feet per second per day. Again, the discharge through a submerged orifice or sluice gate may be determined from the basic formula

$$Q = CA\sqrt{2gh}$$

where A is the area of the opening in square feet, h the net head on the center of opening, and C a coefficient which may range from 0.50 or less to nearly unity. The value of C should be determined by experiment, if possible; otherwise, an average value will have to be taken from reference tables. Discharge through such rectangular openings as logways and fish ladders may sometimes be ascertained by current-meter measurements and ratings developed in this manner; otherwise, recourse must be had to some variation of the basic Francis formula for the flow over weirs.   It should be emphasized that in the development of all such auxiliary ratings the current meter should be used wherever possible and that theoretical considerations should be relied upon only when all opportunities for actual investigational work in the field have been exhausted.

Sharp-Crested Weirs as Control Sections. Sharp-crested weirs [5] are much used as a means for measuring the flow of water and consequently as artificial controls, especially in hydraulic laboratories and in the distributary ditches of irrigation systems.   In the laboratory, they are or may be accurately calibrated in place, preferably volumetrically by measuring the flow over them by means of a calibrated tank.   When so calibrated and if properly installed, sharp-crested weirs constitute one of the best and most accurate devices for the measurement of flowing water.   In the distribution of irrigation water among several or many users, the system must be operated by "rule-of-thumb" methods applied by water masters, ditch riders, and other nontechnical men.   For such purposes, the sharp-crested weir and sharp-edged notches of trapezoidal, V-shape, or rectangular shapes serve probably more satisfactorily and more accurately than any other available device.   Such shapes have been well standardized for field service and acceptably calibrated by models in hydraulic laboratories, and the field users are carefully instructed with respect to their setting so that the available standard weir tables will apply reliably.

There is also a limited use of weirs in systematic stream gaging, especially on streams that have so little water that reliable discharge measurements cannot be made by current meter.   Sharp-crested weirs are not practicable for obtaining records of the flow of large streams because of the considerable expense involved in their construction. If sharp-crested weirs are used, their ratings should be checked by current-meter measurements or other means to insure that the tables based on laboratory tests of models are applicable to the weirs as they are installed, in spite of the unavoidable differences in placements, in shapes and sizes of channels of approach, and in the directions and velocities of the currents of water as they approach the weirs.   A general assumption that a record obtained by means of any sharp-crested weir is of unquestionable accuracy is not justified, and the engineer must proceed in the use of such weirs with the same painstaking care that he exercises with respect to other phases of a stream-gaging program.[6]

[5] Chapter 8.
[6] Bibliog. 8·1.

BIBLIOGRAPHY 11

1. C. H. PIERCE, Structures for Artificial Controls, *U.S.G.S. Mimeographed Circular,* 1933.
2. HARTWELL, LEE, and PIERCE, Preliminary Report on Studies of Artificial Controls, *U.S.G.S. Mimeographed Circular,* 1935.
3. M. C. BOYER, Determining Discharge at Gaging Stations Affected by Variable Slope, *Civil Engineering,* Vol. 9, No. 9, pp. 556–558 (September 1939).

CHAPTER 12

INSTALLATION OF GAGES

Installation Requirements. The type and placement of a gage will depend on the purpose which it is to serve. The types of gages commonly used in systematic stream gaging are described in Chapter 8, and the establishment of gaging stations, including the selection of sites, is described in Chapter 10. Because of its effects on the economy and efficiency of the station and the accuracy of the records, the type of the station gage and the details of its installation rank second in importance only to the selection of the gaging-station site itself.

Only one gage at each gaging station is considered the "station gage," that is, the gage which yields the records of stage from which the subsequent records of discharge are derived. There may or may not be other gages at and near a gaging station. If there are other gages, each has its specific use but none of them serves as the station gage except perhaps in an emergency. If a staff, chain, or wire-weight gage is the station gage, there will probably be no other gage. If the station is equipped with a water-stage recorder, such recorder may be considered the station gage in that it produces a graphic record of stage which is referenced to a hook gage or other permanent reference gage in the well. At a water-stage recorder station, therefore, there will always be a reference gage or gages in the well and, in addition, there should be a staff or other auxiliary gage outside the well. The operation of a water-stage recorder is possible only in conjunction with a permanent reference gage, and whether the water-stage recorder itself or the reference gage upon which the precision of its operation depends is considered the station gage is really beside the point. At a slope station, two gages are always required for measuring the slope. If two water-stage recorders are used, neither can be called the station gage to the exclusion of the other; if, on the other hand, one water-stage recorder and one staff gage are used, the water-stage recorder might well be considered the station gage. The problems related to the installation of a gage vary with its type, the particular purpose which it is to serve, and the physical conditions at the site where it is to be installed.

187

The types of gages used at any gaging station may depend on the amount of money available for equipment, the nature of the river and its fluctuations in stage and discharge, and the availability of potential local observers. Water-stage recorders are now generally preferred for all gaging stations because of the continuity of records of stage and the greater resulting accuracy that may be attained with respect to the records of discharge. Other types of gages, however, may be used with reasonably satisfactory results on large and slowly fluctuating rivers, but water-stage recorders are indispensable equipment for stations on rivers or streams in which rapid fluctuations occur. Also, in regions where the use of water approaches the limit of supply and where there are likely to be conflicts in rights of use, any type of gage other than a water-stage recorder is likely to yield inadequate and, therefore, unsatisfactory records. Whatever the type of gage, the suitability of the site and the stability of the gage are of prime importance.

Since the function of a station gage, whether recording or non-recording, is to provide the means for obtaining accurate and reliable records of stage which will subsequently be converted into records of discharge, it is necessary that the gage (1) have its datum plane below the lowest stage of the river; (2) be so placed that it will not be overtopped by the highest anticipated flood; (3) be so constructed as to be rigid, secure, and safe; (4) be so placed as to be in contact or connected with the water of the stream at all stages; (5) be so situated as to be accessible at all seasons of the year and at all stages of the river; and (6) be so installed that it may be kept reasonably free from ice.

The first of these specifications requires (a) reliable information, if available, with respect to minimum stages of the river at the site, as well as knowledge of the elevation of the lowest part of the river bed at the control section when maximum erosion at that point occurs; and (b) the establishment of the gage in such position that the lowest stages of the river will be recorded as positive readings thereon. In order to be certain that this requirement is fulfilled in the absence of sufficient information as to the lowest possible stage of the stream, it is advisable to establish the datum plane of the gage so far below the bed of the river at the control section that there will be no possibility of negative gage readings which are liable to confuse the local observer and to lead to errors in the computations and consequently in the final records.

The second specification involves, among other things, the availability of knowledge concerning the stages of the highest floods of the past, and in this respect there will always be much greater uncertainty than in the matter of information concerning low stages. Low stages have zero flow as a lower limit; high stages have no upper limit that can be determined with assurance. Any appraisal of the stage of the highest anticipated flood is a most difficult matter because it generally involves assumptions that may be unsound. If no record of stage is available at the site, flood marks may be used to indicate the heights of recent floods, and the frequently unreliable, though truthful, testimony of local residents may be obtained with respect to the stages of the highest floods of the past. The theory of probability may be employed, if some data are available with respect to known floods, in order to determine the height of, for instance, the theoretical one-hundred-year flood. Unfortunately, natural phenomena do not occur with mathematical precision or in accordance with any fixed or known law, and consequently the determination of the theoretical heights of maximum floods in periods of any selected length involves a basis of assumption that is not necessarily true in fact. From a mathematical point of view, the use of the theory of probability to project into the future flood occurrences of the past may be convincing; in actual practice, the results so obtained may lead to unwarranted conclusions. Regardless of the meagerness and unreliability of basic data, however, it will be necessary to make some decision concerning the stage of the maximum anticipated flood, and it is evident that such determination will involve, more than anything else, the exercise of judgment based upon experience. Such an appraisal, of course, is necessary in order to forestall the loss of records of high stages regardless of the type of gage used and especially to prevent the loss of or damage to equipment if a water-stage recorder is to be installed. The higher the stage of the anticipated flood, the greater will be the costs of installation, particularly if a water-stage recorder is used, because of the greater height of the well structure. Unfortunately, because of the general lack of knowledge of what to expect in the way of high floods, as well as the natural desire to avoid unnecessary construction expense, the overtopping of recorder structures by high floods is not uncommon. The exercise of proper foresight will not wholly prevent such occurrences, but it will reduce their incidence to a minimium.

The third specification involves so placing the gage that it will not be unnecessarily exposed to the dynamic force of water, to the pressure of ice, or to the accumulation of drift against it. The gage should be set on a solid and stable base, and whatever supporting structure is used should not change appreciably in elevation or deteriorate rapidly. For a water-stage recorder, the walls of the gage well should preferably be constructed on a foundation of ledge rock or on a slab of concrete on a bed of earth, sand, or gravel that will not be eroded or changed in elevation. In soft material, piles may be used if proper facilities for driving them are available, or a heavy timber grillage, extending if necessary beyond the walls of the well, may serve acceptably as a foundation. The table or shelf on which the recorder is placed must be so supported as to be stable and rigid with no undue danger of settlement or other change in position. A nonrecording gage should be attached to a structure or natural feature that is stable and of fixed elevation. If a special supporting structure is built, it should be firmly bedded on a good foundation and should be of durable construction. If an existing abutment, pier, or wall is used, it should be both stable and durable. Trees or structures that may be affected with respect to elevation by wind, water, frost, or ice are generally unsatisfactory as supports for gages that are to be used for any considerable periods of time.

For water-stage recorder installations, the fourth specification requires that there be an intake pipe leading from the gage well to the river at an elevation that is definitely below the lowest river stage, and, for a nonrecording-gage installation, the use of a supporting structure that is in contact with the water of the river at all stages. Such an installation may involve two or more sections of staff gage in order to obviate the necessity for unduly high or expensive structures that would be exposed to the danger of damage by floods, and especially by ice or drift.

The fifth specification involves placing the gage in a bank that is above high-water stages, or, if that is impracticable, the providing of a bridge, boat, or other means by which the gage may be reached during high-water periods.

The sixth specification involves, for a nonrecording gage, the daily clearing of ice during the frozen season from that part of the staff gage that extends into the river or the cutting of a hole through the ice under the chain or wire-weight gage in order that the water beneath the ice will rise to its static level and readings of stage may be made. For a water-stage recorder, this specification involves the construction of the gage well at such distance from the bank of the river and at such depth below the ground surface that the surface of the water in the well will be, if possible, below the frost line of the bank. It requires, too, the placing of the intake pipe at as low an elevation as the stream bed at the outer end will permit, in order that the pipe may be protected by the greatest possible depth of earth cover and that it may be well below the zone of ice formation in the stream, to the end that the danger of ice formation within the pipe will be minimized.

Datum Plane of Gage. The datum plane of any gage is preferably mean sea level if a bench-mark elevation referred to that datum is reasonably available; otherwise, any arbitrary datum plane may be chosen. The datum plane adopted has no significance with respect to the collection of records of stage, the computation of records of discharge, or local uses of the records. It is highly desirable that all records in a river basin be referred to a common datum plane, thereby affording information with respect to the "fall" of the river or the average slope in the water surface between successive gages and at different stages. For this purpose, the datum plane of mean sea level will generally be used if practicable, but any other datum that is common to all gages in the river basin will be equally satisfactory. The datum of mean sea level will be more readily utilized than any arbitrary or local datum if bench-mark elevations above mean sea level are available at several different points in the basin.

The datum of the gage should, if practicable, be referred also to any municipal, railroad, or other datum plane that is used in the vicinity in order to increase the possible utility of the records of stage in connection with slope and flood studies.

Since it is essential that a fixed datum plane be maintained for all records of stage at any gaging station, all gages must be referred to and frequently checked with bench marks of permanent elevation. This procedure is necessary because gages are sometimes damaged or destroyed and must be repaired or replaced, the chains and wires of chain and wire-weight gages change in length with use, and the structures upon which gages are supported change in elevation. The establishment of bench marks and the referencing of the gage datum are therefore essential phases of the installation of every gage. Naturally, the referencing should be done promptly after the gage is placed in position.

If ledge rock is available at a gaging-station site, a tablet set into the rock should be used as a bench mark. In the absence of ledge rock, the tablet may be set in the top of a reinforced-concrete post. The post should be tapered from bottom to top and should extend above the surface of the ground to such height as to be readily found. It should, of course, be long enough so that its base will be well below the depth of frost. Bench marks on roots or trunks of trees are not to be recommended; neither should a bench mark be set on any part of a gage structure. Bench marks established on bridge abutments or piers, on the foundations of buildings, or on large boulders do not always prove to be permanent, and for that reason two or more bench marks should be utilized in order to insure against loss of the datum. At some times and in some places, such bench marks are the best that can immediately be obtained without undue delay or expense; they should be regarded as temporary, to be replaced at the earliest opportunity.

In addition to one or more permanent bench marks at each gaging station, it is advisable to have auxiliary bench marks or reference points for convenient use. Even though such reference points apparently are unquestionably permanent in elevation, they should be checked occasionally by level through comparison with the permanent bench mark. Reference points should be so placed, if practicable, that the datum plane of any gage may be checked by means of one setup of the level.

Recorder Wells. A recorder well is essentially a stilling well in which the recorder float is protected while it rises and falls with the changes in stage of the river and in which accurate readings of the stage may be made on a reference gage or gages. A well should have sufficient height to provide for the full range of stage of the river without danger of submerging the water-stage recorder. It should be of sufficient size not only to permit the free operation of the float and counterweight without danger of conflict with each other or contact with the side of the well, but also to provide the space needed by the engineer or observer for entering the well to clean or repair it, to read a staff or hook gage, or to adjust the float or counterweight.

In order that the water in the well may be at the same level as the water in the river, there must always be open connection below the water surface between the river and the well. This is usually accomplished by means of an intake pipe.

One of the simplest forms of a recorder well is a galvanized-iron culvert pipe attached in a vertical position to a bridge pier or abutment or to the side of a rock cliff (Fig. 44). This type of well is particularly appropriate for rivers which have wide overflow areas, but it is unsuitable in northern latitudes because of its vulnerability with respect to frost. Such a pipe well must be large enough for the free action of the float and counterweight but would seldom be of sufficient size to permit a man to work in it. It should have an entrance door near the bottom or, preferably, two or more doors spaced at different elevations in order to provide easy access to the interior for the purpose of reading the inside staff gage, if one is installed, or of making necessary repairs. The bottom of the pipe, if so

FIG. 44. Corrugated steel pipe well attached to bridge pier, Colorado River near Eagle Lake, Texas. Note clean-out door in well and vertical staff gage.

supported that it is not in contact with the bed of the stream, may consist of a hollow inverted cone truncated at its lower end to form a circular entrance, perhaps 2 inches in diameter, through which water will pass into and out of the well. Such a finishing of the lower end of this type of well serves two purposes; it eliminates both the action of waves and the danger of silt troubles within the well.

FIG. 45. Corrugated steel pipe well (36-inch diameter) in river bank, Wild Rice River near Twin Valley, Minn. Note box shelter.

Galvanized-iron culvert pipes are also used as wells in river banks (Fig. 45), the principal objective being economy, since a pipe well is both cheaper in cost of materials utilized and in construction costs than a standard concrete well. This type of well is provided with an intake pipe and with an inside gage of some kind. Since access to the well is usually from the top, this well will be satisfactory only if it is of sufficient size (not less than 36 inches in diameter) to permit entrance by the engineer. Pipe wells make satisfactory temporary installations and frequently serve well on a permanent basis. The principal objection to their use must always lie in their necessarily small size.

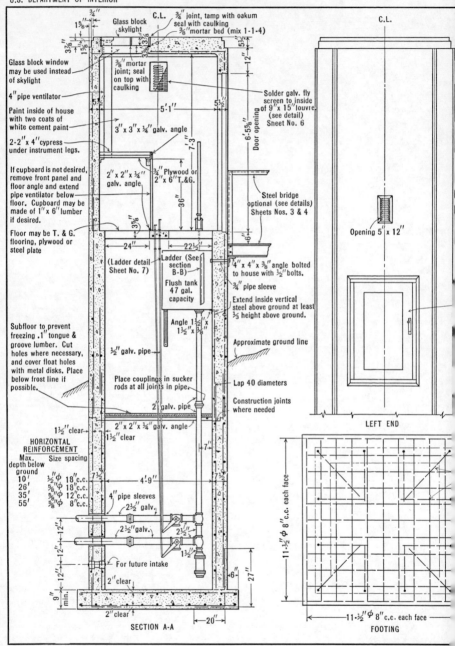

FIG. 46. Plans f[

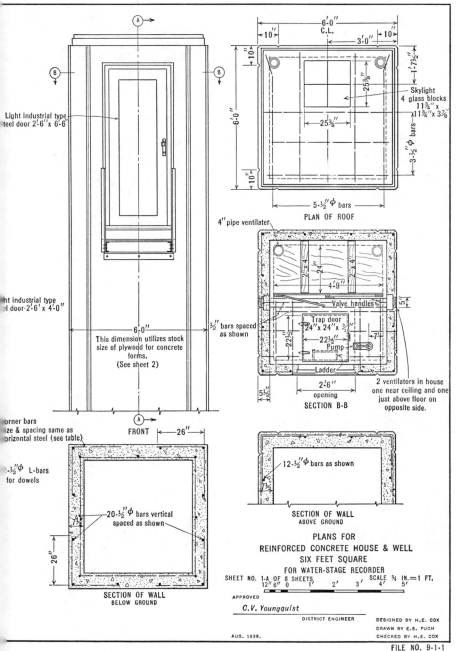

Light industrial type steel door 2'-6" x 6'-6"

6'-0" C.L.
10" 3'-0" 10"
10"
25⅜"
Skylight
4 glass blocks
11¾" x
11¾" x 3⅞"
25⅜"
6'-0"
3-½" ϕ bars
1'-7½"
5-½" ϕ bars
PLAN OF ROOF

ht industrial type
el door 2'-6' x 4'-0"

6'-0"
This dimension utilizes stock size of plywood for concrete forms.
(See sheet 2)

½" bars spaced as shown

4" pipe ventilator
2" x 4" 24" 2" x 4"
4'-9"
Valve handles
22½"
Trap door 24" x 24" x ¾"
22½"
Pump
7"
Ladder
5½"
2'-6"
opening
SECTION B-B
5"
2 ventilators in house one near ceiling and one just above floor on opposite side.

FRONT 26"

orner bars
ze & spacing same as
orizontal steel (see table)

-½" ϕ L-bars
for dowels

20-½" ϕ bars vertical spaced as shown
26"
SECTION OF WALL
BELOW GROUND

12-½" ϕ bars as shown
SECTION OF WALL
ABOVE GROUND

PLANS FOR
REINFORCED CONCRETE HOUSE & WELL
SIX FEET SQUARE
FOR WATER-STAGE RECORDER

SHEET NO. 1-A OF 8 SHEETS   SCALE ¾ IN.=1 FT.
12" 6" 0 1' 2' 3' 4' 5'

APPROVED
C.V. Youngquist
DISTRICT ENGINEER
DESIGNED BY H.E. COX
DRAWN BY E.S. PUGH
CHECKED BY H.E. COX
AUG. 1939.

FILE NO. 9-1-1

inforced-concrete well and shelter.

The gage well should be built on a solid foundation, if possible, because with the present type of concrete construction the weight of the walls and shelter is considerable. Bed rock is the best foundation, of course, but may be impracticable because of prohibitive excavation costs. Concrete floors or foundations are generally used for gage wells, but it is sometimes difficult, because of excessive water, to lay the concrete properly. Under such conditions, if the well is of no greater than ordinary height, a timber floor, built of two thicknesses of 2-inch planks laid crosswise, will be found very satisfactory. Such a floor is permanent, since wood under water will not decay. Since the costs of excavation for the well and intake pipe and of the necessary shoring and pumping are considerable, the walls of wells are now generally constructed either of mass or reinforced concrete in order to assure many years of service, and the well is made not less than 4 feet by 4 feet, inside dimensions, in order to afford ample space for the installation of the various gages and other appurtenances of a water-stage recorder and for entrance by the engineer for cleaning, adjustments, and repairs. If the use of concrete is not practicable and a wooden well is constructed, it should be made of such size, perhaps 5.5 feet by 5.5 feet, inside dimensions, that its walls will serve as outside forms for a concrete well when replacement becomes necessary, thereby eliminating the necessity for re-excavation of the well in connection with its reconstruction. Figure 46 shows a plan for a concrete well and shelter, the layout of the reinforcing steel, and a suggested arrangement of gage appurtenances. For wells up to 25 feet, the thickness of the walls may be increased to 12 inches and the steel reinforcement omitted.

Intake Pipes. An intake pipe is an essential element of any water-stage recorder well that is not set directly in the channel of the flowing water. The installation of the intake pipe may be difficult, and the cost will necessarily vary with the length and size of the pipe, its depth below the ground surface, and the nature of the materials to be excavated, whether solid rock or unstable sand or clay. In many situations, shoring of the sides of the trench may be anticipated. Since the excavations must extend below the level of the water in the stream, pumping of water from the well and trench will ordinarily be necessary. Under unfavorable conditions of excavation, the driving or jacking of the intake pipe through considerable distances of unexcavated material may be attempted, not always successfully, or various methods, such as draining, grouting, or freezing, may be adopted for the purpose of stabilizing the unconsolidated material through which the excavation for the trench must be made.

Intake pipes of steel have been found as satisfactory as those of wrought iron and are much cheaper. Galvanizing is unnecessary unless the pipe is exposed to corrosive action of some kind. Cast-iron soil pipes have been used as intake pipes but are not recommended because of the difficulty attending their proper placement in the trench and in making good joints. The intake pipe must be large enough, commonly from 2 inches to 4 inches in diameter, to insure that the water in the well shall follow the rise and fall of the water in the river with no considerable lag, but not so large as to permit waves in the surface of the water in the river to affect appreciably the stages of water in the well. The larger sizes of pipes should be used in those places where the water carries a bed load or suspended load of silt, because a small pipe will become obstructed much more quickly than a larger one. Intake pipes may range in length from a few feet at some sites to 300 feet or more at others. At some sites, two or more intake pipes at different elevations are used in order to increase reliability of action and to decrease the lag of the water in the well during floods when the changes in stage of the river may be rapid. The reliability of action is thus improved by providing second and third intake pipes to come into action whenever the water reaches them and especially to afford means for the entrance of water if the lower pipe becomes covered by shifting sands or is otherwise obstructed.

The intake pipe should be laid as nearly level as practicable or, if necessary, on a uniform small slope, but irregular gradients should be avoided. Its invert should, if possible, be not less than 6 inches above the floor of the well in order to prevent obstruction of the intake by silt deposited inside the well and to provide a sufficient depth of water for the proper operation of the float at all times. Throughout its length, it must be below the lowest stage of the river, must if possible be free from the danger of freezing, and should extend from the well to a point in the stream where there is a considerable depth of water at the lowest stage. In other words, the outer end of the intake should be above the bed of the stream in order to lessen the danger of its being covered by deposits of silt or gravel. It is well to remember that the lowest stages of northern rivers frequently occur during the winter when precipitation is in the form of snow and there is no runoff from the surface of the ground over a period of three or four months.

Flushing Devices. Many streams, particularly in the South and West, carry heavy loads of suspended silt at all stages, although, of course, such load is greatest during flood stages. At a gaging station on a stream of this type, this condition leads to heavy deposits of silt, not only in the well itself, but also within the intake pipe, with the result that the intake pipe soon becomes obstructed to such an extent as to be largely or wholly inoperative. To combat this trouble, the intake may be flushed or cleaned at periodic intervals and so kept in proper operating condition. If the deposits of silt are small, the intake may be kept open and in proper operating condition by occasionally running collapsible sewer rods through it. A piece of canvas or burlap pulled through the pipe by a stiff wire will also clean the pipe effectively if no great obstruction is present. Many different devices are available for flushing intake pipes, the general principle behind all of them being the sudden release of a quantity of water under sufficient head to wash out the accumulated silt as the water passes outward through the intake pipe.

The simplest means of cleaning a well and intake pipe by flushing is by the use of a public water supply through a fire hydrant or service connection. If a hydrant stream is used, the procedure of cleaning the well and intake is made simple by the unlimited amount of water under high pressure which is thus available. Usually, however, resort must be had to other means. At every gaging station where serious silt troubles may be expected, the well end of the intake pipe should be provided with a check valve and means for its operation from or near the floor of the gage shelter. Incidentally, this valve, in addition to its principal use in connection with flushing operations, may, if required, be of value in dampening the effects of wave action within the well by reducing the effective size of the intake opening. Where only infrequent flushing is necessary, the procedure is first to close the valve and then build up a head of water in the well by pumping from the river into the well by means of a portable gasoline pump. When a considerable head of water has been so created, the check valve is opened and the water passes out through the intake pipe with sufficient velocity to dislodge and carry away the accumulations of silt therein. Much of the accumulated silt in the bottom of the well will also pass out through the intake pipe if it has first been agitated and loosened before water is pumped into the well.

Another method of flushing the intake (Fig. 47) utilizes a tank on the floor of the shelter which is connected by piping directly to the intake pipe outside its valve. This tank is filled by the engineer or observer by pumping water from the well with a hand pump. After the tank is filled, the valve between the intake pipe and the well is closed and the valves in the pipe leading from the tank to the intake are opened. This method is appropriate at stations where frequent flushing, as at weekly intervals, is necessary, as it provides a relatively small amount of water under a high head which is usually effective in keeping the intake clear.

Prevention of Ice Formation in Gage Wells. It is important that means be provided to prevent the formation of ice in gage wells, since

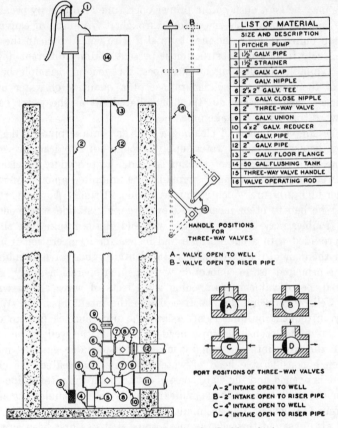

LIST OF MATERIAL	
	SIZE AND DESCRIPTION
1	PITCHER PUMP
2	1½" GALV. PIPE
3	1½" STRAINER
4	2" GALV. CAP
5	2" GALV. NIPPLE
6	2"x 2" GALV. TEE
7	2" GALV. CLOSE NIPPLE
8	2" THREE-WAY VALVE
9	2" GALV. UNION
10	4"x2" GALV. REDUCER
11	4" GALV. PIPE
12	2" GALV. PIPE
13	2" GALV. FLOOR FLANGE
14	50 GAL. FLUSHING TANK
15	THREE-WAY VALVE HANDLE
16	VALVE OPERATING ROD

HANDLE POSITIONS
FOR
THREE-WAY VALVES

A - VALVE OPEN TO WELL
B - VALVE OPEN TO RISER PIPE

PORT POSITIONS OF THREE-WAY VALVES

A - 2" INTAKE OPEN TO WELL
B - 2" INTAKE OPEN TO RISER PIPE
C - 4" INTAKE OPEN TO WELL
D - 4" INTAKE OPEN TO RISER PIPE

Fig. 47. Details of typical intake flushing device.

a very thin layer of ice on the surface of the water may so impede the rise and fall of the float as to render the gage-height record of little or no value. The usual means of preventing ice formation in gage wells fall under the following headings: (a) subfloors or frost barriers, (b) oil tubes, (c) heating devices, and (d) miscellaneous expedients.

Subfloors or Frost Barriers. At many gage sites, the earth cover around the gage well is of insufficient depth to provide full protection against freezing, but, if there is any depth of penetration into earth or rock, protection may be supplemented by the construction of a subfloor or frost barrier. This is a light floor of either temporary or permanent construction placed in the well as far as possible below the ground surface but at the same time high enough to avoid submergence by the usual small winter floods. Such a subfloor prevents freezing of the water surface by utilizing in a closed space the natural heat of the ground surrounding the well and to some extent that of the water.

A subfloor may be constructed temporarily of plywood, composition board, or similar light material, or permanently, of tongue-and-groove lumber, the floor of either type being supported by 2 inch by 4 inch timbers wedged in place at the desired elevation or bolted to the walls of the well. A small opening with removable cover is left, through which the hook gage may be set with the aid of a flashlight, and one or more circular holes are cut, through which the float or floats may rise when stages exceed the elevation of the subfloor. These float holes may be closed by removable covers which will rise with the float and settle back into place after the float passes through the hole on the receding stage. Subfloors, though quite effective in regions where, because of long-continued cold weather, material fluctuations in stage seldom occur during the winter, are not so successful under conditions involving frequent breakups. Under such conditions, it is seldom possible to place the subfloor at a sufficiently low elevation to be effective and at the same time to avoid frequent submergence which may involve fouling of the float with consequent impairment of the gage-height record. Subfloors of fixed elevation and position are superior to loose floors which float upward with a rising stage, because the loose floors may foul the floats and they must be reset in place after the water has receded. Frost barriers or subfloors make access to the well difficult, thus complicating the reading of the hook gage, and are generally to be recommended only when no preferable method of frost prevention is available.

Oil Tubes. Where weather conditions are not too severe and where, in addition, some protection is afforded the well by the surrounding earth, the use of oil tubes will frequently make possible an uninterrupted winter gage-height record. An oil tube is essentially an open galvanized-iron cylinder, usually 14 inches or 16 inches in diameter, either set on legs or with holes punched near the bottom to provide free access of water. The seam of the tube is soldered so as to be watertight. Several gallons of kerosene or other oil are placed in the tube, and the float is thus immersed in oil rather than in water. Since the specific gravity of oil is less than that of water, the surface of the oil in the tube will be higher than that of the water in the well and the float will ride lower in the oil than it would in water; consequently, the setting of the water-stage recorder must be adjusted on the basis of hook or other reference gage readings for the new position of the float. The operation of oil tubes is in general satisfactory, provided that too low temperatures are not experienced, in which event ice may form under the oil and thus defeat the purpose of the oil tube. The disadvantages of oil tubes are the frequent great heights to which they must be carried in order to prevent overtopping and consequent loss of oil, the tendency to foul the well by oil escaping at either low or high stages, and the gage-height corrections which are introduced if the recorder is not set at all times to the datum of the reference gage.

Heating Devices. It is probable that heat is in general the most effective means of preventing the formation of ice in gage wells. This method of combating ice formation has the advantage of being adjustable to varying outside temperatures, is relatively clean, and does not obstruct the well. Heat may be provided in several different ways, some of which are cited below.

The most satisfactory form of heat for a gage well is electric heat, but unfortunately relatively few gaging stations are situated near power lines and consequently the use of electricity is necessarily limited. Electric heat in the well is provided by a resistance element such as a space heater, although in shallow wells where there is only a slight tendency to icing a single large electric bulb will furnish sufficient heat to keep the air temperature above the freezing point. If a space heater is used, it may be installed on a float or it may be suspended in the well above flood stage. Immersion heaters are also used, but they are less satisfactory than space heaters because they tend to fill the well and shelter with water vapor which creates undesirable humidity.

Kerosene heaters of various types have been frequently used but are not entirely satisfactory. Aside from the ever-present danger of fire, it has been found difficult so to regulate the wick or burner that the lamp or heater will burn properly for a week between an observer's visits. Such heaters are prone either to go out or else to flare up, filling the well with soot. A kerosene lantern, if attended daily, may provide sufficient heat to prevent freezing, and it may be resorted to if other methods are not practicable.

Gas burners are coming into constantly increasing favor where electric heat is not available. This method of heating utilizes so-called bottled gas, which is readily obtainable commercially in tanks containing about 100 pounds of gas. The gas tank is installed in the shelter, and the gas is conducted by flexible metal tubing to the burner, which is set on a bracket attached to one of the walls of the well. The burner is usually surrounded by a perforated metal shell which serves both as a radiator and as a guard for the gas flame. Such commercial gases are explosive but not toxic; they are heavier than air and will settle in gage wells. Therefore, special care must be taken to air out wells if free gas is present. The combustion of gas or oil in the well requires oxygen, and consequently fresh air must be provided at all times through the well ventilators. It is believed that gas burners provide, next to electric heat, the most desirable means of heating gage wells, and, if they are attended by the observer at frequent intervals, the element of danger involved appears small.

Occasionally a gaging station is so situated that either live or exhaust steam is available. This may be piped into the well and used to heat either the air or the water. Steam pipes in the well show satisfactory performance, but steam as a means of heating the water is open to the same objection as immersion heaters.

Miscellaneous Expedients. Efforts have been made to provide protection against freezing in situations where the outside temperatures are not excessively low by the injection of some chemical into the water in the well for the purpose of so lowering the freezing point of the water as to prevent the formation of ice. Rock salt, among other chemicals, has been tried for this purpose. The objection which applies to the use of one chemical applies to all. The water in the well is subject to constant change by the flow through the intake pipe as a result of changing stages in the stream, and the well water is thus subject to continual dilution so that the effect of any chemical is soon lost.

One method which frequently has been found effective in preventing the formation of ice in gage wells has been to bank up the walls of the well with well-rotted manure at the beginning of the winter. This method, though often satisfactory so far as results are concerned, can scarcely be recommended from an aesthetic standpoint.

Although, as has been pointed out elsewhere, wooden wells are not to be recommended for any except the most temporary construction, it is of interest to note that they provide much better protection against winter cold than concrete wells in the same locations. Greater vulnerability with respect to cold is therefore one of the minor drawbacks in connection with the use of concrete wells in preference to timber construction.

Recorder Shelters. However modest or pretentious a recorder installation may be, housing for the water-stage recorder must always be provided in order both to protect it from the elements and to secure it from molestation by irresponsible persons. A recorder shelter

Fig. 48. Typical reinforced-concrete well and shelter, Auglaize River near Defiance, Ohio. Note steel clean-out door and vertical staff gage.

may vary in type from a small box just large enough to cover the instrument itself to an elaborate and completely appointed house of considerable size. The present tendency is in general away from both extremes and toward a shelter of standard size and design which, though unpretentious, nevertheless provides every necessary facility for the proper and efficient operation of a water-stage recorder.

Reinforced-concrete shelters (Fig. 46) are regarded as standard construction by the Geological Survey, and most of the permanent recorder installations made in recent years have been of that type. Figures 48 and 49 show typical all-concrete installations. Reinforced-concrete shelters have several advantages over all other types: first, the shelter construction is integral with that of the well and may be standardized through the use of removable panel forms; second, since concrete and steel are used exclusively as construction materials, the danger of damage or destruction by fire is largely eliminated; and,

Fig. 49. Typical reinforced-concrete well and shelter, Delaware River at Montague, N. J. Photograph by W. S. Eisenlohr, Jr.

third, since no wood or wood trim is used, annual maintenance work, such as painting and repairing roofs, is very small. Although, in general, wooden shelters have a reasonably long life, wooden floors are subject to decay because of dampness and must be renewed from time to time. The floors of concrete shelters, being of concrete, are permanent.

Certain features apply to all standard shelters, whatever their type of construction may be. These include a solid table or shelf on which the water-stage recorder is set. A similar setting, usually on the same table or shelf, must be provided for a float-tape gage, if one is to be used. Other appurtenances include a hook gage, flushing equipment, if necessary, electric lights and heat, if obtainable, or other protection against freezing of the well, and provision for ventilation of well and shelter and for natural light in the shelter. In concrete shelters, steel is to be preferred for the recorder shelf, for the door and door frame, the window frames and shutters, and for the approach to the shelter, if it is far above the ground surface. Windows of glass brick have

Fig. 50. Typical installation, concrete well and wooden shelter, Black River near Boonville, N. Y.

been used both in side walls and in the roof, but in regions where snowfall is heavy the roof windows are less satisfactory than wall windows. Glass-brick wall windows, however, being unprotected by shutters, are liable to malicious breakage.

Although concrete shelters have undeniably important advantages over wooden shelters, under certain conditions wooden shelters on concrete wells still offer the best possible combination for recorder installations. Experience in northern latitudes has shown that under winter conditions much less frost is present in wooden shelters than in

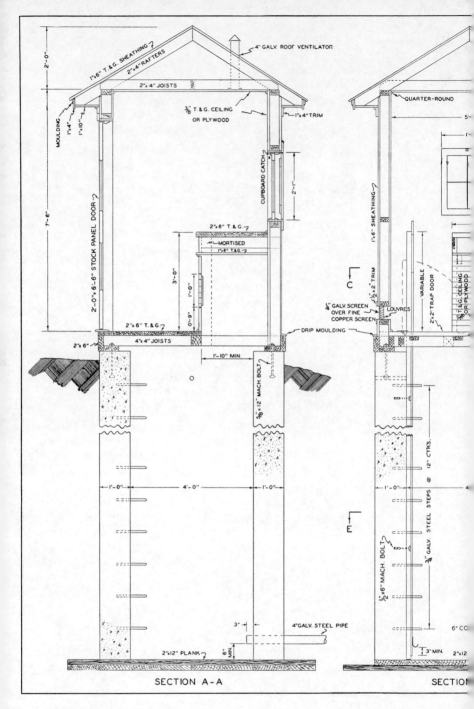

FIG. 51. Plans for plain concrete

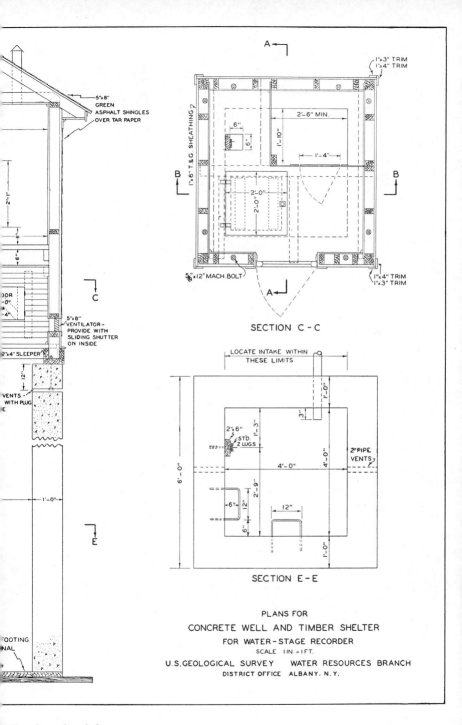

5"x8"
GREEN
ASPHALT SHINGLES
OVER TAR PAPER

2'-1"

6"

6"

OOR
-0"
4"

C

5"x8"
VENTILATOR -
PROVIDE WITH
SLIDING SHUTTER
ON INSIDE

2"x4" SLEEPER

12"

VENTS
WITH PLUG

1'-0"

E

FOOTING
NAL

A

1"x3" TRIM
1"x4" TRIM

1"x6" T.&G. SHEATHING

B   B

2'-6" MIN.

6"

1'-10"

6"

1'-4"

2'-0"

2'-0"

5/8"x12" MACH.BOLT

A

1"x4" TRIM
1"x3" TRIM

SECTION C - C

LOCATE INTAKE WITHIN
THESE LIMITS

1'-0"

3"

2'-6"
STD.
Z LUGS

1'-3"

6'-0"

4'-0"

4'-0"

2"PIPE
VENTS

2'-9"

6"

12"

12"

6"

1'-0"

SECTION E - E

PLANS FOR

CONCRETE WELL AND TIMBER SHELTER

FOR WATER-STAGE RECORDER

SCALE 1 IN. = 1 FT.

U.S. GEOLOGICAL SURVEY   WATER RESOURCES BRANCH
DISTRICT OFFICE   ALBANY. N.Y.

well and wooden shelter.

level after the bed piece and face board have been placed in position, since readings on the gage must relate to vertical distances and not to distances along its inclined face.

Staff gages may consist of vertical sections and inclined portions (Fig. 55) of different slopes that may best fit the topography and

FIG. 55. Staff gage installation, consisting of vertical and inclined sections.

facilities of a particular site. The only requirements are that the sections shall be securely placed, that the datum plane for every part of each section shall be the same, and that all parts shall show true vertical distances or changes in elevation.

As an inclined section of a staff gage will rest on two or more supports, it is especially subject to error in datum because each support may be liable to changes in elevation which can ordinarily be ascertained only by means of an engineer's level. Inclined staff gages, therefore, require more careful attention than vertical ones.

concrete ones. Such frost is troublesome in connection with the operation of a water-stage recorder because it tends to collect on moving parts and may eventually stop the recorder. From the standpoint of cost, there is little to be said in favor of either the wooden or the concrete type of shelter construction. Figure 51 shows plans for a typical wooden shelter and plain concrete well from which the details of construction will readily be noted. Figures 50 and 52 show typical

FIG. 52. Typical installation, concrete well and wooden shelter, Cayuga Inlet near Ithaca, N. Y. Note A-frame and cableway.

installations of this kind. One of the features of wooden-shelter construction is a boxed-in table upon which the water-stage recorder rests. The floor is cut away underneath this table to an extent sufficient to allow the float, in case of extremely high stages, to rise above the floor and to be effective until it hits the under side of the table. In this way, some 30 inches of additional head room is made available, which may occasionally be utilized to very good advantage when extremely high floods occur. The exteriors and roofs of wooden shelters may be finished with asbestos, or composition shingles or clapboards may be placed on the sides and wood shingles on the roofs. Composition shingles are desirable because they require no painting. Since it is customary to ceil wooden shelters on the inside, an air space is thus provided which is quite effective in keeping shelters of this type reasonably warm in winter and cool in summer. With a color scheme such as may be expressed in green shingles and door and white trim, structures of this type are quite attractive in appearance.

At certain sites and under certain conditions, it may be expedient and desirable to adopt other types of construction than those above referred to. In parks and other public places, shelters may be constructed either of natural stone or of brick with special ornamental

Fig. 53. Combination stone and concrete installation, Bennett Spring at Bennett Springs, Mo.

treatment. These considerations apply mainly to the exteriors of the structures, of course. The inside arrangements will be similar to those in other standard shelters. Figures 53 and 54 show examples of such special installations.

In dry climates and under circumstances where temporary recorder installations are required, a simple box 3 feet by 2 feet by 1½ feet in size, with one side hinged to form a door, may serve as a shelter. This type of installation (Fig. 45) was formerly quite common in the West but has been largely superseded except for stations on irrigation canals and ditches and on streams of minor importance.

Installation of Gages. The installation of a water-stage recorder involves its placement in the recorder shelter in such a position on a level support or shelf of fixed elevation that the float and counterweight will operate without interference with each other or contact

with the walls of the well, at the same time being so far removed the ladder that the engineer or observer may enter the well and therein without interfering with the float and counterweight If a float-tape gage is installed in the well, the matter of in the free operation of the recorder float is further complicated presence of another float and another counterweight. Great should be taken in accurately locating and cutting the holes table for the clock weight and recorder float and counterweight

Fig. 54. Combination concrete and brick installation, Cedar Swamp Glen Cove, L. I., N. Y. Note concrete artificial control.

since these cables must pass cleanly through the holes witho bing on their edges.

A vertical staff gage (Figs. 7 and 12) is installed by atta timber back piece by anchor bolts or otherwise to the face o abutment, or other structure, or in rare instances to the f cliff, and fastening thereto a graduated scale in a vertical Preferably, the scale consists of one or more graduated enam tions, or, if such sections are not available, a painted board by coopers' staples to feet and tenths may be used and af the same manner to the backing timber. Whatever the typ it should be accurately graduated, the enameled sections s rectly with the aid of a steel tape, and the whole gage set datum by means of an engineer's level.

The installation of an inclined staff gage differs from vertical staff gage in that the graduation must be made b

The important aspects of chain and wire-weight gages (Figs. 13, 14, 15) relate to their placement over a section of the river channel that has flowing water at all stages and on a part of the bridge or other structure that does not vary in elevation as a result of loading or change in temperature. Such gages should not be placed on any part of a suspension bridge, because this type of bridge is especially unstable in elevation, or at or near the center of a truss span which may change appreciably in elevation with a heavy snow or ice load or with the passage of a heavy live load, or with considerable changes in

Fig. 56. Float-tape gage.

temperature. If erected on a metal bridge of any type, a chain or wire-weight gage should be placed as near an abutment or pier as practicable and in all instances it should be securely attached to the structure.

One of the potent reasons for using chain or wire-weight gages is to avoid the hazards of ice and drift and the cost of expensive supporting structures. They cannot serve to replace all staff gages, however, because in general their use is limited to a small proportion of gaging stations by the absence of existing rigid bridges or other structures that extend across or project over the flowing water.

A float-tape gage (Fig. 56) is commonly installed in conjunction with a water-stage recorder. It serves as an expeditious means for checking the record made by the recorder and for comparing the stage of the water in the well with that in the river. Its datum plane must, of course, be the same as that of the station gage. It may be installed on and attached to the shelf on which the water-stage recorder is placed or on an independent and separate mounting attached directly to the wall of the well, in such position that its float and counterweight will not come into contact with any other device that may be placed in the gage well and will not prevent the entrance into the well of the operating engineer. Water-stage recorders are now available equipped with integral float tapes which perform all the functions of float-tape gages and so make possible the elimination of one float and one counterweight from the well.

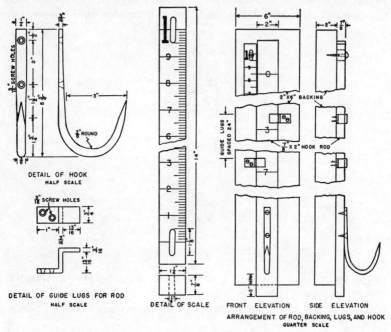

FIG. 57. Details of hook gage.

A hook gage (Fig. 57) is commonly installed in a gage well as a reference gage for the water-stage recorder. It may or may not be provided if a float-tape gage is used, as both are designed to serve essentially the same purpose. Experience, however, has shown that a hook gage will in general maintain its datum more satisfactorily than a float-tape gage. An integral float-tape gage on the water-stage recorder should never take the place of a hook gage as a reference gage for the recorder.

The hook-gage rod is attached to the bed piece or back board by means of Z-lugs so spaced that the rod will move freely, though with some resistance. The hook-gage scale should be set correctly to station datum and fastened tightly in place.

CHAPTER 13

STRUCTURES FROM WHICH DISCHARGE
MEASUREMENTS ARE MADE

Characteristics. Few rivers can be measured at all stages by wading, and for this reason structures from which discharge measurements can be made must be provided at gaging stations. The particular facilities provided for that purpose will be determined variously by the availability of suitable existing bridges or other structures, the physical characteristics of the site, and the amount of available funds. It is unfortunate that because of limited funds it is sometimes necessary to choose a somewhat inferior site for a gaging station in order to obtain the financial advantage that will result from the use of an existing bridge or other structure.

The principal means of support for the engineer in making discharge measurements are cableways, bridges, and boats. The surface of the ice which may cover the river during the winter may also be considered a means of support. These different facilities will be discussed in this chapter.

In the making of discharge measurements, determination of the area of cross section is necessary, which, of course, means that not only must accurate soundings be had at the points where velocity observations are taken but also that the progressive distances from an initial point on one of the banks must be known and recorded. Fixed structures, such as cableways and bridges, provide for an accurate determination of the cross section by means of graduations on either the cable or the bridge structure at regular intervals measured from an initial point. With such fixed graduations, the areas of discharge measurements made from cableways and bridges will be truly comparable with each other when the soundings of successive discharge measurements are taken at the same points. A firm cover of ice constitutes essentially a type of bridge that has the characteristics of a fixed structure during the period of its availability. A boat, however, when acting as a means of support for the engineer, must be held in successive positions along a cable that may serve the dual purpose of holding the boat in place and of affording by graduations either on the cable or on an auxiliary tag line a means of measuring distances from some initial point. In the absence of such a cable, the successive positions of the boat must be determined from the shore by the cumbersome means of range lines or angular measurements.

In the interest of economy, the facilities used by the engineer should, if practicable, be such that he may, working alone, be able to perform all the necessary operations incident to the making and recording of a discharge measurement. Such conditions are usually provided by cableways and bridges. If such facilities cannot reasonably be made available, recourse may be had to boat equipment, which will invariably require additional personnel. It is important that the number of assistants required to man the boat itself and to perform auxiliary functions on shore be kept at a minimum.

In the selection of the site and in the establishment and operation of a gaging station, the structure from which the measurements of discharge are to be made may well be of controlling importance. Existing highway and railroad bridges were formerly largely utilized for this purpose, but in more recent years cableways have been installed wherever practicable. In selecting the type of structure, consideration should be given to the possible saving in funds by utilizing an existing structure, to the costs involved in building a special structure, and above all to the accuracy and over-all cost of the records of discharge to be obtained.

Cableways. Cableways are generally to be preferred to bridges because frequently it is possible by means of them to utilize superior measuring sections in the stream and also because angularity of flow as well as disturbances in flow caused by bridge piers and abutments may thus be avoided. Obviously, the better the section, the more reliable will be the rating, and consequently, discharge records of higher accuracy will result. From the financial standpoint, initial costs for installation of stations with cableways are somewhat greater than of those using existing bridges, but operating costs are generally in favor of cableways.

Cables. Cables for cableways consist of steel-wire ropes of varying diameters, varying grades of steel, and varying sizes and numbers of strands. For any given type of rope, the size needed will be determined in part by the length of the span and in part by the grade of steel used; the longer the span, the greater the size of rope; the better the grade of steel, the smaller the size of rope, within limits, of course. The costs per foot of cable obviously increase with the size of cable and with the grade of steel. In general, the shorter spans will afford a wider range in the choice of the wire rope than the longer spans. Galvanized, improved plow-steel, yacht-rigging rope is suitable for all spans up to about 800 feet and is generally preferred for the shorter spans.

Improved plow-steel tramway cable is much smoother and stiffer than yacht-rigging rope, and a cable car can be operated on it more easily. For long spans it is frequently almost mandatory since because of its greater unit strength and resulting lesser weight it makes possible installations with much smaller sag than would be required for the heavier yacht-rigging rope. As this feature makes also for easier operation of cable cars, tramway cable is being more and more used for shorter spans. However, a tramway cable can have no short bends; it must not be used with thimbles and clips; and its exact length must be known before the cable can be ordered because a socket at each end of the cable must be attached at the factory.

The following formulas give the tension in cables which are supported at the same elevation at both ends and which are subjected to both uniformly distributed and concentrated loads:

$$H = \frac{WS^2}{8D} + \frac{PS}{4D} = \frac{S(WS + 2P)}{8D}$$

$$T = H\sqrt{1 + \frac{16D^2}{S^2}} \quad \text{(approximate)}$$

in which H = horizontal tension, in pounds.
T = maximum tension, in pounds.
W = weight of cable or uniformly distributed load, in pounds per foot.
S = span between supports, in feet.
D = sag, in feet.
P = concentrated load at center of span, in pounds.

The following formula, derived from the above formula for H, may be used to determine the sag for a given horizontal tension in a uniformly loaded cable:

$$D = \frac{S(WS + 2P)}{8H}$$

The following formula gives the length of cable (L) needed for a span (S) between supports of an unloaded or uniformly loaded cable:

$$L = S\left(1 + \frac{8D^2}{3S^2}\right)$$

The following sizes of cable are generally regarded as standard for a concentrated live load of 750 pounds:

⅝-inch cable for spans under 200 feet
¾-inch cable for spans from 200 to 400 feet
⅞-inch cable for spans from 400 to 600 feet
1-inch cable for spans from 600 to 800 feet

Weight per foot and allowable working strength (one-sixth minimum breaking strength) of galvanized yacht-rigging rope (6 strands of 7 wires each) are shown in the following table:

Diameter (inches)	Approximate weight per foot of cable (pounds)	Working strength (pounds)		
		Cast steel	Plow steel	Improved or extra-strength plow steel
⅝	0.63	3,470	4,140	4,800
¾	0.90	4,930	5,940	6,840
⅞	1.23	6,700	8,040	9,240
1	1.60	8,700	10,400	12,000

Weight per foot and allowable working strength (one-fifth the minimum breaking strength) of galvanized plow-steel tramway cable are shown in the following table:

Diameter (inches)	Number of wires	Approximate weight per foot of cable (pounds)	Working strength (pounds)
⅝	19	0.86	8,000
¾	19	1.24	11,700
⅞	19	1.69	15,800
1	19	2.20	20,000
1⅛	37	2.70	25,000
1¼	37	3.23	30,400
1⅜	37	4.01	37,600
1½	37	4.88	45,600

Towers. A cableway should, if possible, be supported at a sufficient height above the river to permit the use of the cable car in making discharge measurements at the highest known or anticipated flood stages. In rare instances, the banks of a river may consist of cliffs of sufficient height, steepness, and quality of rock that the cable may be attached directly to anchor bolts in the rock at elevations which will insure the necessary clearance. In order to insure safe anchorages at such sites, the ledge rock must be carefully inspected for massiveness, soundness, and quality. The heavy expansion bolts generally used as anchors should be leaded or grouted securely into the rock. This method of anchorage, however, is open to some criticism because of the difficulty of determining by ordinary inspection in subsequent years the condition of the rock and of the anchor bolts themselves.

In wooded country, it is not uncommon to find large trees that may serve as cableway supports for relatively short spans. If the trees are sound, of sufficient size, well rooted, and properly placed with respect to the direction of the stream, they may provide inexpensive and reasonably satisfactory supports. If a tree is utilized as a support, the cable should be so attached that the life of the tree will not be endangered by girdling. This may be accomplished by placing wooden blocks under the cable wherever it encircles the tree. The ends of the cable should be anchored in the ground in the usual manner. The swaying of the trees in the wind may, of course, cause unusual and unpredictable stresses in the cable, and such effects of swaying will increase with the height of attachment of the cable. Sometimes, at sites where the banks of the stream slope upward steeply enough to provide the necessary clearance for the cableway, the ends of the cable may be anchored directly into the ground without supports. In general, however, an artificial support or tower is necessary for at least one end of the cableway and usually for both ends. Two towers will generally be found more satisfactory than any other means of support, although for short spans different combinations of natural and artificial supports may be used, depending upon the physical conditions at the site.

The most common artificial supports or towers under present average conditions consist of modified A-frames, usually of wood, although even for low towers steel is now coming into general use. The height of towers, of course, will vary with the elevation of the natural ground surface and with the necessary elevation of the cableway. The elevation of the cableway is governed by the stages of anticipated floods, by the length of the span, by the load to be carried, and by the sag of the cable itself. Obviously, it is desirable that the opposite ends of the cableway should be supported at the same elevation.

For comparatively short spans and where relatively low supports are required, modified A-frames of timber will serve adequately. Such a support consists essentially of two inclined members forming the legs, which are framed into a sill set on concrete or rock piers or on such other suitable supports as will keep all wood of the structure above the surface of the ground and so make possible its periodic

Fig. 58. Typical low timber A-frame and wooden cable car. Note sheave supporting cable at top of A-frame.

inspection and painting (Fig. 58). The sill should never be omitted and the legs set into the ground, because of the certainty of gradual decay below the ground surface and the consequent danger of the eventual collapse of the cableway, with the attendant risk of injury to an engineer. These inclined members are connected at the top and carry a sheave which supports the cable itself. Diagonal bracing should be added as required by the height of the tower or A-frame. A landing platform for the convenience of the engineer in stepping into and out of the cable car may also be provided. The sill and legs ordinarily vary in size from 6 inches by 6 inches to 10 inches by 10 inches, and they should be made of timber which is suited to the

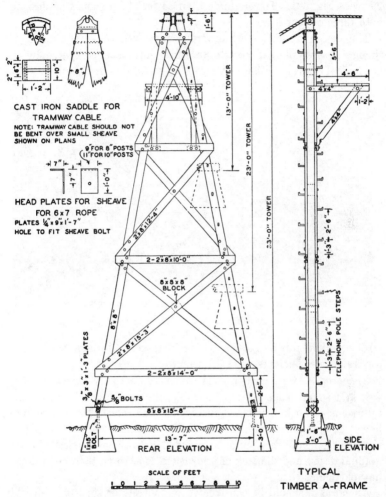

FIG. 59. Plans for timber A-frame. (From Equipment for River Measurements, Plans and Specifications for Structures from Which Discharge Measurements are Made, *U. S. Geological Survey Mimeographed Circular,* 1933.)

purpose and of good quality. The tower or A-frame should of course be backstayed to prevent its listing forward or toward the stream. Figure 59 shows plans for typical cable towers of different heights.

The height of wooden towers should not exceed 33 feet; higher towers should be built of fabricated steel. In the interest of good practice, it is probable that steel towers are to be preferred for heights above 25 feet (Fig. 60). Towers more than 33 feet high should be designed with three or four legs.

The design of high steel towers cannot well be standardized, although general plans for such structures have been prepared by the Geological Survey. Figure 61 shows a typical design for a steel tower

Fig. 60. Steel tower for cableway. Note metal gaging car.

30.6 feet high; this design may, if desired, be readily adapted for steel towers of lesser heights.

Anchorages. Safe anchorage is obviously necessary for every cableway. If sound ledge rock is available, the anchorages may be made by means of anchor bolts set firmly into the rock. More commonly, however, and preferably, deadmen are utilized. The use of logs or timbers as deadmen should be avoided because of the certainty of gradual decay and the lack of knowledge concerning their condition at any particular time.

Anchorages should be constructed of concrete or steel or preferably of a combination of the two. A design for a simple concrete-steel anchorage is shown in Fig. 62. Anchorages must be of sufficient weight and so designed as to provide an ample factor of safety for the cableway, not only when the cable is stretched to provide for the minimum sag and is fully loaded, but also where large emergency stresses may be induced by the fouling of the weight or meter by drift during flood measurements.

Whatever the type of anchorage, it is important that the cable be connected above ground to the anchorage or deadman by means of a U-bar or clevis. Under no circumstances should the ends of the cable

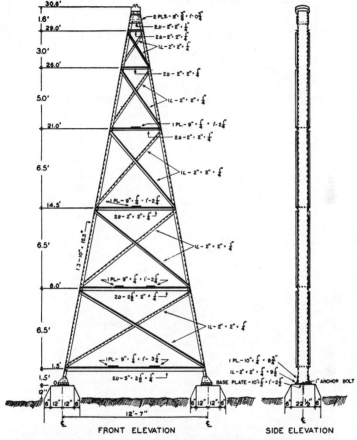

Fig. 61. Design for typical steel tower for cableway. (From Equipment for River Measurements, Plans and Specifications for Structures from Which Discharge Measurements are Made, *U. S. Geological Survey Mimeographed Circular*, 1933.)

be placed in the ground or in the concrete anchorage. Figures 63 and 64 show typical connections of cable to anchorage.

Erection of Cable. The towers having been erected and the anchorages completed, the procedure to be followed in erecting the cable will depend largely upon the length of the span and the consequent weight of the cable. For short spans, the cable may be dragged directly across the stream by means of a boat or by a light wire or

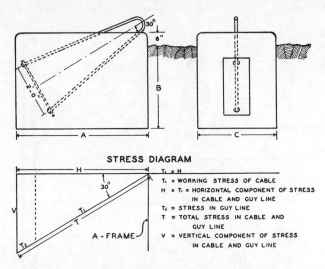

STRESS DIAGRAM

$T_1 = H$
T_1 = WORKING STRESS OF CABLE
$H = T_1$ = HORIZONTAL COMPONENT OF STRESS IN CABLE AND GUY LINE
T_2 = STRESS IN GUY LINE
T = TOTAL STRESS IN CABLE AND GUY LINE
V = VERTICAL COMPONENT OF STRESS IN CABLE AND GUY LINE

A - FRAME

ANCHORAGE DATA

SIZE AND KIND OF CABLE	STRESSES ON ANCHORAGE IN POUNDS			ANCHORAGE DIMENSIONS					RESISTANCE AGAINST HORIZ. MOVEMENT			F.S. AGAINST SLIDING
	$T_1 = H$	T	V	A	B	C	VOL.	WT.	BLOCK	EARTH	TOTAL	
5/8"GALV. CAST STEEL	3470	4010	2000	5'-0"	3'-6"	2'-6"	44 FT.³	6160	1080	8750	9830	2.8
3/4"GALV. CAST STEEL	4930	5700	2850	5'-0"	4'-0	3'-0"	60 FT.³	8400	1350	10500	11850	2.4
5/8"GALV. 6x19 PLOW STEEL	4980	5760	2880	5'-0"	4'-0	3'-0"	60 FT.³	8400	1320	10500	11820	2.4
3/4"GALV. 6x19 PLOW STEEL	7110	8210	4110	5'-0"	4'-0	4'-0"	80 FT.³	11200	1500	14000	15500	2.2

SAMPLE COMPUTATION
TO DETERMINE FACTOR OF SAFETY
(5/8" GALVANIZED CAST STEEL RIGGING ROPE)

VOLUME OF BLOCK   2'-6"x 3'-6"x 5'-0" = 43.75, SAY 44 CU.FT.
WEIGHT OF BLOCK = 44 x 140 = 6160 POUNDS
NET WEIGHT OF BLOCK = TOTAL WEIGHT − 2 V = 6160 − 4000 = 2160 POUNDS
RESISTANCE OF BLOCK AGAINST HORIZONTAL MOVEMENT = NET WEIGHT OF BLOCK x COEFF.
OF FRICTION = 2160 x 0.50 = 1080 POUNDS
RESISTANCE OF EARTH AGAINST HORIZONTAL MOVEMENT = END AREA OF BLOCK x EARTH
RESISTANCE = 2'-6"x 3'-6" x 1000 = 8750 POUNDS
TOTAL RESISTANCE AGAINST HORIZONTAL MOVEMENT = 1080 + 8750 = 9830 POUNDS
FACTOR OF SAFETY AGAINST HORIZONTAL MOVEMENT = $\dfrac{\text{TOTAL HORIZONTAL RESISTANCE}}{T_1}$ =
$\dfrac{9830}{3470}$ = 2.83

FIG. 62. Plans for concrete anchorages for cables. (From Equipment for River Measurements, Plans and Specifications for Structures from Which Discharge Measurements are Made, *U. S. Geological Survey Mimeographed Circular,* 1933.)

hemp rope which has previously been carried across by boat or by wading. For longer spans and heavier cable, a light cotton or hemp rope may be carried across the stream by boat, the rope in turn being used to drag across a light wire rope. This wire rope is then stretched

Fig. 63. Typical connection of cable through turnbuckle to anchorage. Note U-bolt in concrete, clevis, cable backstay for A-frame, and standard bench-mark tablet.

Fig. 64. Typical connection of tramway cable through bridge bolt to anchorage. Note U-bolt in concrete, tramway cable and socket, and auxiliary U-bolt for cable backstay.

and fastened in place. The principal cable is suspended from the light wire rope by hooks and is pulled across the stream by means of a boat or rope block and tackle.

After the cable has been hung loosely in place, it may be stretched to its approximate final position by means of differential chain blocks before being attached to the turnbuckle, which has previously been let out to its full length and connected to the anchorage. After the end of the cable has been looped through the eye of the turnbuckle and secured with clips, it will be possible to remove the chain blocks and to take up with the turnbuckle as much of the remaining sag as may be necessary. Tramway cable, which cannot be looped, is connected to the anchors by means of bridge bolts, the ends of the cable itself being securely held in the sockets of the bolts through spreading and leading of the strands.

During the process of erection, the cable should be handled carefully to avoid kinks, and, for the same reason, as well as to prevent personal injury, it should be unrolled or uncoiled with extreme care. Wire rope, before being cut, must be tightly bound with several wraps of wire on both sides of the cut to prevent raveling of the strands.

As a matter of convenience, the two cable-car sheaves with the cable car attached to them should be placed on the cable before it is erected. This will eliminate the work of hoisting the cable car to position and placing it on the cable, often with some difficulty, after the cable has been erected.

Final Adjustment of Cable. As has been previously pointed out, the amount of sag in the cable is one of the factors which determine the elevation of the cable and consequently the height of the supports. In some instances, the amount of permissible sag will be the controlling factor in determining the size of the cable, but usually other considerations will govern and the size of the cable will be selected after a consideration of length of span, height of recorded or anticipated flood stages, and the limitation, if any, on height of supports, always, of course, taking into consideration and allowing for the amount of sag for the size of cable selected. It is assumed that all these factors were considered and properly evaluated long before the cable was erected and that the cableway is now complete except for final adjustments.

Figure 65 shows a sag diagram for various sizes and specifications of galvanized wire rope. From this diagram may be determined the proper amount of sag for the newly erected cable. By taking up or slacking off on the turnbuckle or bridge bolts, the cable may be readily adjusted to the proper sag. Since newly erected cable will stretch, frequent adjustments of sag should be made. As an aid in the making of such adjustments, the proper amount of sag may be measured down from the cable at each support and the point so obtained permanently marked on the supporting structure. By sighting between these marks on the opposite supports, the sag of the cable may be easily checked, and corrected when necessary.

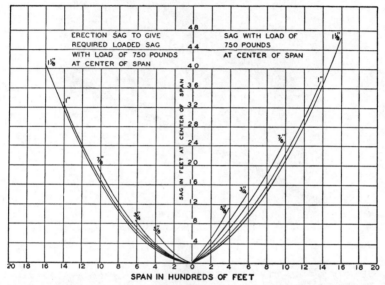

Fig. 65. Sag diagram for galvanized plow-steel tramway cable. (From Equipment for River Measurements, Plans and Specifications for Structures from Which Discharge Measurements are Made, *U. S. Geological Survey Mimeographed Circular*, 1933.)

The length of the cable will vary with changes in temperature, and, since in northern latitudes temperature variations from winter to summer of 140° F. or more are not uncommon, adjustment of the sag with the seasons is highly important. The cable should be slacked off in winter and taken up in summer in order on the one hand that no undue stresses may be induced in it and on the other hand that the cable car may be operated without unnecessary difficulty.

The amount of sag in a cable directly affects the operation of the cable car; with each increase in sag, the operation becomes increasingly difficult because of the steeper slope which must be ascended by the cable car in order to reach the river bank or the supporting structure. This consideration is of major importance when long spans are used. The weight of the cable car may have an important effect on the allowable sag because this weight, as well as that of the engineer or engineers in the car and of the miscellaneous equipment utilized in making measurements of discharge, must be pulled up the

FIG. 66. Cable-car puller in position on cable. Note brake-lining stop for cable car.

slope of the cable by the muscular power of the occupants of the car, using either bare or gloved hands or some form of "puller" (Fig. 66). Since this is at best an arduous task, the importance of keeping the cable adjusted to the minimum permissible sag is evident.

Each cableway, except those in which tramway cable is used, must be provided with a turnbuckle for the final stretching of the cable and for making such subsequent adjustments in the sag as may be necessary. Since the turnbuckle carries the full cable stress, it is highly important that it form no element of weakness in the cableway. Although, theoretically, smaller turnbuckles may be appropriate for short spans and cables of small diameter, a standard 1½-inch turnbuckle with a 36-inch takeup is recommended for all spans utilizing cables of diameters up to and including 1 inch. Turnbuckles should be made of mild steel, galvanized, with an eye at each end, which should be forged rather than welded.

The turnbuckle should be so placed as to permit of easy operation. In some instances, the U-bar of the anchorage is passed through one eye of the turnbuckle before being set in the concrete. This method of attachment to the anchorage does, it is true, eliminate one connection with cable clips, but it also makes replacement of the turnbuckle impossible. Turnbuckles should be connected to the U-bar of the anchorage by means of a clevis or anchor shackle. In attachments with cable clips at the turnbuckle connections, at least five clips should be used, and care should be taken that the U-bolts of the clips bear on the short or dead end of the cable. Cable clips should be inspected periodically and the bolts tightened when necessary. A thimble should always be used when the cable is looped through the eye of a turnbuckle.

Cable Cars. Cable cars must be of adequate strength and of proper design to convey engineers and their measuring equipment to any desired points or stations on the cableways. They must also provide safety and reasonable comfort for the engineers while they are making discharge measurements and must afford adequate means of support for the reels that may upon occasion be utilized.

Two types of cable cars are in common use. The type shown in Fig. 58 was developed many years ago and is still widely used. Except for the sheaves, the main and foot-rest hangers, and the necessary bolts, this car is constructed of wood. From it, discharge measurements are made by hand line over a roller-bearing sheave or by means of a small reel. The engineer sits in this car with reasonable comfort and has sufficient freedom of motion for efficient work. It was developed for one-man use, although it will easily carry two men, and, since it is comparatively light, it can be moved with greater ease than a heavier car. This type of car is well adapted to the work of gaging rivers in which the depths and velocities are not so great as to require heavy weights and the bulky equipment needed for their handling.

The type of cable car shown in Fig. 67 has been recently developed for work primarily on large rivers of great depth and high velocities. Except for the floor system, which is of wood, this car is ordinarily constructed of aluminum alloy, although steel may be used. It is designed to carry two men who stand while working, heavy sounding equipment, and a heavy reel. The sides of the car afford sufficient protection for safety and for efficiency in working. On southern rivers,

Fig. 67. Metal gaging car on tramway cable. Note reel and measuring equipment.

a canopy top is sometimes provided for protection from the sun or rain during the progress of a discharge measurement which may require several hours to complete.

Comparison of these two types of cable cars is perhaps without purpose since each car has its own field of usefulness. The aluminum car is heavier and, except for the fact that it is usually operated on a tramway cable, is not handled as easily as the old-style wooden car.

Furthermore, it requires over 2 feet more of vertical clearance than
the wooden car, which bears a direct relation to the necessary elevation of the cableway. Generally speaking, the wooden car is still to
be preferred in situations where the river conditions are such that
adequate discharge measurements can be made from it.

Bridges. Because of the costs involved, it is only occasionally and
on relatively small streams that bridges can be built solely for stream-
gaging purposes. If so built, they may be footlogs, simple trusses, or
suspension spans designed for foot traffic only (Fig. 68).

Fig. 68. Footbridge for stream gaging adapted from discarded steel girder.

Generally speaking, bridges used by engineers in making discharge
measurements must be utilized as they are found, and it is merely a
coincidence if they prove to be entirely suitable for this purpose.
The sites of such bridges have been selected primarily with reference
to street, highway, or railroad systems and not with respect to the
requirements of stream gaging; consequently, they frequently do not
afford the best sites for gaging stations or for making measurements
of discharge. The piers and abutments may contract and obstruct
the channel, provide lodgment places for drift, and disturb the currents of the flowing water. Under such unfavorable conditions, which
of course do not always obtain, the probable accuracy of the discharge
measurements is reduced, with a consequent adverse effect on both the
rating of the gaging station and the resulting records of discharge.

The advantages of using cableways wherever possible in preference
to bridges have already been pointed out in this chapter. Granting
the general superiority of cableways, it is recognized, however, that
the use of existing bridges as sites for gaging stations may in some

instances be amply justified, aside from the deceptive justification of lower first cost. Some single-span bridges provide excellent measuring sections and acceptable sites for gaging stations. Furthermore, bridges usually have the advantage of ready accessibility, particularly in times of high water. Frequently, moreover, particularly in the South, the use of cableways is precluded by excessively wide overflow sections. Under certain conditions, therefore, the use of bridges can be defended as fully justifiable and desirable.

Both highway and railroad bridges have been used as sites for gaging stations in the past and to a lesser extent they are being so used at present. In addition to the objections that have been cited, problems of traffic interference and interruptions must be considered and solved as well as the difficulties involving much raising and lowering of the current meter and weights that generally arise from working through bridge floors or trusses. The trucks, cranes, and reels for handling the heavy weights that may be required must be so designed or modified as to meet these peculiar conditions at the individual sites (Chapter 8).

Boats. Discharge measurements at relatively few gaging stations are obtained by means of boats, although boats are essential for the operation of gaging stations on large rivers that are too wide for spanning by cableways and that have no nearby bridges. Under such conditions, boat stations are accepted, but they would seldom be selected in preference to a practicable bridge or cableway station, because of the probable higher cost of operation and the lower accuracy of the records of discharge.

As a rule, discharge measurements made from boats require the services of a greater number of men (generally two or more) than measurements made by other means. In using a current meter from a boat, a short extensible boom with a sheave at its outer end over which the meter cable will pass extends from the bow of the boat. By means of this boom, the current meter may be so placed and operated as to be unaffected by any disturbance in velocities that may be induced by the hull of the boat itself. The boat must be large enough to be steady, to carry the necessary number of men, and to support the reel that may be needed for handling the weights, the size of which will be determined by the depths and velocities to be measured. On a large river, a power boat with a crew varying in number with the size of the boat will be needed (Fig. 69).

If the width of the river is too great for spanning by a tag line, or if, for navigational or other reasons, the use of a tag line is impracticable, the successive positions of the meter must be determined by range lines on shore, by measured angles between fixed lines on the banks and the successive positions of the boat during the measurement, or by stadia observations from the shore. Obviously, measurements of dis-

Fig. 69. Boat equipment for discharge measurement. Note boat boom and boat line reel, Canfield gaging reel, tag line, and meter equipment. Photograph by I. A. Cooper.

charge obtained under these conditions are more expensive to make and to compute than measurements made from a cableway or a bridge where the engineer, usually working alone, makes all the observations at intervals that are directly measured and regularly spaced.

Discharge measurements made from boats are liable to errors in depths and velocities that may be caused by the rise and fall of the boat as the result of wave action. This rise and fall will be greatest at the outer end of the boom and will cause a vertical motion of the meter that will accelerate the rotation of the cup-type meter and decelerate the rotation of the screw-type meter. Thus, discharge measurements made by the cup-type meter will appear too large and those

Fig. 70. Gaging reel mounted on collapsible support with skis for discharge measurements under ice cover.

made by the screw type will appear too small. Therefore, such measurements should be made, if practicable, when wave motion is at a minimum.

Ice Surfaces. In regions where below-freezing temperatures persist for sufficiently long periods to form a safe ice cover, the ice may afford an excellent support for the engineer while making discharge measurements. In making discharge measurements through the ice a somewhat different procedure is required from that followed under open-water conditions. Axes and ice chisels are needed for cutting holes through the ice where observations of depth and velocity are to be made. Shear poles or collapsible tripods (Fig. 26), or reels with or without cranes, are required for handling the meter and weights if depths and velocities are great. The reel may be advantageously mounted on a low collapsible standard placed on skis or runners (Fig. 70). In using a current meter in low temperatures, it is necessary to move the meter quickly from one hole in the ice to the next in order to avoid congealing of the water in the bearings of the instrument and so affecting the accuracy of its operation. A movable shelter is sometimes utilized for relieving to some extent the discomfort of the engineer while making current-meter observations.

BIBLIOGRAPHY 13

1. G. J. LYON, Equipment for Current-Meter Gaging Stations, *U.S.G.S. Water Supply Paper* **371**.

CHAPTER 14

OPERATION OF GAGING STATIONS

Objectives. The operation of a gaging station involves four principal objectives: (1) the collection of systematic records of stage; (2) the making of the measurements of discharge that are required for the development of a station rating curve to express the stage-discharge relation; (3) the periodic instruction of the local observer with respect to his assigned duties, giving special attention to his success or failure in understanding and performing those duties; and (4) the maintenance in proper condition of the structures and instrumental equipment used in obtaining the records of stage and in making the measurements of discharge. The statement of objectives is simple; the difficulties in attaining them are many and varied.

Difficulties. The continuous or periodic records of stage and the records of discharge derived from them must, theoretically at least, be equally reliable for all stages of the stream, for all conditions of flow, and for all changes in the stage-discharge relation. Changes in the stage-discharge relation may be due to a variety of conditions, including shifting controls and variations in the cross section of the channel caused by shifting bed and banks. Temporary and seasonal changes may be caused by the accumulation of drift, the formation of an ice cover of varying thickness, anchor ice or frazil, the jamming of broken ice, or aquatic vegetation in the channel. Each of these conditions presents its own problems and difficulties. In general, the more stable the channel and conditions of flow, the fewer difficulties will be encountered.

Added to the difficulties related to the physical conditions at and near the gaging station are problems related to travel and transportation; human inefficiencies, lapses, and errors; faulty operation of instruments; and wide and sudden variations in temperature, precipitation, and wind movement, with correspondingly wide and sudden fluctuations in stage and discharge. The difficulties vary at all times at different gaging stations and with the seasons and the years at individual stations. Because of their number and variety, their enumeration, except in general terms, is impracticable. Some can be anticipated and so can be met with reasonable ease or even prevented; others cannot be foreseen and are therefore overcome with much greater difficulty.

Records of Stage. Records of river stages not only serve as bases of computations of records of discharge but also furnish direct information which may be important in litigation or as an index of the severity of droughts or the heights of floods. Usually, of course, the value of records of stage is greatly enhanced by parallel records of discharge. Records of lake and reservoir stages, involving no consideration of discharge, are valuable from the standpoint of storage and in other ways. In connection with the computation of discharge, the relative accuracy of the records of stage affects to a large extent the degree of accuracy that may be attained in the records of discharge. It follows, therefore, that the degree of refinement to which gage-height records should be observed or computed will be determined largely by the nature and anticipated quality of the discharge records. Gage-height records, especially those from water-stage recorders, are generally expressed in terms of feet and hundredths of a foot, although in situations involving small streams and low flows it may be frequently desirable, during critical periods, to carry the gage-height record to the nearest half-hundredth of a foot. In some special studies, the use of gage heights which have been carried to thousandths of a foot may be fully warranted. For purposes other than the computation of discharge, less precise records of stage may suffice and gage heights observed to the nearest half-tenth or tenth of a foot may occasionally be satisfactory. The stream-gaging engineer, however, being primarily concerned with records of discharge, must strive for the highest practicable degree of accuracy in the records of stage. Such accuracy, of course, will serve all other purposes, even though the degree of refinement may be greater than is necessary.

Stability of Gage Datum. It cannot be too strongly emphasized that, if reliable records of stage and discharge are to be obtained, the maintenance of a fixed gage datum is necessary. The most common causes of instability, expressed in movement of the station gages, are settlement of structures, rise and fall with changes in temperature, heaving as a result of frost action, undermining, and the stretching and wear of moving parts. A listing of the various possible causes of instability in different types of gages is clearly impossible, but as an example the chain gage may be considered. The accuracy of chain-gage readings may be adversely affected by stretching and wear of the chain itself, by loosening of the gage box, or by gradual or seasonal changes in the elevation of the bridge or other structure to which the gage is attached. Such typical changes in gages are discovered and corrected by means of periodic comparisons of the datum of the gage with that of one or more bench marks of known permanent elevation.

The elevation of each gage must be carefully checked by level at least once a year, preferably in the late spring after the effects of freezing have disappeared, and oftener if there have been conditions other than freezing, such as high stages of the stream or scouring of the bed or banks near the gage, that might cause doubt as to the stability of the gage. There is some advantage in situations where inclined staff gages are involved in deferring the annual check-up until the period of lowest river stages, in order that the lowest portions of the gages may be tested, which would generally not be possible at times of medium and high stages. In northern latitudes, a midwinter check will sometimes disclose small temporary variations in the elevations of the outside gages and even of the gages inside of and firmly attached to the concrete walls of the wells, due to frost action. Such variations are not disclosed by the usual check levels because they will have disappeared by early summer.

In checking gages, a standard level in good adjustment and an accurate rod should always be used. The leveling should start by interchecking all the bench marks, and, when there is a discrepancy, the elevation of the basic, or most reliable, bench mark will ordinarily be used. The elevation of the hook-gage scale should be determined, if possible, by a direct level reading on the scale. Elevations of staff gages in the well may be ascertained by measuring down with a steel tape from a reference point in the shelter. Inclined staff gages are tested by taking level shots on each foot or half-foot graduation. Outside vertical staff gages are checked by level readings directly on them and the correctness of the graduations or of the spacing of enameled sections, if used, should be verified by a steel tape. A chain gage is tested by sighting directly on the bottom of the weight at the height of instrument, comparing this elevation with the reading on the chain-gage scale. Measurement of the length of the chain is also necessary. This is done by removing the chain, stretching it out on the bridge floor, and using a steel tape to determine its length from the bottom of the weight to the index mark. The chain is always measured under a standard "pull," usually 12 pounds, as measured by a spring balance. Wire-weight gages of various types are checked by sighting on the bottom of the weight at the height of instrument and noting the reading on the counter or scale. The elevation of the check bar, if there is one, is also determined. In addition to these determinations of various elevations by level, the positions of the hooks, if a hook gage is used, should be verified by measuring with a steel tape the distance from each point of hook to the zero mark on the hook-gage rod. Even the foot marks on the hook-gage rod should be checked with a steel tape in order that no possibility of error, however slight, may be overlooked. In all these situations, appreciable errors must be corrected by resetting or regraduating the gages, correcting the lengths of chain, adjusting the positions of the hooks, or by such other means as will restore the original datum. Small errors may be expressed as plus or minus corrections to be applied to the observed or recorded gage heights, but such datum corrections, for the sake of simplicity, should be eliminated wherever possible.

Some of the check measurements indicated above should also be made at periodic intervals or perhaps at the time of each discharge measurement. Some vertical staff gages may be tested approximately by measuring down from a reference point of known elevation to the water surface by means of a tape or rod; chain lengths should be measured with a steel tape, and the positions of hooks verified in the same manner.

While the stability of the control section bears no direct relation to the stability of the gage datum, it is desirable, when running the annual levels, to obtain elevations of various points on the crest of the artificial control, if the station has an artificial control, because of the value of such elevations in connection with apparent changes in the stage-discharge relation. Such elevations should be ascertained for the lowest point of the control crest or of the notch, at the ends of the control, at the quarter points, and at such other intermediate points as may be considered necessary.

Observers. In connection with the use of nonrecording gages, where twice-daily gage readings are usually required, the services of local observers must be arranged for. Observers are also commonly employed to attend to the routine operation of water-stage recorders and to make inspections at periodic intervals.[1]

Since the quality of the observer's work has a direct bearing on the accuracy of the records of stage, and consequently of discharge, great care should be taken in the selection of the observer and in acquainting him fully with his duties. Other considerations being equal, the most competent man who lives within a reasonable distance from the gage should be employed. Unfortunately, for one reason or another, it is not always possible to employ first-class observers or even the most promising prospects, and recourse must then be had to men of lesser ability.

[1] Chapter 10.

The instruction of observers is a continuing process, not only because of the unavoidable changes which occur from time to time, but also because such nontechnical people may be able to comprehend and remember only one step at a time in the technical aspects of their work and its relation to the purpose for which the gaging station was established. Observers generally appreciate the compliment of being told why particular steps are taken in the work, and are led to put forth their best efforts to help the field engineer who has taken the time to explain to them the broad aspects of the work and to show them how their duties constitute an essential part of it.

Because of the importance of the observer's records in relation to the discharge records for the station, the field engineer must inspect and check the observer's work in every practicable way. To this end, he may visit the station when he is not expected, inspect the observer's notes before there is an opportunity to modify them or bring them up to date, and in other ways assure himself that the observer's work is being done carefully and methodically. Instances have been found where the observer's records were several days in arrears; and, more surprising, other instances have been reported where the records were written up a week or more in advance. Such deficiencies and delinquencies must, of course, be discovered and eliminated, either by improving the facilities for making observations, by correcting the observer's objectionable practices, or, if circumstances permit, by replacing him by someone who gives promise of being competent and reliable in all respects.

It should not be assumed, however, that all or any considerable number of gage observers are unfaithful in the performance of their work, because the opposite is true, and many observers turn in records that are undoubtedly comparable in accuracy with the work of engineers. The careful supervision of all observers is necessary simply because it is difficult to detect the occasional dishonest one and to make a sure case against him.

Operation of Nonrecording Gages. The fact that the integrity and accuracy of records of stage at nonrecording gaging stations depend almost entirely upon the work of local observers is one of the important causes of possible weakness in such records. In order to promote the efficiency and reliability of the observer, the conditions for reading the gage must be so maintained that the gage reader, although perhaps deficient in education, can make and record the necessary observations without undue possibility of error. The means must be provided and maintained for safe approach to the gage at all stages of the river, and the face of the gage must be clearly visible from the place of observation. The gage must be plainly and completely graduated and must at all times be kept clean and legible.

Because of the fact that a gage-height record based on twice-daily gage readings may, at times of rapid change in stage, be an inadequate basis from which to compute a record of mean daily discharge, the observer will be expected at such times to obtain additional gage readings in order that flood peaks may be more adequately delineated. The judgment and interest which the observer exhibits with respect to the furnishing of such supplemental data constitute a fair measure of his value as an employee.

The support for a nonrecording staff gage and the gage itself may at times be subjected to the danger of change in position, damage, or destruction by the action of ice or drift that may be either floating or attached to or lodged against the gage structure. The danger varies with the area of exposure offered by the gage structure to these various destructive forces and also with the number and size of supports or anchorages which may be subject to the lifting or heaving action of ice or frost. Whether a vertical staff or an inclined staff gage is the more vulnerable will depend entirely upon the conditions of their respective installations. As has already been pointed out, changes in elevation must be determined by level through comparison with permanent bench marks. The comparison is facilitated if the bench marks are so situated that it can be made by a single setup of the level. Changes in elevation of the gage, if appreciable, should be corrected either by restoring the gage to its original position, by replacement, or by so regraduating it in its new position as to maintain the relation to the datum plane that was established when it was first set.

Operation of Water-Stage Recorders. In order that a water-stage recorder may function properly, the well and shelter must be maintained in good physical condition, the intake pipe kept open, the well protected against ice formation, and the reference gages, both inside and outside the well, maintained at correct elevation.

The routine operation of the water-stage recorder itself involves periodic changing of the record paper, filling the pen or sharpening the pencil, oiling the instrument, and winding, setting, regulating, and otherwise caring for the clock. Some of these duties are performed by an observer, if one is employed; others by the field engineer, the exact division of specific duties being dependent upon circumstances.

When the record paper is changed, care must be exercised that the time and stage are correctly indicated on the new paper or chart. In order that the proper gage-height and time corrections applicable to the graph may be known, the watch time and the stage indicated by the staff, hook, or float-tape gage inside the well should be recorded by pencil notation on both the old and new record sheets near the terminal and starting points, respectively, or, when a weekly recorder is used, in the spaces provided on the charts for this purpose. The pen should be kept filled, although not to capacity, in order to obtain a legible graph, and the ink used should be of such composition that it will flow evenly and continuously, not clogging in the pen or spreading over the surface of the paper, which may at times be damp. When pens are filled to capacity, there is danger of their overflowing, as the ink will sometimes, under humid conditions, absorb considerable moisture from the air. The pencil, if one is used, must be of such a grade of softness that it will make a legible trace on the record paper even if the paper becomes somewhat softened by moisture. It must be kept sharp, but not so sharp as to penetrate and tear the paper. In some regions and seasons of dampness, specially treated paper is sometimes required to insure a legible and otherwise satisfactory graph and to prevent tearing of the paper by the pen or pencil. Dampness causes expansion of the record paper and resulting errors in the gage-height record. So-called foil-backed charts, which have been used successfully on weekly recorders, serve to eliminate entirely corrections induced by such expansion.

Reliability in the action of the clock is the most important requirement of a water-stage recorder. The stopping of clocks has been responsible for more breaks in records than all other causes combined. To insure against fragmentary records, high-grade clocks are essential. They must be cleaned and oiled by an expert at reasonable intervals, perhaps from one to two years. High-grade oil is necessary to prevent friction, corrosion of the metals, or gumming of the bearings. The continued use of unsuitable oils will lead to clock stoppages and to interruptions in the records.

In order that the exchange of clocks may be effected with reasonable facility, recorders and recorder clocks are now so made that any clock may be easily removed from or attached to any recorder of similar type, thereby reducing to a minimum the number of spare clocks needed. The clock should be wound regularly by the observer, if one is employed, otherwise by the engineer at the time of each visit. Such visits must be made at least at such frequent intervals of time as may be determined by the available clear distance in the well through which the clock-driving weight may fall. The clock and recorder must be inspected at every opportunity. If they are not operating properly they must be adjusted or replaced in order that there shall be no break in the gage-height record.

A field engineer who has several different types and "makes" of water-stage recorders to keep in operation, some of which may be old and whose clocks are therefore not interchangeable, is forced by circumstances to become expert in diagnosing clock and recorder troubles and in taking the steps necessary to insure proper operation. At the very least, he must be able to interchange clocks and to remove and install recorders with reasonable dispatch and without damage to their delicate mechanisms. Some engineers who are mechanically inclined learn to take apart, clean, oil, reassemble, and adjust recorder clocks as satisfactorily as the ordinary commercial clock repairer.

Inspection of Graph. It is the duty of the engineer whenever he visits a gaging station to assure himself that the water-stage recorder is in proper operation and to inspect critically the graph as to legibility and accuracy. In this connection, he should make such notes over his initials or signature either on the record sheet itself or on a separate inspection report sheet as will indicate the gage-height and time corrections that will be necessary. Notations should be made of the readings on all gages, both inside and outside the well, and of the stage indicated by the pen or pencil. The time by watch, by recorder clock, and by pen or pencil will also be recorded, together with a notation of any changes made in the setting of the pen or pencil. Careful inspection of the notes made by the observer on the record sheet or on his weekly reports to the central office is also essential for checking the reliability and completeness of his work. His notations of stages observed periodically on the hook, float-tape, and staff gages are very important and should be carefully watched, not only with respect to their reasonableness and probable accuracy but also as an indication of what further instruction should be given him.

Inspection of Intake Pipe. As already stated, comparison should be made, at each visit of the engineer, between readings on the outside staff gage, on the staff, hook, or float-tape gages inside the well and the record made by the water-stage recorder. Along with the notation of these readings, there should be a statement as to any action taken or changes made that might affect the records of stage as indicated by any of the gages.

If there is a material difference between the elevations of the water surfaces in the gage well and in the river at the gage, the reason therefor should be investigated, and, if the difference is due to obstruction of the intake, steps should be taken to remove the obstruction by flushing or pipe-cleaning facilities at the stations or by other means. However, not all differences in readings of inside and outside gages are due to obstructions in the intake. One of the most troublesome reasons for such differences is the suction caused by the current as the water flows past the end of the intake. If the velocity of flow, and consequently the "draw-down," are definite functions of the stage, no error will be introduced into the records of discharge, provided that the station rating applies to the record of stage within the well. If, however, the records of stage are to be employed in connection with determinations of water-surface slopes, it is evident that readings of stage on an outside gage, or their equivalents, must be used. In connection with flood heights, the records from outside gages should be utilized if they are materially different from those made by the water-stage recorder.

At the National Hydraulic Laboratory, engineers of the Geological Survey have tested various devices for attachment to the outer end of the intake, or for altering the intake pipe itself, in such manner that the effect of draw-down may be reduced. Some of these devices were found to be reasonably effective in bringing into closer agreement the readings on the inside and outside gages.[2] Differences in readings of outside and inside gages may, therefore, be of importance even though they are stable in character and have no significance in connection with the computations of discharge. Causes of such differences should be investigated, and those that are variable and erratic should be corrected, if possible; otherwise, serious errors may be carried into the records of discharge.

In northern latitudes, intake pipes are occasionally rendered inoperative by the formation of ice therein. This effect is usually the result of an insufficient depth of overlying earth cover between the well and the stream or of an insufficient depth of water over the exposed part of the pipe. Whatever may be the cause of such obstruction, the result will be to render the gage-height record valueless until water again passes freely through the intake. Except at the end of the winter, the opening of a frozen intake pipe is often wasted effort, because, unless protective measures of some kind are adopted, the same trouble may recur with the next cold spell. Intake pipes may be thawed out by electricity, if electric current and appropriate apparatus are available, by heating the water in the well with an immersion heater or in some other manner, by adding calcium chloride or other chemical to the water in the well, or by passing the exhaust from an automobile into the intake pipe through a flexible hose. The intake pipe will tend to resist freezing much longer if heat of some kind is provided to prevent the formation of ice within the well.[3]

[2] Bibliog. 14·2.
[3] Chapter 12.

Current-Meter Measurements of Discharge. The field operations involved in making a current-meter measurement of discharge consist essentially in obtaining observations of depth and velocity at several points or stations transversely across a stream, each of which points is at a known distance from an *initial point* on one of the banks. The velocity observations are made, of course, with some type of current meter. Depths are obtained by sounding either with a graduated rod or with a line to which a weight is attached. Distances from the initial point are taken directly from fixed graduations on the cable or bridge structure or from a tag line or tape stretched across the stream. Since the total discharge of a stream is the sum of the increments of discharge between successive measuring stations and since each increment of discharge is the product of mean depth by mean velocity, it will be seen that the observations cited provide all the basic information ordinarily required for a measurement of discharge.

In order to establish the relation of stage to discharge by means of a rating curve, the results of each measurement of discharge must be correlated with the mean stage of the stream at the station gage. To this end, the stage should be observed when the discharge measurement is started, when it is finished, and at one or several intervening times if the stage is fluctuating and considerable time is involved. Under ideal conditions, stage and discharge should not fluctuate during the time of the measurement, but discharge measurements must frequently be made under much less favorable conditions. If the stage changes during the time of the measurement, even though at a uniform rate, it is not possible to correlate the stage and discharge with absolute accuracy because the graph of their relation is curvilinear. If the rates of fluctuation are not uniform, the correlation will be still less exact. Under such conditions, provided that the measurement is made in the vicinity of the station gage, the accuracy of the discharge measurement may be improved by weighting the mean stages for groups of partial sections, or even of single partial sections, with the discharges for such groups or sections. The quotient of the sum of these weighted values divided by the total discharge of the measurement will be the weighted mean gage height of the measurement.

When the discharge measurement is made at some distance from the gage under conditions of changing stage, the correlation of stage and discharge becomes increasingly difficult because of the time element which is introduced and also because of channel storage between the gage and measuring section. Various methods [4] are employed to cor-

[4] Bibliog. 14·3.

rect either the stage or discharge of measurements made under such conditions, none of which is entirely satisfactory since all of them are approximations at best. The mean gage height of the measurement may be corrected in a roughly approximate manner by estimating from observed velocities the time of travel of the water from the gage to the measuring section, or vice versa, and then determining from the graph of the water-stage recorder the mean gage height for a period equal to the elapsed time of the discharge measurement but earlier or later, as the case may be, by an interval of time equal to the time of travel.

When the measurement is made at some distance from the gage, plus or minus corrections to the discharge of the measurement may be required because of inflow or diversion between the gage and the measuring section. Corrections for inflow may be made on a straight drainage-area basis, which is inexact because it depends upon the assumption that the discharge from the area intervening between the gage and measuring section is at the same rate as from the area above the measuring section. The application of an assumed coefficient to the theoretical discharge from the intervening area is a questionable procedure, although sometimes necessary. Actual measurement of the inflow, if possible, is preferable to its estimate by any theoretical means. Diversions between the gage and measuring section must be measured unless their amounts are known.

It is obvious that such adjustments to stage and discharge tend to reduce the accuracy of discharge measurements and that therefore they should be avoided by making the discharge measurements as near the station gage as possible, to the end that the actual amount of water passing the gage may be measured and that such discharge may be precisely correlated with the corresponding mean gage height. Obviously, the greater and more rapid the fluctuations, the less accurate, in general, will be the measured discharge and its correlation with the stage, and the shorter should be the time involved in making the measurement. At times of changing stage, therefore, it will often be necessary to consider the importance of the time element and to plan the discharge measurement accordingly.

The observations of depth and velocity will generally progress from one bank to the other, although, if the time element is important and sufficient personnel and equipment are available, the observations may be made simultaneously from both banks toward the center, or vice versa. The spacing of the points of observation across the stream will so vary with its width, with the unevenness of its bed, and with its velocities as to disclose the essential variations in velocity and the contour of the bed. The points or stations of observation will be spaced closest where either or both the depths and the velocities of current are most variable, and farthest apart where the depths and velocities vary but little (Fig. 71). In general, at least 20 observations of depth and velocity should be made, even in a narrow stream. The number of observations required will ordinarily increase with the width of the stream, with the unevenness of its bed, and with the variations in its velocities. The points of observation should always be spaced

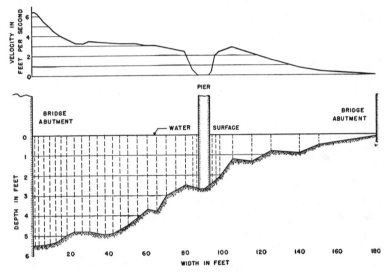

Fig. 71. Diagram showing distribution of measuring points in cross section of unusual shape with abnormal distribution of velocities.

so closely that no section between successive stations shall contain an increment of discharge greater than 10 per cent of the total discharge. The number of observation stations should be determined primarily by the variations in depth and velocity and by the fluctuations in stage rather than by the width of the stream, it being always kept in mind that the two necessary objectives are a discharge measurement that is as accurate as it is practicable to obtain and the proper correlation of that measurement with the corresponding stage.

In making a measurement of discharge, the depth is measured first at each observation station because the depth must be known before the current meter can be properly placed in the vertical and the observation or observations of velocity made in accordance with one of the methods described below before moving to the next observation station.

In general, discharge measurements should be computed and the results plotted on the station rating curve (copy of which should be carried by the field engineer) before the engineer leaves the general vicinity of the station. If the plotting presents unusual or unexpected aspects or if the stage of the river is critically high or low, a check measurement of discharge should be made. In other words, before he proceeds to another station, the engineer should assure himself that he has made the most reliable discharge measurement possible under existing conditions.

The time required to make a discharge measurement is usually much less than the nonproductive time spent in travel to the station. Obviously, therefore, it is poor judgment to attempt to save time at the station by shortening the time of the discharge measurement or by failing to make a check measurement which is clearly indicated. Unsupported discharge measurements at critical stages or measurements which are of doubtful reliability do not inspire confidence, to say the least.

Difficulties and Precautions. Theoretically, the making of a current-meter measurement of discharge is a simple matter, and in some situations, where all the conditions are favorable, this may perhaps be true. Generally, however, the making of a discharge measurement is subject to many complications, and to meet them the engineer must exercise extreme care as well as, at times, much ingenuity. Skill in making accurate measurements of discharge can be acquired only through long and varied experience, and any detailed listing of even typical difficulties with which the engineer may be confronted would have no particular value. However, it is proper to point out certain difficulties that may be encountered and certain precautions that should be observed, especially with respect to the determination of depths and velocities.

Perhaps one of the most difficult operations, particularly in connection with the making of discharge measurements at high stages, is the accurate determination of the depth at each observation point. Except in a wading measurement, soundings are made by means of a weight attached to the same line or cable which carries the current meter. Sounding weights vary in weight from 15 pounds to several hundred pounds. A simple discharge measurement may require the use of only a 15-pound weight on a hand line, such equipment being appropriate in situations where velocities are relatively low and depths not excessive. The procedure of making a sounding with hand-line equipment consists in bringing either the bottom of the weight or the center of the meter to the surface of the water, marking the point on the hand line where it intersects the handrail on the bridge or the zero of the scale on the side of the cable car, then lowering the meter and weight to the bottom and measuring, either with a metallic tape or graduated stick, or on the scale in the cable car, the length of line so paid out, which is the depth, except that if the center of the meter was placed initially at the water surface the distance between the center of the meter and the bottom of the weight must be added to the observed depth to obtain the true depth. Some engineers prefer to reverse this procedure and to make soundings upward from the bottom to the surface. In situations involving greater depths and higher velocities, 50-pound or 75-pound weights are used, being operated from bridges, cable cars, or boats by means of reels and cranes specially designed for that purpose.[5] Under such circumstances, soundings are indicated directly on the counter of the reel, which is set at zero when the bottom of the weight is at the water surface. Care must always be taken to insure that the recorded soundings closely approximate true vertical depths.

If the velocities are high and depths great, the meter and weight will be carried downstream so that the measured depth will be greater than the true depth and will consequently require corrections if there is a considerable vertical angle. As will be seen from the diagram (Fig. 72), in situations where large vertical angles are induced by high velocities, great depths, insufficient sounding weight, or any combination thereof, two separate corrections will be required: an "airline" correction for that part of the line between the crane and the surface of the water, and a "wetline" correction for that portion of the line which is in the water. The wetline correction will usually be less than the airline correction, so much so that it is often possible to neglect it by making the soundings by means of tags on the lower part of the line. These tags may consist of cloth streamers at carefully spaced 5-foot or 10-foot intervals, held in place by friction tape or beads of solder. Similar tags on a hand line may also be a convenient means of facilitating the making of soundings if the depths are greater than 5 feet.

In the most extreme situations, weights of several hundred pounds may be necessary. Such weights must be handled and operated by power-driven reels and cranes because under these conditions manually operated equipment would be entirely inadequate. It will be seen from the above that large vertical angles, if not taken into consideration, may induce erroneous soundings. These angles should therefore be measured whenever necessary, using the protractor on the crane, a

[5] Chapter 8.

hand protractor, or some other means, and the soundings corrected in whatever way may be appropriate under the circumstances. Cross-sectional areas may also be incorrectly measured if the angle of the

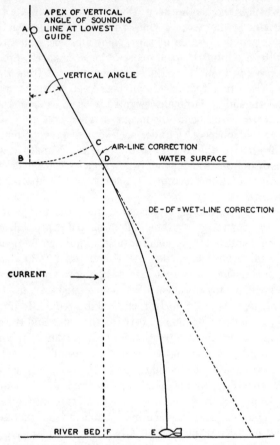

Fig. 72. Airline and wetline corrections to observed depth. (From Method for Correcting Soundings of Deep Swift Rivers, *U. S. Geological Survey Mimeographed Circular*, 1931.)

current is not normal to the measuring section. In such situations, the indicated distances between successive observation points will be too great and coefficients must be applied to such distances, or widths, based on the cosines of the angles which the thread of the current makes with a line normal to the measuring section. In practice, such horizontal angles are determined while the measurement is being made, by means of an angle indicator or by a card which shows the cosines of various indicated angles and consequently the coefficients which should be applied, theoretically to the widths, but which in practice, and for the sake of simplicity, are usually applied to the mean velocities at the observation points concerned. If no means is at hand for the measurement of such angles, the direction of the current may be indicated at each observation point by a line drawn on a sheet of paper and the proper coefficient determined subsequently.

At times of floods, rivers carry large quantities of drift and frequently of broken ice, which under the high velocities that obtain at such times constitute a real menace to the measuring equipment. Careful watch must be kept upstream for such drift so that in case of danger the meter may be raised out of the water without delay. At all times the meter must be carefully watched to guard against entanglement in it of grass, weeds, and other such matter which will seriously affect its operation. Great care should be taken in making observations adjacent to bridge piers and abutments because in such places there is not only great variation in the depth but also variable velocity.   When approaching a bridge pier the distances between points of observation should be shortened and the final observation made as close to the pier or abutment as the safety of the meter will allow.   The depth and velocity at the face of the abutment or pier may then be estimated from the results at the adjacent observation points.

The 0.6-Depth Method. The 0.6-depth method is based on the fact, established by many determinations of vertical curves of velocity (vertical velocity curves), that the mean velocity in any vertical generally occurs at about six-tenths of the depth. The value of this method rests in the comparatively small number of velocity observations (one at each observation station), the essential accuracy of the results, and the relatively short time required for a measurement of discharge. In using this method, the depth of water is measured at each observation station, the current meter is placed at a distance below the surface equal to six-tenths of the depth, and a predetermined number of revolutions of the meter wheel (usually multiples of 5, depending upon the meter rating table) is timed by a stop watch for a period of not less than 40 seconds and preferably for about 50 seconds. Some meter rating tables require that the number of revolutions be observed for a fixed time, such as 50 seconds. The 0.6-depth method is not so commonly used as formerly because of the higher degree of accuracy obtained by the 0.2–0.8-depth method described below. It is of great value, however, in supplementing other methods which may not be usable because of shallow depths or for other reasons. The 0.6-depth method will generally give slightly greater results than those obtained by the 0.2–0.8-depth method.

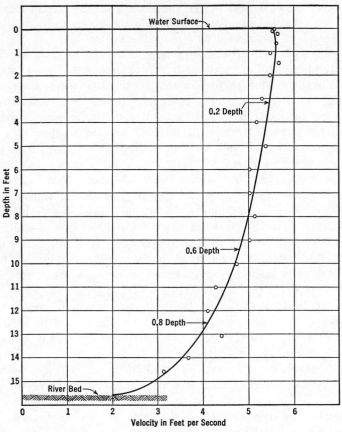

FIG. 73. Typical vertical velocity curve.

The 0.2–0.8-Depth Method. The 0.2–0.8-depth method rests on the theory that the vertical velocity curve is typically parabolic in form and therefore that the mean of all ordinates to the curve is essentially equal to the mean of the ordinates at two-tenths and eight-tenths of the depth, and on the observational finding obtained from many vertical velocity curves that this relationship holds for essentially all streams of water having a free surface (Fig. 73). This method requires more time in its application than the 0.6-depth method, but the results obtained are of higher accuracy. Therefore, it is the preferred method unless the stage is changing so rapidly that the time involved in the measurement is of controlling importance, in which situation the inaccuracy involved in using the quicker (0.6-depth) method may be much less than the inaccuracy which would result from the greater change in stage that would occur if the somewhat slower (0.2–0.8-depth) method were used. It is obvious that in practice the 0.2–0.8-depth method is subject to greater limitations with respect to shallow depths than the 0.6-depth method.

The procedure in using the 0.2–0.8-depth method is the same as that for the 0.6-depth method except that observations of velocity are made consecutively at these two depths at each observation station, the mean velocity in each vertical being the mean of the two velocities so obtained.

Multiple-Point Method. In the application of the multiple-point method, enough determinations of velocity are made at each observation station to define a vertical velocity curve. The mean velocity at the observation station is computed by dividing the area between the axes of plotting and the vertical velocity curve by the depth, or by averaging the velocities obtained from the vertical velocity curve at such a number of equally spaced points as will show essentially the average velocity.

This method is undoubtedly the most accurate of the methods for making current-meter measurements of discharge, since it is the ordinary basis for determining the accuracy of other methods. It is not common in general stream-gaging work because of the amount of time involved in its application and because results by the quicker methods are generally sufficiently accurate for ordinary requirements. The advantages of the accuracy of the method are lost, in part at least, if the stage changes appreciably during the time of the measurement, and it is increasingly inadvisable for use as the rate of change of stage increases.

Other Methods. In addition to the three principal methods for the determination of velocities in the vertical which have been outlined above, there are several other methods which, although not in common use, are nevertheless of occasional applicability and so are at least deserving of mention.

The so-called integration method seeks to obtain a determination of the mean velocity in the vertical by raising and lowering the meter at as uniform a speed as possible, on the theory that since the meter passed through all the velocities in the vertical the number of revolutions in a given period of time would be a fair index of the mean velocity. Aside from the obvious shortcomings of this method, it is unsuitable with the Price current meter because of over-registration under such conditions and consequently is now seldom used at all.

Sometimes, at times of high stages, drift renders impossible the obtaining of velocity readings at both the 0.2- and 0.8-depth points or even at the 0.6-depth points. Under such conditions, actual soundings are also impossible, but depths may be ascertained from observations of stage if the bed of the stream is stable and a standard cross section is available for the measuring section. At such times the "surface method" may be used, with the assurance of results which, although not of high accuracy, are nevertheless greatly preferable to no discharge measurement at all. In this method, if the depth at each observation station is known from a standard cross section, the meter is set as nearly as possible at the 0.2-depth point and a velocity observation made. If the depth of the stream is unknown, the meter may be set at some uniform depth at each observation station, but far enough below the surface to insure the complete submergence of the meter. With any such depth of submergence, the mean velocity in the vertical will be obtained by applying a coefficient to the observed velocity. Such a coefficient can be determined from vertical velocity curves to be obtained for each observation station after the high stages have subsided. If the depths are unknown at the time of the discharge measurement, a cross section must, of course, be developed by later soundings. Obviously, this method cannot be used if the bed and banks shift greatly.

The beds of some streams are so rough or so covered with irregular aquatic growth that the 0.2–0.8-depth method does not give accurate results because of velocity disturbance at the 0.8-depth point. The 0.6-depth method is also not universally applicable because of such disturbance. Under such circumstances, the best results seem to be obtained by averaging the two velocities obtained respectively by the 0.2–0.8-depth and by the 0.6-depth method. This is sometimes known as the "three-point method."

Wading Measurements. Many measurements of discharge, especially at low stages, are made by wading (Fig. 74). For such measurements, the best cross sections are often not those utilized at higher stages at cableways or bridges, and different sections may even be used at different low stages. The lower the stage the greater will be the relative effect of minor errors in the discharge measurement and therefore the greater the necessity for obtaining the highest possible accuracy in all operations incidental thereto. Before starting the measurement, the channels and currents at each possible measuring section should be studied and the best practicable section or sections selected. Wading measurements should be made as near the gage as possible, since small discharges may frequently vary by large percentages in short distances because of seepage gains or losses in the bed of the stream. For this reason, a fair or even poor section near

Fig. 74. Measurement of discharge by wading.

the gage may often be preferable to an excellent section some distance upstream or downstream. Channels in which measurements of small discharges are made may be improved at the time of each measurement by such expedients as the removal of stones and debris or the elimination of shallow portions of the channel by throwing up small temporary earth dams. After such improvements in channel conditions, sufficient time must, of course, be allowed for the stabilization of flow before the discharge measurement is made. At low stages, the use of pygmy meters [6] which operate reliably in shallow depths, may be desirable.

[6] Chapter 8.

In order that low flows in small streams may be measured with greater precision, concrete (or paved) measuring sections may be constructed (Fig. 75). Such a section may consist of a flat concrete slab about 6 feet long (in the direction of flow) with 45-degree sides to confine the flow, constructed at a section of the stream near the gage where the velocities are normally quite regular. The width of the concreted section, of course, will control, to a considerable extent,

FIG. 75. Concrete measuring section.

the depths and velocities therein. Minimum depths of 0.5 foot and minimum velocities of 0.5 foot per second will be satisfactory. Wading measurements (or measurements from footlogs) at such sections will tend to be more consistent because uniform soundings and velocities can be obtained. An auxiliary vertical staff gage at the section will serve further to improve the accuracy of the discharge measurements.

In a wading measurement, the successive points of observation are referred to an initial point by means of either a steel or metallic tape, or, in a stream of considerable width, by a graduated wire tag line. The soundings are made directly by means of the graduated meter rod. In general, the 0.2–0.8-depth method is used for depths greater than 1.5 feet, and the 0.6-depth method for lesser depths. With the pygmy meter, the 0.2–0.8-depth method may generally be used for depths as small as 1.0 foot. Experiments made at the National Hydraulic Laboratory by engineers of the Geological Survey relating to the performance of both standard Price current meters and pygmy meters in shallow depths [7] indicate that for depths less than about 0.5 foot with velocities less than about 0.5 foot per second the 0.6-depth method will require the application of variable coefficients, all greater than unity, to the observed velocities. These experiments show also that, if possible, velocities of less than 0.4 foot per second in shallow depths should be avoided. The importance of choosing a wading section which is relatively as free as possible from these undesirable factors is obvious. It is highly important that the meter rod be held in as nearly a vertical position as possible; otherwise, the center of the meter will not be at the proper depth and also, since the shaft of the meter is not vertical, the instrument will tend to under-register.

In making discharge measurements by wading, the position of the engineer is important. As a result of elaborate studies made by engineers of the Geological Survey at the National Hydraulic Laboratory of the effects of different positions on the action of the meter,[8] it has been found that there is a minimum effect on the action of the meter when the engineer is standing from 1 to 3 inches downstream from the tag line, facing either bank and not less than 18 inches from the meter rod, the meter rod being at the tag line. In measuring very narrow streams, where the feet and legs of the engineer occupy a relatively large part of the cross section, the use of a footlog or temporary measuring bridge, if one can be made available, is greatly to be preferred to wading.

The limiting conditions for wading measurements, being determined by both depth and velocity, may be expressed in terms of the product of these two quantities. In general, it may be stated that, even with good footing, this product should not exceed 10; for example, if the mean velocity is somewhat more than 3 feet per second, measurements may ordinarily be made by wading in depths up to about 3 feet. For the lower velocities, the depth at which wading measurements may be made will be determined by the stature of the engineer or perhaps by the height of his wading boots.

Measurements under Ice Cover. In general, the cross section to be utilized in making measurements of discharge from an ice surface should be selected under open-water conditions, when the velocities of the currents of flow and their distribution can be observed. The flow of water under ice cover is analogous to its flow in a pipe under a pressure head approximately equal to about nine-tenths of the

[7] Bibliog. 8·10.

[8] Bibliog. 14·4.

thickness of the ice, provided that the ice is wholly supported by the water, and the shapes of the vertical velocity curves will consequently differ from those of a stream flowing in an open channel.

Although it is true that the vertical velocity curves of water flowing under ice cover are unique, in general, the 0.2–0.8-depth method applies also for this condition, although the 0.6-depth method does not. The depths of water to be used are those below the under surface of the ice. In making a measurement of discharge under ice cover a sufficient number of holes is first cut through the ice along a line transverse to the direction of the stream. The distances to these holes from an initial point may be measured with a tag line. The water will generally rise in the holes nearly to the top of the ice as a result of hydrostatic pressure. The depth of water beneath the ice is obtained by subtracting from the total depth of water the distance from the surface of the water to the under surface of the ice. This distance may be conveniently measured with a graduated stick or rod, one end of the rod being fitted with a small steel angle, a leg of which, projecting about 3 inches at right angles from the end of the rod, may be hooked under the ice. Total depths of water are measured either with a graduated rod, if the depths are not great, with a hand line and weight utilizing a tripod or shear poles (Fig. 26), or with a line and weight operated from a reel mounted on skis or runners (Fig. 70). If the depths are sufficient to permit the use of the 0.2–0.8-depth method, the measurement proceeds in much the same manner as under open-water conditions. If, however, the depths are insufficient for this method, it is usually customary to make one observation at mid-depth, or in some instances at 0.6 depth, and then from a number of vertical velocity curves obtained at the deeper sections determine the proper coefficient to apply to the mid-depth or 0.6-depth observations to reduce them to mean velocities in the vertical. Where the depths are too shallow for the development of vertical velocity curves, a coefficient of 0.87 or 0.88 is usually assumed and applied to the velocity observations at mid-depth, or, for velocity observations at 0.6 depth, a coefficient of about 0.93 may be used.

Since measurements of discharge under ice cover may frequently involve much discomfort for the engineer, he should be warmly dressed so that the danger of frostbite may be reduced to a minimum. In order to shorten as much as possible the time of his exposure to the elements, and also for reasons of economy, the holes through the ice should be cut coincident with the making of the measurement by a local helper, hired for that purpose by the engineer. A major precaution that must be observed, often with difficulty, is to protect the meter from the formation of ice in the bearings, which would affect its operation most adversely. The meter should therefore be kept in the water at all times except when it is being carried from one point of observation to the next, which transfer should be effected without unnecessary delay. A portable heater is sometimes used to supply warm water with which to "thaw out" the meter if temperatures are extremely low. Since the making of discharge measurements from an ice surface may at times he hazardous, the engineer should be aware of the safety of the ice before venturing upon it, because no discharge measurement, however important, should be made at the risk of a man's life.

Volumetric Measurements of Discharge. The accurate measurement of low flows by means of current meters is frequently so difficult because of shallow depths and low velocities that recourse should be had, wherever possible, to measurement by the volumetric method, although, unfortunately, this method is in general practicable only at gaging stations provided with artificial controls that satisfy certain requirements. Wherever volumetric measurements are possible, the relative accuracy of the results is comparable with, and often superior to, that of current-meter measurements made under favorable conditions. Either of two requirements must be satisfied if the volumetric method is to be used: (1) the flow must be so concentrated in a low section of the control or in a notch that all of it may be diverted for purposes of measurement, or (2) the control must be horizontal and the flow evenly distributed in order that fractional diversion and measurement may be possible.

In the first situation, the entire flow must be diverted, without appreciable loss by leakage, into a wooden measuring box or metal tank which has been so calibrated that its exact cubical contents are known. The water should be conveyed from the artificial control to the measuring receptacle by means of a portable trough or pipe. The measuring box or tank is usually installed permanently in an advantageous position below the control and at some point where it will not obstruct higher flows in the stream or be subjected to damage or destruction by them. It should be located near the control in order to minimize the danger of loss of water in transit and to reduce the time of travel from control to measuring tank. Obviously, it must be placed at such an elevation that the water will flow into it by gravity. Means, of course, must be provided, as by a valve at the bottom, by which the tank may be emptied after each test run. The dimensions and therefore the capacity of the tank will depend upon several considerations, but in any event it should be remembered that the larger the tank the more accurate will be the determination of discharge because of the greater accuracy with which the filling of the tank may be timed. The procedure in making a volumetric measurement of this kind is simple and involves the accurate determination with a stop watch of the time required to fill the calibrated tank. Ordinarily, the observed times for about six runs are averaged, and from the result the discharge of the stream in cubic feet per second or other unit may be easily calculated. Obviously, for accurate results, the flow of the stream must be practically constant during the time required for each series of runs.

When the control consists of a horizontal crest with essentially uniform flow passing over it, a different procedure will be required. Metal troughs 2 inches or 4 inches wide, provided with some means whereby they may be tightly fastened to the control, are utilized to divert sections of the flow into a portable measuring tank of 2 cubic feet capacity, the time required to fill the tank being carefully observed with a stop watch. Trials are made at numerous points along the control, and the total discharge is then the product of the average flow diverted by the trough and the ratio of the length of the control to the width of the trough. This method, though obviously not as accurate as the method mentioned above, because much greater flows are ordinarily involved, has nevertheless been found to give more consistent results than those by current meter at such low stages.

Computation of a Discharge Measurement. As already indicated, the total discharge of a stream, when measured by the velocity-area method, is computed as the sum of the partial discharges through the subareas into which the total cross section is divided by the observation stations. The field observations used in computing the partial discharges consist of the depths and velocities at stations variously spaced across the stream at distances measured from an initial point on one bank. A partial discharge is commonly computed for any subarea of the cross section, extending, for example, from Station 5 to Station 6 on the assumption that the average depth for the subarea is the average of the depths observed at the two stations and, similarly, that the average velocity is the average of the velocities observed at those stations. On that basis, the partial discharge for the subarea between Stations 5 and 6 is

$$q = w \left(\frac{v_5 + v_6}{2} \right) \left(\frac{d_5 + d_6}{2} \right)$$

in which q is the partial discharge, d is the depth, v is the mean velocity, w is the width of the subarea, and the subscripts indicate the stations at which the depths and velocities have been measured. Stevens [9] has found that this formula, which is simple and easily applied, is also the most accurate for general use.

If the stations are evenly spaced, some engineers have preferred the formula

$$q = w\left(\frac{v_5 + 2v_6 + v_7}{4}\right)\left(\frac{d_5 + 2d_6 + d_7}{4}\right)$$

for obtaining the discharge in the subarea extending from halfway between Stations 5 and 6 to halfway between Stations 6 and 7. Other engineers have preferred the prismoidal formula, which gives somewhat greater weight to the depths and velocities observed at the middle observation point. They compute

$$q = w\left(\frac{v_5 + 4v_6 + v_7}{6}\right)\left(\frac{d_5 + 4d_6 + d_7}{6}\right)$$

It is probable that the simple formula now commonly used gives results that are as accurate as the basic data warrant and, in any event, that, for smooth-flowing streams of fairly uniform depths, the differences in the total computed discharge will not generally be great, whether one or another of these formulas is used. The formula that is simplest and most easily applied is, therefore, accepted as best for general use, thereby requiring a minimum time for the computations and running a minimum risk of arithmetical errors. Figure 76 shows note sheets of a typical discharge measurement on which the details of computation have been carried out, by the first of the three methods referred to above, which is standard in the Geological Survey.

Operation of Slope Stations. Since slope stations are used where variations in the slope of the water surface for the same stage make the ordinary methods for stage-discharge stations inapplicable, that is, where velocity of flow is not necessarily a function of the stage, they must be so equipped that continuous records of stage made by water-stage recorders yield the information from which the slope of the water surface at any time may be computed. To this end, two water-stage recorders are installed in a stretch of river of essentially uniform surface slope, separated by a distance that may be several hundreds or many thousands of feet. The two recorders are set to record elevations above the same datum plane, and either the two graphs must correspond closely as to time or the differences in time

[9] Bibliog. 14·6.

9-275 c
(July 1935)

UNITED STATES
DEPARTMENT OF THE INTERIOR
GEOLOGICAL SURVEY

WATER RESOURCES BRANCH

DISCHARGE MEASUREMENT NOTES

Meas. No. 221
Checked by C.L.W.
Date 10/2/41

Sacandaga River near Hope, N. Y.

Date Sept. 30, 1941 Party H.W. Fear (M) R. Forrest (N)

Width 88 Area 135 Vel. 0.61 G. H. 1.46 Disch. 82.0

Method 2-.8 .6 No. secs. 30 G. H. change 0.00 in 1¼ hrs. Susp. rod

Method coef. 1.00 Hor. angle coef. See notes Meter No. 1629 Susp. coef. 1.00

GAGE READINGS			Hook Inside	Outside
Time		Recorder	Inside	Outside
4:00 p.m.		1.48+	1.465	1.47
4:35	Start	1.48	(1.465)	
5:50	Finish	1.48	(1.465)	
6:10		1.48	1.465	—
Weighted M. G. H.		1.48	1.465	
G. H. correction		−0.015	.000	
Correct M. G. H.		1.465	Use 1.46	

Date rated Nov. 12, 1938 Used rating for rod susp. Meter — ft. above bottom of wt. Tags checked —

Spin before meas. 2′—25″ after 2′—7″

Meas. plots +3.0% diff. from 9/2/41 rating

Wading, ~~cable, ice, boat, upstr., downstr., side bridge~~ 0.6 ~~feet~~, mile, ~~above~~, below gage, ~~and~~

Chain, wire, found —

changed to — at —

Correct length —

Levels obtained —

Measurement rated ~~excellent (2%)~~, good (5%), ~~fair (8%), poor (over 8%)~~, based on following conditions: Cross section rough

Flow uniform Weather cloudy; light showers

Other —

Gage operating properly

Record removed no Intake flushed no

Observer not seen

Control clear

Remarks #7 numeral placed on outside gage

Sheet No. 1 of 4 sheets. G. H. of zero flow — ft.

U. S. GOVERNMENT PRINTING OFFICE 6—7440

FIG. 76*a*. Sheet 1 of notes for typical discharge measurement.

80 •   75 •

UNITED STATES
DEPARTMENT OF THE INTERIOR
GEOLOGICAL SURVEY
WATER RESOURCES BRANCH

9-275 January 1925

Meter 1629
watch 1974

Date Sept. 30, 1941 DISCHARGE MEASUREMENT NOTES start 4:35 p.m.

Sacandaga River, near Hope, N.Y.

Dist. from initial point	Angle coefficient	Depth	Depth of observation	Revolutions	Time in seconds	At point	Mean in vertical	Mean in section	Area	Mean depth	Width	Discharge
L.E.W.												
108	.90	0.2	est same as 107			.461 (e)						
							.461	0.20	0.20	1	0.09
107	.90	.2		10	45	.512	.461					
							.230	.60	.30	2	.14
105	1.0	.4	.2	0	0	.00						
							.077	1.00	.50	2	.08
103		.6	.4	3	51	.154	.154					
							.077	1.20	.40	3	.09
100		.2		0	0	.00						
Rock						.00		0	0	0	—
100	1.6		.3	5	45	.268	.377					
			1.3	10	47½	.486		.648	4.35	1.45	3	2.82
97	1.3		.3	20	49	.919	.919					
			1.0	20	49	.919		.862	3.40	1.70	2	2.93
95	2.1		.4	20	48	.938	.804					
			1.7	15	51	.669		.861	4.00	2.00	2	3.44
93	1.9		.4	20	44	1.02	.918					
			1.5	15	41½	.816		1.00	5.70	1.90	3	5.70
90	1.9		.4	30	56	1.20	1.09					
			1.5	20	46	.977		1.02	5.70	1.90	3	5.81
87	1.9		.4	30	62	1.08	.948					
			1.5	15	41½	.816		.884	5.55	1.85	3	4.91
84	1.8		.4	20	42½	1.06	.819					
			1.4	10	39½	.578		.776	6.80	1.70	4	5.28
5:00 p.m.	(1.6)						(.734)	38.50		28	31.29

No. 2 of 4 Sheets. Comp. by ____ Chk. by CLW

U.S. GOVERNMENT PRINTING OFFICE 6—7082

FIG. 76b. Sheet 2 of notes for typical discharge measurement.

must be known so that the graphs can be adjusted to the same time basis. By means of the two graphs, the difference in stage at the two gages, or the *fall*, can be obtained for any time, and this difference, divided by the distance between the gages, will give the average slope of the water surface between the gages.

In the operation of a slope station, great care must be exercised, therefore, to preserve the stability and identity of the datum plane of the two gages, to coordinate the time shown by the two graphs, and to correlate each measurement of discharge with the slope or fall and with the stage. In all other respects, the field operation of a slope station is similar to that of a regular stage-discharge station. In the respects indicated, there are really no essential differences except in the degree of care that must be exercised with respect to the correlation of time between the two graphs, since relatively small differences in time may lead to relatively large errors in the records of slope during periods when the slope is changing.

Field Reports. An essential feature in the operation of a stream-gaging program relates to the scheduled and nonscheduled reports made by the field force.

Each observer[10] must make periodic reports to the office. If a non-recording gage is used, the records of gage height should be entered in a book provided for the purpose, which should be sent to the office at the end of the period of three months for which the book was designed. In addition, the observer should send a weekly report card showing the gage-height entries in his book for the preceding week, thus keeping the office currently advised as to stages of the river and insuring against loss of records by the sending of the same basic information twice; he should send nonscheduled reports of unusual stages, conditions, or events daily, and by telephone or telegraph, if necessary, as they may occur. If a water-stage recorder of the weekly type is in use, the observer must change the record sheet at the end of each week and mail the chart to the office; regardless of the type of water-stage recorder, he should report periodically on a form furnished for the purpose as to the gage height shown on the record chart at a specific time and the simultaneous readings of the float-tape, staff, and hook gages. He should report chart time, his watch time, and, if the gage clock has a dial, the gage-clock time. If there is lack of agreement in gage-height readings or in the indicated times, he should, if possible, explain the discrepancies. He should make also nonscheduled and prompt reports of all unusual conditions or events

[10] Chapter 10.

that relate to the stages of the river or the operation of the recorder.

The field engineer should mail promptly to the office, on a card designed for that purpose, the results of each discharge measurement and a report of all conditions at each gaging station visited by him, with a detailed account of all work done. If he is in the field for several days and makes measurements of discharge at several gaging stations, he should mail to the office, daily if possible, the original loose-leaf notes of all measurements, completely computed, that have been made since the last previous transmittal of data. This should be done in order to keep the office fully informed, to permit prompt checking of the computations, and to insure against the loss of original records, as accidents will sometimes occur on rivers, cableways, bridges, and highways, and unnecessary risk should not be taken with respect to valuable and irreplaceable records. The field engineer should mail also to the office any recorder charts removed by him unless he is about to return to headquarters. As a rule, the observer will not be expected to remove the record roll from a continuous water-stage recorder, but the field engineer will remove it at appropriate intervals of time.

Office Work Related to Operation. In order that the field work of operating gaging stations may be properly executed, it is essential that the work of analyzing, plotting, and filing reports from observers and field engineers be kept current and that the office engineer keep the field engineers advised as to any situation which may affect their work or the order in which it should be handled. By such orderly procedure, lapses by the observers are promptly detected, reports of difficulties at gaging stations are given immediate attention, unusual or significant changes in stage are noted without delay, and the field engineer is kept currently advised as to critical situations at all gaging stations in his route of travel with respect to stages and conditions of flow, operation of water-stage recorders, damage to structures, needed repairs or replacements, and the work of observers.

In order to serve efficiently in this work, the office engineer must see that the office records are methodically handled in accordance with a satisfactory system of checking, "follow-up," and filing; he should be familiar with the gaging stations and their equipment, and alert to the significance of information received from the observers or other local sources.

Maintenance of Structures. The details of the maintenance of a recorder shelter, including the well, will be determined by its type, whether of wood, concrete, brick, or other material, or of a combination of such materials. All wooden structures should be kept well painted and of course must be repaired or replaced wholly or in part from time to time as they deteriorate. Concrete wells and shelters require a minimum of maintenance, but wooden wells must eventually be replaced after varying lengths of service. Wooden shelters built on concrete wells will give long and satisfactory service, if properly constructed and if the exposed woodwork is kept painted and the roof is well maintained. At gaging stations in northern latitudes, various devices, such as subfloors, oil tubes, gas burners, and electric heaters, may be installed for the purpose of preventing ice formation in the well. Before the beginning of winter, all such appurtenances should be carefully inspected and put in proper condition for service by such repairs and replacements as may be necessary.

Towers, A-frames, and cable cars, whether of wood or steel, must also be kept well painted and any defective parts of these structures replaced as may be necessary to maintain their strength. Graduations on the cable to indicate distances from the initial point must be kept clearly visible and should be repainted frequently. Cable clips, turnbuckles, sheaves, and all connections should be examined frequently for deterioration or vandalism. Cable clips should be tested with a wrench and tightened if necessary and the threads of turnbuckles greased at least once a year to prevent rusting and to permit of easy adjustment.

If a bridge has been built for stream-gaging purposes, it must be painted and the wooden parts replaced as may be necessary for convenience in use, durability, and strength. As with cableways, graduations on bridges to indicate distances from the initial point must be repainted frequently to insure proper visibility.

The various auxiliary and reference gages at every gaging station usually require a certain amount of annual maintenance work. Bed pieces for both inclined and vertical staff gages may need repair or replacement, graduations must be renewed where required, enameled faces replaced if illegible or damaged, and hooks and scales adjusted or replaced. A listing of all the small operations which may be involved in routine maintenance work is quite impracticable and in fact superfluous, if it is remembered that the purpose of such work is that the various structures at a gaging station be kept in a condition approximating as nearly as possible that when they were installed or erected.

Cost of Operation and Maintenance. The cost of operation and maintenance of a gaging station is made up of many items, some of which relate to the physical characteristics of the station and its equipment, some to the grouping of stations, some to the degree of accuracy expected in the records, and some to the cost of services, technical and otherwise, required in connection with such operation and maintenance. Various phases of this subject have been discussed in Chapter 10.

Low costs of operation and maintenance are desirable only if they can be attained by the exercise of careful planning and efficient work. Otherwise, low costs are only too often indicative of records of indifferent accuracy and reliability. It is false economy to consider costs of operation ahead of quality of records, and it is much more desirable, if funds are very limited, to operate a smaller number of gaging stations in the most approved manner than to distribute the available funds too thinly over the slipshod operation of a larger number of stations.

Use of the Radio. The availability of a radio in the automobile of the field engineer may have considerable importance in periods of high water. At such times, it often happens that the engineer in the field may not be readily reached by telegraph or telephone because without notice he may interrupt or modify his schedule of travel in order to reach distant stations where the stages are unusual and where discharge measurements are urgently needed. Changes in his schedule will occasionally be made necessary also by the submergence of roads or destruction of bridges which may render the regular routes impassable.

During floods, local radio broadcasting stations commonly broadcast flood bulletins at stated times for the information of the people of the region. The broadcaster will often be willing to include in his broadcast information from the engineer's headquarters office or from gage observers at key stations which will be of great value and assistance to the field engineer. With such timely information, both general and specific in nature, the field engineer will be greatly aided in planning the routes to be traveled in reaching the stations where his services are most urgently needed. Discharge measurements of flood flows are difficult to obtain because of the frequently sudden incidence and generally short duration of floods and also because of the travel difficulties which may be experienced. The radio gives promise of becoming a factor of increasing importance in such work and at such times.

Transportation. The most common means of transportation utilized by field engineers in connection with the maintenance and operation of gaging stations are light motor trucks, coupés, and sedans. Trucks of one-half-ton capacity are particularly useful in construction and maintenance work since they will carry in locked compartments all the instruments, tools, and equipment needed. Tripods and leveling rods must be collapsible to the length of the locked space provided. For routine stream gaging, coupés, sedans, and sedan delivery cars have been found satisfactory, since they are light in weight and easy to handle, provide facilities for carrying ordinary stream-gaging instruments and equipment, and are reasonably inexpensive to operate. Sedan delivery cars are preferred by many engineers because of their capacity for carrying all necessary stream-gaging equipment in a locked compartment. Any of these types of cars are also especially useful at times of high water, when it is imperative that gaging stations be reached in the shortest possible time.

More unusual, in the sense of uncommon, methods of transportation in stream-gaging work are by airplane, on horseback, with teams of horses, by rail, and on foot. Travel on foot is often necessary for distances of varying length when the engineer has proceeded by automobile or other means as far as possible and must complete the journey to the gaging station under his own power. In the winter, snowshoes or skis are occasionally utilized, when the roads or trails to the gaging stations can be traversed by no other means. Pack animals may even be required to supplement travel by foot or on horseback if for any reason the transportation of materials or extensive equipment is involved. Airplanes are not commonly used but have been found valuable in reaching isolated stations, where the high cost of obtaining records of discharge may offset the expense of airplane travel. Horses are now used only to reach gaging stations located far from highways or otherwise inaccessible by more usual means of transportation. Railroads and busses may be considered emergency means of travel which would be used only when the opportunity to obtain discharge measurements at critical stages occurs and for one reason or another no other means of transportation are available. Travel by rail and by bus is complicated by the difficulties involved in transporting equipment from the railroad stations or bus terminals to the gaging stations; in addition it is time-consuming and frequently costly.

In general, for all ordinary stream-gaging purposes, automobiles offer the most economical, reliable, and satisfactory means of transportation and are generally used throughout the country, with one or more of other auxiliary means mentioned above to meet special conditions as required.

Schedules of Travel. The arrangement of schedules of travel of field engineers in connection with the operation of gaging stations involves the consideration of several factors. Not all stations require the same amount or spacing of work, and the differences in such requirements relate to a variety of reasons. Some gaging stations are equipped with water-stage recorders of the 7-day or 8-day type which require weekly winding of the clocks; other stations have continuous recorders operated by weight-driven clocks that will run as long as the weights continue to fall and which may not require winding for long intervals of time. With some recorders, the record chart must be changed weekly, whereas with others a roll containing a year's supply of record paper is used and the record may be removed at convenient irregular intervals. At some stations, observers are employed who change the charts and wind the clocks; at others no observers are employed and all work of operation must be done by field engineers. Some stations have reasonably permanent control sections and the stage-discharge relations change slowly or not at all so that relatively few discharge measurements are needed except at critical stages; others have constantly shifting control sections with stage-discharge relations changing accordingly, thus requiring many discharge measurements; still others are between these extremes in their requirements for timely work by the field engineer. In addition to the above, it may be pointed out that special trips to individual stations or groups of stations may be required at any time for any one of an endless number of reasons.

So far as the differences in gaging stations relate to natural conditions, they must generally be accepted as they are or else be definitely modified, perhaps at considerable expense; so far as the differences relate to equipment, they may be modified practically at will, although not without added expense for services, materials, and instruments. Whatever may be the reasons for differences in gaging stations, the stations should be so grouped for the attention of field engineers that at each station whatever work may be necessary to obtain reliable and continuous records of discharge will be done.

The cost of operating any gaging station will be affected to a considerable extent by the size and compactness of the group in which it is placed in the field engineer's schedule of travel; the less the distance of special travel by the field engineer to reach a station, the less will be the demands on his time, and therefore, other things being equal, the less the cost of operation. The organization of field work with special reference to the grouping of gaging stations, the coordination with the office work, and the planning of schedules of travel are certain, therefore, to present important problems affecting the accuracy of the records and the efficiency and costs in the operation of gaging stations in a broad stream-gaging program.

BIBLIOGRAPHY 14

1. W. G. Hoyt, The Effects of Ice on Stream Flow, *U.S.G.S. Water Supply Paper* 337.
2. C. H. Pierce, Investigations of Methods and Equipment Used in Stream Gaging, Part 2, Intakes for Gage Wells, *U.S.G.S. Water Supply Paper* 868-B.
3. B. E. Jones, A Method for Correcting River Discharge for a Changing Stage, *U.S.G.S. Water Supply Paper* 375-E.
4. C. H. Pierce, Preliminary Report on Position of Engineer in Discharge Measurements by Wading, *U.S.G.S. Mimeographed Circular,* 1941.
5. Corbett and others, Stream-Gaging Procedure, *U.S.G.S. Water Supply Paper* 888.
6. J. C. Stevens, Comparison of Formulas for Computation of Stream Discharge, *Engineering News,* Vol. 59, pp. 682–684.

CHAPTER 15

COMPUTING AND PREPARING RECORDS FOR PUBLICATION

Interrelation of Field and Office Work. The field work related to the operation and maintenance of gaging stations represents the first step toward the ultimate objective of obtaining accurate and continuous records of daily discharge because by means of it the basic and underlying data are obtained from which those records will eventually be deduced; the second step is taken in the office and is concerned with those processes and procedures which are necessary for the conversion of field data into discharge records; and the third and final step, taken also in the office, involves the arrangement of the computed records in proper form for publication, if they are to be published. Although the office work related to the computation of records of daily discharge has many ramifications, which cannot be discussed in the limited space available in this chapter, an attempt is here made to outline the basic principles and procedures involved. With a knowledge of the general basic principles and procedures, the engineer will aways be able to devise appropriate methods for solving special problems as they may arise.

Analyzing Field Data. As has been pointed out, it is absolutely necessary, before routine computations are undertaken, that there be available a sufficient number of discharge measurements, well distributed with respect to both stage and time, to define a station rating curve or curves, to verify or revise an existing rating curve, or to provide a basis for use with other data in computing discharge by the slope method. Discharge measurements will also be required to indicate, as well as may be, the amount and extent of backwater from ice, aquatic vegetation, debris, or other cause. Also necessary, of course, is an adequate and reliable gage-height record or record of stage covering the period for which the computations of discharge are to be made. This gage-height record may be based on a record of daily or twice-daily gage readings by a local observer, on a graph from a water-stage recorder in the form of a continuous record or of a series of weekly records, depending upon the type of instrument used, or even on a printed record of instantaneous gage heights at regular fixed intervals of time, such as an hour or fractions thereof, if a printing recorder is used.

The practice of the Geological Survey is, in general, to compute records of daily discharge once a year on the basis of a so-called climatic year ending on September 30.[1] Frequently, however, it is necessary to compute in a provisional manner current records of daily discharge for special purposes, but experience has shown that such current computations are subject to later revision because of the inability of the computer always to recognize currently from the field data changes in the stage-discharge relation which may have taken place recently, and because such changes will make necessary corresponding shifts or alterations in the station rating curve. When a whole year's record is computed at one time, it is possible to obtain a broad general picture of all changes in the stage-discharge relation which may have taken place during the year and to have complete information relating to backwater from various causes and concerning other field phenomena which may have an important bearing on the accuracy of the records.

Discharge measurements are generally computed in the field by the engineer shortly after he has made them and are then forwarded to the office to be added to the permanent records of the station. Because such field computations may be made under difficulties, including pressure of time, they are liable to error. Therefore, discharge measurements should be carefully checked in the office as soon as possible after they are received from the field. The checking of a discharge measurement involves not only checking the computations related to discharge but also checking, so far as may be possible, the mean gage height applicable to the measurement, because in the plotting of a discharge measurement on a rating curve sheet the element of gage height is just as important as the element of discharge. The checking of the mean gage height involves applying to the gage-height observations made during the measurement whatever datum correction may be shown by the most recent levels and also comparing these observations with the graph from the water-stage recorder. It may also involve weighting mean gage heights for increments of time with corresponding increments of discharge or making allowance for elapsed time, if the discharge measurement was made under conditions of changing stage or at some distance from the station gage.[2] The checking of the discharge computations involves verification of the velocities

[1] Chapter 17.
[2] Chapter 14.

indicated by the recorded number of meter revolutions in the observed time; these velocities, of course, are obtained from the meter rating table applicable to that particular suspension of the individual meter which was used during the measurement. The application of coefficients to the velocity figures for horizontal angles and to the depths for vertical angles, if any of those angles were of significant size, should also be checked. Also involved is the checking of the mean depths, section widths, areas, mean velocities, and, finally, the increments of discharge which are obtained as the products of the appropriate mean velocities and the increments of area. The total discharge is the sum of these increments of discharge. The technique of checking discharge measurements made under ice cover is similar to that of checking open-water discharge measurements, but with the added responsibility of checking the effective depths and the application of any coefficients which may have been necessary because only one velocity observation in a vertical was made under the ice.

Occasionally it is necessary to apply an over-all coefficient to the discharge apparently indicated by the measurement. For example, if the suspension of meter and weights was different from any of the various suspensions for which the meter was rated, a coefficient may be applicable to the total discharge. This "suspension coefficient" may be greater or less than unity and ordinarily will be within less than 2 per cent of unity. Again, it may have been impracticable to obtain current-meter observations at either 0.2- and 0.8-depth or 0.6-depth points in the vertical, and "method coefficients" must be applied to the indicated velocities, usually in the office, on the basis of vertical velocity curves. Discharge measurements made by wading will occasionally require correction by coefficients applicable to the individual observations if the depths or velocities, or both, are very small.[3]

After the discharge measurements have been checked, they should be plotted both on the office rating curve sheet and the field rating curve sheets, and the notes filed until the computation of the discharge record is undertaken.

As soon as possible after their receipt from the field, the records of gage height should be critically examined by the office engineer, principally from the standpoints of continuity and quality. For non-recording stations, the observer enters his daily or twice-daily observations and the time at which each was made, in a small book for that purpose, which usually covers a three-months' period. It is important that the observer's readings be compared with the occasional

[3] Bibliog. 8·10.

independent readings made by visiting engineers, in order that at least sporadic checks may be had on the accuracy of his work. Promptly after their receipt in the office, weekly recorder charts or continuous record rolls should be dated, preferably by typewriter if of the former type. With continuous record rolls, particular attention must be given to time corrections, since it is only rarely that a continuous recorder operates over long periods of time without some small errors in time. Time corrections are ascertained either from a midnight-marking device, if the water-stage recorder is so equipped, or from the results of periodic inspections and notations of time and stage made by the observer and of occasional inspections and notations or reports made by visiting engineers.

Since integrity of the gage-height record is dependent on the maintenance of a fixed datum for the gage, levels must be run at least annually, frequently oftener, to the station gages from the station bench marks. The level notes should be carefully analyzed in the office as soon as they are received; if inconsistencies are found, the field engineer should be instructed to run check levels. It is imperative, if datum corrections must be applied to the recorded gage heights, that the amount and duration of such corrections be accurately known before any attempt is made to compute records of daily discharge.

Station Rating. The first step preliminary to the actual computation of the discharge at any gaging station consists in the determination of the stage-discharge relations throughout the range of stage (rating curve), and the arrangement of such determination in the best form for use (rating table). This step is necessary in order to obtain a practicable means for converting or translating a record of mean daily gage height into a record of mean daily discharge.

RATING CURVES. For a newly established station, of course, no previous rating curve will be available, and it will be necessary to develop an initial station rating curve. The available discharge measurements are assembled and the results plotted on a sheet of cross-section paper with gage heights as ordinates and discharges as abscissas and with the point of origin in the lower left corner. The cross-section paper should be of such light weight as to permit the making of blueprints for field or other use. If rectangular cross-section paper is used, the vertical and horizontal scales should be so chosen that the rating curve will occupy a position corresponding roughly with the diagonal of the paper. It is highly desirable that discharge measurements be available at well-distributed stages throughout the whole range of stage of the record in spite of the fact that extremely high and exceptionally low discharge measurements are difficult to obtain because such extreme stages do not occur often and do not ordinarily persist for any considerable periods of time. A proper definition of the lower end of the rating curve will be facilitated if the stage of zero flow has been determined by observations made in the field. This point, which is a theoretical one for a perennial stream, is ascertained by measuring the depth of water over the lowest point of the control section and subtracting such depth from the stage indicated at the gage, thus giving the probable gage height of zero flow which would occur just as the water ceases to flow in the stream. From a mathematical standpoint, most rating curves have the general form of a parabola or of a combination of parabolas. Because of this fact, it is frequently possible to utilize to advantage a logarithmic scale, to which reference will be made later in this chapter, in plotting discharge measurements and drafting station rating curves.

The results of the discharge measurements having been plotted, together with the point of indicated zero flow, if available, a smooth curve is drawn, averaging the plotted points as nearly as possible. In general, at least ten well-distributed discharge measurements should be available to define an initial rating curve; assuming that these measurements were properly made under reasonably steady conditions of stage and that they apply to a stable stage-discharge relation, it should generally be possible to draw a curve that will not miss any of the accredited discharge measurements by as much as 5 per cent. In order to obtain a satisfactory definition for the lower portion of the rating curve, the low-water part of it may advantageously be re-plotted to a larger scale in the upper left part of the rating curve sheet.

Rating Curve Extensions. If, as frequently happens, discharge measurements have not been made in the current year or previous years at stages equal to or greater than the highest stages recorded during the current year, it will be necessary to extend the rating curve upward by other means than discharge measurements. One method of doing this, assuming that all the medium- and high-stage measurements were made at the same section of the river, as from the same cableway or the same bridge, is to plot the cross-sectional areas of discharge measurements against corresponding mean gage heights and to draw a mean curve on the basis of these points, thus obtaining a stage-area curve. If there is no bank overflow, such a curve will be very nearly a straight line that may be projected upward to the point of maximum stage. Similarly, a stage-velocity curve is constructed by plotting the mean velocities of the discharge measurements against the corresponding mean gage heights. This curve usually has little curvature and can be extended upward with a fair degree of confidence. Values of discharge for the higher stages may be deduced from these two curves with the degree of confidence that pertained to the extensions.

High-water extensions may also be made advantageously by logarithmic plotting since, because of its parabolic shape, a rating curve obtained by such plotting will usually approach a straight line, at least for medium and higher stages. For such plotting, a log-log sheet 10 inches by 15 inches, consisting of three horizontal and two vertical cycles, will be found convenient. In plotting, the gageheight scale should be so selected that zero gage height will refer roughly to zero flow, and this may be accomplished by subtracting from or adding to the gage heights to be plotted a proper correction, usually in even feet. Since, under the best conditions, rating curves will tend to plot on log-log paper as straight lines, it will be possible to make high-water extensions in this manner with considerable confidence, provided, of course, that there is little or no bank overflow or no great change in other control conditions at high stages.

In rare instances and in situations where there is more than one gaging station on the same stream, it may be possible to extend the rating curve for one station by utilizing corresponding discharges at another station either upstream or downstream. This method is not to be recommended except under the most favorable conditions, because it involves many difficulties, such as the correlation of peak stages, with resulting problems related to the time of travel of such peaks, the adjustment of discharges for differences in drainage areas by means of a drainage-area ratio or some modification thereof, and the difficult and uncertain problem of channel storage. In spite of these difficulties, this method, particularly in situations involving bank overflow where other methods are not applicable, may give surprisingly good results, if the contributory conditions are favorable and if it is used with extreme care by an engineer of wide experience in hydrometric work.

In Chapter 8, the determination of peak flows by the slope-area method was discussed. Such determinations, particularly if made under favorable conditions, may be very valuable in providing bases for extensions of rating curves, and they may serve for such purpose either as isolated data or as information that supplements or corroborates data obtained by other methods.

Experienced engineers frequently follow the practice of making the initial and sometimes the only plotting of the results of discharge measurements on log-log paper. Even when such plotting is made for purposes of study only, engineers have found that it is possible to obtain a better-shaped and smoother curve than would be possible without considerable difficulty by direct plotting on rectangular cross-section paper (Figs. 29 and 77). Logarithmic plotting is generally of little value for extremely low stages, and plotting on rectangular cross-section paper must be relied upon. If the gage-height scale has been properly adjusted before plotting on logarithmic paper, there will usually be little curvature except at the lower end, where, because of the narrowing of the channel at low stages, the logarithmic curve will tend to be concave downward, somewhat similar to its shape on rectangular cross-section paper. If the upper end of the curve tends to be concave upward, a restrictive channel effect, perhaps at some distance below the station, is indicated. A logarithmic rating will generally be concave downward at the upper end only when there is bank overflow.

Multiple Rating Curves. In plotting normal rating curves, care should be taken to recognize only those discharge measurements which were made under good conditions, that is, with the control and channel free from ice, aquatic vegetation, or other obstructions which might cause backwater at the gage. At gaging stations where the channels and controls are not entirely stable because of the movement of the materials which form them, shifts in rating may occur several times within a year as a result of ice jams, flood stages, or other reasons. Under such conditions, the station rating will consist not of one curve but of several successive curves. If material is scoured from or deposited on the control more or less uniformly across the stream, the shift will generally be to a rating curve that is roughly parallel, for low and medium stages, to the one that preceded it. By "parallel" it is meant that the two ratings will be separated by a constant or nearly constant gage-height distance. As the conditions which determine the stage-discharge relation at high stages are usually complex, involving many channel features, small shifts in control at low stages may not be apparent at high stages. If the scour or deposition takes place in an irregular manner across the control, a curve of entirely different shape may result, perhaps even crossing the preceding curve. The construction of a series of rating curves under such conditions requires not only the availability of a sufficient number of discharge measurements to define the various shifts with reasonable precision but also a most careful analysis in which all the factors which may have contributed to such shifts are considered and properly evaluated (Fig. 78).

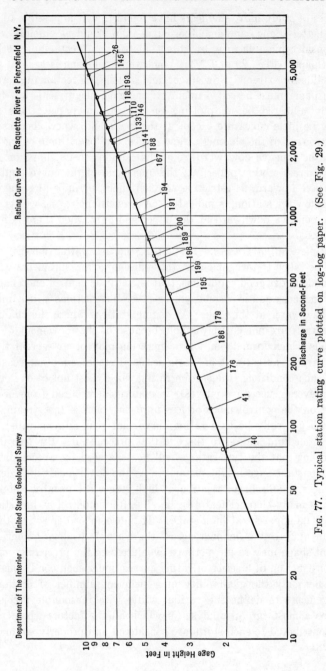

Fig. 77. Typical station rating curve plotted on log-log paper. (See Fig. 29.)

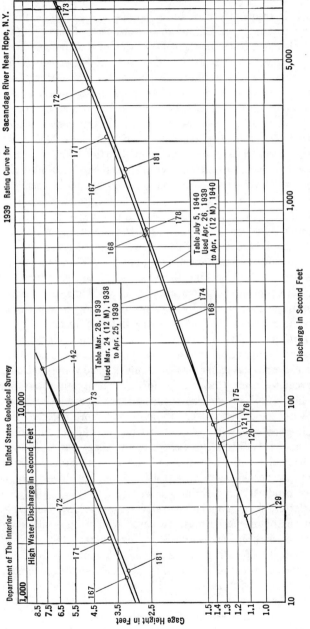

FIG. 78. Station rating curve illustrating shift in stage-discharge relation.

Use of Weir Formula. The well-known basic weir formula $Q = Clh^{3/2}$ is frequently used by engineers, not only as a ready and convenient means of estimating an instantaneous flow over a dam or weir, but also as a basis for the construction of a rating curve or table for use in connection with a continuous record of daily discharge at a gaging station situated within the backwater of such a structure. The value of the coefficient C may be determined by various means, ranging from laboratory experiments on models to pure assumption. The fact that values of C may vary greatly for different heads on the same dam is not always recognized. Gaging stations that are so situated that the control sections consist of dams or weirs should, therefore, be rated in the usual manner by discharge measurements and rating curves developed on the basis of such measurements. Such rating curves may be used with full confidence, which might not always be true if they were based wholly on the theory of similitude. A rating curve based on the results of actual discharge measurements, aside from its inherent reliability and its corresponding value in the determination of a continuous record of daily discharge, is also of value as a means of checking the value of C and showing its range of variation under varying conditions of flow. Thus, a determination of this sort becomes essentially a laboratory study made with a full-sized model and conducted under actual field conditions.

Loop Rating Curves. The above discussions have related to typical rating curves for stations on streams where the gradients are sufficiently steep and the capacities of channels below the stations sufficiently great to insure that, except for occasional shifts, any particular gage height will always indicate one corresponding discharge. On streams with somewhat flatter gradients and more constricted channels, a different situation may obtain and the higher stage-discharge relations may be affected by a condition of exaggerated and variable channel control resulting from rapid rise to peak stages, inadequate capacity in the reaches below the station, or other causes. Such conditions may produce "loop rating curves" (Fig. 79). If the gradients are still flatter, there may be no stable stage-discharge relations, and computations of discharge must be based wholly on a slope method. This situation is discussed elsewhere in this chapter.

Not only will loop rating curves assume different shapes at different gaging stations, because of varying channel conditions and other physical reasons, but also they will vary in shape at each gaging station, as a result of variations in the heights of peak stages and in the rates of rise and recession of the high stages. Whatever the individual shapes may be, all loop rating curves comprise a normal low-

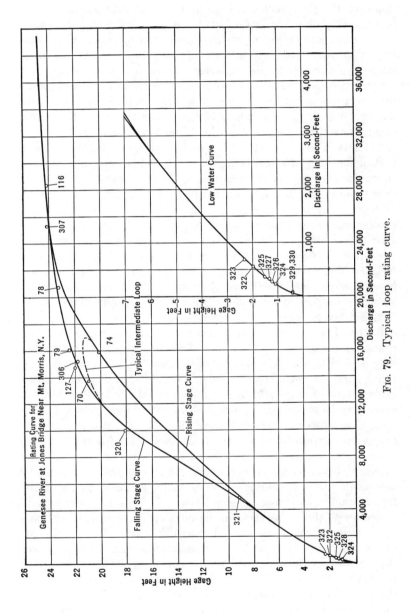

FIG. 79. Typical loop rating curve.

water curve, a rising-stage curve which loops to the left as stages approach the peak, and a falling-stage or backwater curve that lies to the left of the rising-stage curve and joins the normal low-water curve at a more or less constant stage within the range of medium or low stages. Although theoretically any rating curve for rising stages probably should lie somewhat to the right of a rating curve for falling stages, the normal rating curve generally represents a compromise between the two because discharge measurements are made during both rising and falling stages. The normal rating curve should be and generally is near the falling-stage curve, and properly so, because the stages of a river are in recession during a major part of the time. Normal rating curves, therefore, will show one discharge for one gage height, regardless of falling or rising stages. Loop rating curves, on the other hand, will show two different discharges for each stage in the loop range, one discharge on the rise, and a smaller discharge on the recession. Since, at any gaging station characterized by the loop rating, these curves vary as the different peaks vary, it usually is necessary to construct a special loop rating curve for each high peak. Loop rating curves are most characteristic, perhaps, of large southern streams of relatively flat slope, but they may occur in any part of the country, wherever river and channel conditions are favorable.

RATING TABLES. When the station rating curve or curves and their respective periods of use have been decided upon, the station rating may be said to have been completed for those periods. However, the rating curves in themselves provide no convenient means of translating a record of stage into one of discharge. In order that a rating curve may be really usable, it is necessary to convert it into a *rating table* (Fig. 80), which shows for each tenth of a foot or less in gage height the corresponding discharges in second-feet; a third column contains the consecutive differences between discharges, usually for successive tenths of feet in gage height. A rating table is prepared by ascertaining from the rating curve the indicated discharges, generally for each tenth of a foot in gage height. It is usually necessary to "smooth up" the rating table somewhat after these values have been taken from the rating curve, and this is ordinarily done by a study of the differences and second differences, the second differences being the successive differences between the entries in the third column of the table. Theoretically, for a rating curve of ordinary shape, both the first and second differences will tend to increase gradually from the low-water to the high-water end of the rating table, although at high stages many rating curves become nearly tangential in shape, in which situations the second differences approach zero as a limit. It is usually customary to express in a rating table the values of discharge to three significant figures only, although in some instances it may be desirable to show the discharge to four significant figures for a short distance above 1,000 second-feet.

UNITED STATES
DEPARTMENT OF THE INTERIOR
GEOLOGICAL SURVEY
WATER RESOURCES BRANCH

File No. Washington ____
Field ____ 126 ____

Rating table for _____ SACANDAGA RIVER NEAR HOPE, N. Y. _____

_____, from __Apr. 26__, 19 39 , to __Apr. 1(12 noon),__ 19 40

Gauge height	Discharge	Difference	Gauge height	Discharge	Difference	Gauge height	Discharge	Difference	Gauge height	Discharge	Difference	Gauge height	Discharge	Difference
Feet	Sec.-ft.	Sec.-ft.	Feet	Sec.-ft.	Sec.-ft.	Feet	Sec.-ft.	Sec.-ft.	Feet	Sec.-ft.	Sec.-ft.	Feet	Sec.-ft.	Sec.-ft.
1.00			3.00	1,230	130	5.00	5,030	260	7.00	11,600	400	.00		
.10	22	14	.10	1,360	140	.10	5,290	270	.10	12,000	410	.10		
.20	36	16	.20	1,500	140	.20	5,560	280	.20	12,410	420	.20		
.30	52	19	.30	1,640	150	.30	5,840	280	.30	12,830	430	.30		
.40	71	23	.40	1,790	150	.40	6,120	290	.40	13,260	440	.40		
.50	94	28	.50	1,940	160	.50	6,410	300	.50	13,700	450	.50		
.60	122	33	.60	2,100	170	.60	6,710	310	.60	14,150	460	.60		
.70	155	40	.70	2,270	170	.70	7,020	310	.70	14,610	460	.70		
.80	195	45	.80	2,440	180	.80	7,330	320	.80	15,070	470	.80		
.90	240	53	.90	2,620	190	.90	7,650	330	.90	15,540	480	.90		
2.00	293	60	4.00	2,810	190	6.00	7,980	340	8.00	16,020	490	.00		
.10	353	68	.10	3,000	200	.10	8,320	340	.10	16,510	490	.10		
.20	421	75	.20	3,200	210	.20	8,660	350	.20	17,000	500	.20		
.30	496	83	.30	3,410	210	.30	9,010	350	.30	17,500	500	.30		
.40	579	92	.40	3,620	220	.40	9,360	360	.40	18,000		.40		
.50	671	97	.50	3,840	220	.50	9,720	360	.50			.50		
.60	768	102	.60	4,060	230	.60	10,080	370	.60			.60		
.70	870	112	.70	4,290	240	.70	10,450	380	.70			.70		
.80	982	118	.80	4,530	250	.80	10,830	380	.80			.80		
.90	1,100	130	.90	4,780	250	.90	11,210	390	.90			.90		

The above table is not applicable for ice or obstructed channel conditions. It is based on __7__ discharge measurements made during __1939-40 and previous curves__.

_____

and is _____ well defined between ____ 50 ____ second-feet and __18,000__ second-feet. At and above 8.2 feet this table is identical with table dated Mar. 28, 1939.

_____

Computed by __R.O.M.__

Checked by __H.W.F.__

Date __July 5, 1940__

March, 1915

6—7347

FIG. 80. Station rating table. (See corresponding rating curve, Fig. 78.)

The rating table having been tentatively completed and checked, its accuracy should be tested by computing for each discharge measurement its percentage of variation from the rating table. This is done by ascertaining from the rating table the discharge corresponding to the gage height of the measurement. The difference between the discharge obtained from the rating table and the discharge obtained by the measurement, expressed with proper sign, divided by the rating table discharge, will be the percentage, plus or minus, of variation from the rating table. In general, in a group of discharge measurements, plus percentages should tend to balance minus percentages, and frequently a careful study of these variations will indicate slight changes in the shape or position of the rating curve that may well be made before it is accepted as final. Discharge measurements which show minus percentages, particularly if made at times when backwater from ice or aquatic vegetation might be expected, should be closely scrutinized in order to ascertain, if possible, whether they were actually made under normal channel conditions. All discharge measurements which vary from the rating table by as much as 5 per cent should be critically examined in order to determine the reason for such variation, because ordinarily most discharge measurements will plot well within that limit.

In common practice, mean daily gage heights to hundredths of a foot are used in obtaining mean daily discharges. In order to expedite computation, it is usually customary, therefore, to prepare from the rating table a computer's table, which shows the discharge for each hundredth of a foot throughout the range of most commonly occurring stages. Discharges for hundredths of feet are ordinarily obtained by straight-line interpolation between successive values for tenths of feet. This procedure is not mathematically correct, since by this method the rating curve is considered a series of chords. For all except very low stages, however, no appreciable error is introduced by simplifying the work of computation in this manner. For very low stages, the curvature of the rating curve may be relatively so great that it is expedient, if not necessary, to take discharge values for hundredths of a foot directly from the rating curve and to prepare the computer's table on the basis of curvilinear expansion rather than on the basis of straight-line interpolation.

Computing Records of Stage. The station rating curves and tables having been prepared, the next step in computing a record of discharge consists in computing and tabulating mean daily gage heights (or daily mean gage heights, the term preferred by some engineers) for the year or period. For a nonrecording station, the mean daily gage height used is ordinarily the single observation or the mean of the morning and afternoon gage readings, with datum correction applied if necessary. This procedure is reasonably accurate if no material change in stage occurs between successive readings; otherwise, a special procedure, explained below, will be necessary. Ordinarily, the only corrections to be applied to gage heights observed on a nonrecording gage are those indicated by levels. For a recorder station, mean daily gage heights are taken from recorder charts by inspection, or, when there are only minor fluctuations in stage, they are ascertained by averaging the gage-height records for equal portions of the day. After the mean daily gage heights have been determined, any necessary corrections should be applied to them. Such corrections may include the datum correction as shown by the most recent levels run at the station or corrections which originate on the sheet or chart as indicated by observer's or engineers' inspections and which may be due to expansion or contraction of the record paper, to the presence in the well of oil that has escaped from the oil tube, to incorrect setting of the pen or pencil, or perhaps to a lack of agreement between the float-tape gage and the standard reference gage, the reference gage usually being either a hook gage or a staff gage in the well.

Since stage-discharge relations do not generally follow a straight line, the ordinary rating curve being parabolic in shape, it is not accurate to apply mean daily gage heights directly to the rating table to obtain mean daily discharge if the gage-height record for any day shows considerable fluctuation. If the gaging station is situated closely below a hydraulic power plant or on a stream which is otherwise subject to sharp diurnal fluctuations resulting from industrial operations, the methods described above for obtaining mean daily gage heights will not apply because of the curvilinear stage-discharge relations, and the discharge integrator should be used, if one is available. For a station on a stream without artificial regulation and where only normal fluctuations occur, the discharge integrator ordinarily will not be required. For days of considerable natural fluctuation, the discharge is ascertained by taking out mean gage heights for parts of the day, with discharge values from the rating table corresponding to each, and then weighting and combining such partial discharges to obtain the mean discharge for the whole day. The manner in which the day is divided for this purpose will depend upon the amount and rapidity of the fluctuation in gage height.

It is common practice to require that, if a rapid change in stage occurs, the average error introduced in any part of the record caused by ignoring the curvature of the rating curve shall not exceed 1 per cent. Accordingly, it is customary to prepare from the station rating table a curve showing the allowable range of stage at different gage heights to meet this requirement. For days of considerable fluctuation in stage, observed gage heights from nonrecording gages should be plotted on recorder-chart sheets and the points connected smoothly to simulate a continuous gage-height graph. Such graphs having been prepared for critical days or periods, the discharge is obtained, as described for a graph obtained from a water-stage recorder, by averaging the discharges for parts of the day. For nonrecording stations, the curve of allowable range of stage is usually prepared on the basis of a 2 per cent average error, on the theory that a gage-height record based on a nonrecording gage may be expected to be less accurate than one from a water-stage recorder.

Before water-stage recorders came into their present general use, nearly all gaging stations were of the nonrecording type and the application of limits of refinement in gage-height observations on nonrecording gages was common, if not almost universal. These limits were based on the theory that for low stages of the river it was usually possible to read a staff or chain gage accurately to within 0.02 foot, but, as the stage of the river increased, greater turbulence and wave action made accurate gage reading more and more difficult, so that for high stages the gage could not be read within 0.10 foot, or perhaps more, of the true stage. Accordingly, on the basis of the tolerance of an average 2 per cent error, two limiting stages were determined for each rating table, below one of which gage heights were used to hundredths and above the other to the nearest tenth of a foot, gage heights to the nearest half-tenth being used between these two limiting stages. This system is still in fairly general use in connection with records from nonrecording stations.

For a time, varying limits were applied in connection with gage heights obtained by means of water-stage recorders, but it was soon realized that, with properly designed stilling wells, the gage-height record for higher stages presumably was as accurate as for low stages. With such recorders and for ordinary streams, it is now customary to use gage heights to the nearest hundredth of a foot, regardless of stage. In some special investigational work, usually where very small amounts of water are involved, it may occasionally be necessary to express gage heights to the nearest thousandth of a foot. For such work, water-stage recorders with large gage-height ratios, usually 1 : 1 or 1 : 2, are necessary. Occasionally, also, it may be necessary to express gage heights obtained by means of water-stage recorders to the nearest half-hundredth of a foot in order to avoid the rather large errors that would result from the use of hundredths when the streams are at very low stages. Other situations may require special consideration to achieve the accuracy desired or needed in the final records of discharge.

The Discharge Integrator. The discharge integrator, a modification of the rolling planimeter, is an instrument of precision originally designed about 1914 by Edwin S. Fuller, then an assistant engineer with the Geological Survey, and first constructed by him in 1915. Since that time, the instrument has been greatly improved by other Survey

FIG. 81. Discharge integrator set up for operation.

engineers. Its use is confined almost exclusively to the Geological Survey, since all the fifty (more or less) integrators now in use have been constructed or assembled in the Geological Survey shops in Washington. The instrument when built in lots of ten costs from $500 to $700. Its probable use outside the Geological Survey is so limited that its manufacture apparently is not an attractive commercial venture. The purpose of the discharge integrator is to translate mechanically a continuous gage-height graph into a record of mean daily discharge (Fig. 81).

The essential parts of the discharge integrator are:

(1) A stationary rack and a main roller guide mounted on a beveled straightedge, along which the integrator proper is moved when in operation.

(2) A movable frame supported at three points.

(3) A metal disc which is rotated by a drive wheel beneath it when the frame is moved along the guide.

(4) A recording wheel which rests upon and is turned by the rotating disc.

(5) A flexible metal curve carried by a ladder and in contact with the carriage of the recording wheel.

(6) A tracing pointer attached to the ladder which carries the flexible metal curve.

The discharge integrator is applied to the graphical record of stage procured by a water-stage recorder and the mean daily discharge read from the recording wheel. • • • The translation from stage to discharge is effected by means of the flexible metal curve which is a representation of the station rating curve or table.

In operation the instrument is placed upon the recorder chart so that the beveled straightedge is set along the gage height chosen as the base line. Movement of the frame along the guide causes rotation of the disc and recording wheel. If at the same time the tracing pointer attached to the ladder carrying the flexible curve is made to follow the graph on the chart, the recording wheel carriage will be moved across the disc so that the rate of rotation of the recording wheel at any instant will correspond to the rate necessary for the determination of the discharge represented by the gage height at that instant.[4]

The difference between the readings of the recording wheel at the beginning and end of its run over the day's graph of gage height is the mean discharge for the day.

The integrator will give accurate results when it is carefully set and carefully operated. Ordinarily no difficulty is experienced in having successive independent runs check each other within 1 or 2 per cent.

Various relatively simple and inexpensive devices are used to a limited extent to perform the functions of the discharge integrator. Although they apparently operate satisfactorily under favorable conditions, they lack the universal applicability and accuracy of the discharge integrator and are not likely to supplant it, but they may be used in the absence of an integrator in connection with the computation of the mean daily discharge of rapidly fluctuating streams.

Computation of Discharge during Periods of Backwater. It is obvious that ice, aquatic vegetation, or debris in the control section or in the nearby channel may so raise the level of the water at the gage that the station rating curve will no longer indicate the true discharge. A similar condition may exist when the control and lower channel are "drowned out" by backwater from a lake or from a stream that is tributary below the gaging station. In all situations of this kind, backwater corrections must be applied to the recorded mean daily gage heights before the mean daily discharge can be correctly computed. In northern regions, backwater from ice is very common, occurring at many gaging stations every winter. Such backwater may vary in amount from a few hundredths of a foot to many feet when

[4] Bibliog. 15·2.

ice jams occur. Backwater may be caused by weeds and aquatic growth of various kinds in practically all parts of the country but is of especially frequent occurrence in the South.

The computation of discharge during periods of backwater [5] from ice is a difficult procedure in which judgment and experience always play an important part. On most streams, backwater from ice may occur in several ways. It may be temporary, when caused by anchor ice or frazil, or it may be of long duration, often persisting throughout the whole winter, when caused by the formation of heavy surface ice at the control section and in the channel below the gaging station. When breakup occurs at a low stage of the river, the broken ice may jam and cause heavy backwater, the amount and variations of which are most difficult to ascertain. In some extreme situations, the freezing of solid ice or the deposition of slush or broken ice at the control section or in the channel above it may change so completely the distribution of flow at the station gage that a condition of "negative backwater" may actually exist for periods of several days, thus requiring the application of a plus, rather than a minus, correction to the gage-height record.

The simplest method of determining discharge during periods of backwater from ice, and the one on which all other methods are based, consists first in plotting the daily gage-height record for the winter months and, on the same sheet, the mean gage heights of all discharge measurements made during the period, together with the amounts of backwater and the "effective gage heights" indicated by such measurements. The amount of backwater shown by a discharge measurement is determined by subtracting from the mean gage height of the measurement the "effective gage height" corresponding to the measured discharge as determined from the station rating table. If the backwater is small or temporary in nature, the effective gage height for each day can frequently be determined visually on the gage-height record made by the water-stage recorder. The record of maximum and minimum temperatures and of precipitation recorded at a nearby Weather Bureau station is also plotted, usually on a separate sheet.

The next step is the construction of the graph of effective gage heights, using the results of discharge measurements, weather records, notes by the observer, and all other available information. Generally, but not always, the effective gage-height line tends to fall and the backwater to rise during periods of continued frost, that is, when both the maximum and minimum daily temperatures are below 32° F. The

[5] Bibliog. 14·1.

effective gage-height line will tend to rise when the temperatures exceed 32° F., and such rises, if accompanied by rain, may remove either part or all of the accumulated ice, thereby reducing or eliminating the backwater, or may cause ice jams, with accompanying increase in backwater. An interesting phenomenon that occurs frequently in northern latitudes with a sudden and extreme drop in temperature is an almost immediate sharp reduction in discharge resulting from ice formation upstream, accompanied by backwater conditions, and the consequent creation of a large volume of channel storage. When such storage capacity is filled, usually within twenty-four hours or less, there will be a quick rise or "recovery" in the discharge at the gaging station even though the temperatures still remain below freezing. This recovery will be followed by a more or less normal recession as long as the low temperatures continue.

The general procedure, therefore, is to determine, by the means indicated above, either the effective gage height or the amount of backwater for each day throughout the winter (Fig. 82). Frequently, comparisons by gage-height or discharge hydrograph with the records of other stations on the same stream, or even on streams in adjacent drainage basins, will aid in the proper delineation of the effective gage-height graph. The graphs of effective gage heights and of backwater having been determined, the observed daily gage heights, the backwater, and the effective gage heights are tabulated in that order. The mean daily discharges are then determined from the rating table, after which the discharge may or may not be adjusted to 1 per cent or 2 per cent limits in order to round off the final figures.

At many gaging stations, there will be diurnal fluctuations in stream flow as a result of power operations upstream, which will introduce another variable into the computations, since backwater is a function of stage, to some extent at least. Such conditions introduce serious complications which can be evaluated satisfactorily only by having available the results of very frequent measurements of discharge by means of which diagrams may be constructed for the purpose of showing, for approximately constant over-all backwater conditions, the variation in backwater with respect to stage. Under certain conditions, it is quite possible to make the computations in terms of discharge rather than of gage height. Usually, however, the gage-height method is to be preferred because the gage-height record on the recorder chart frequently furnishes many clues in the study of the various elements that enter into the solution of the problem.[6]

[6] Bibliog. 14·1.

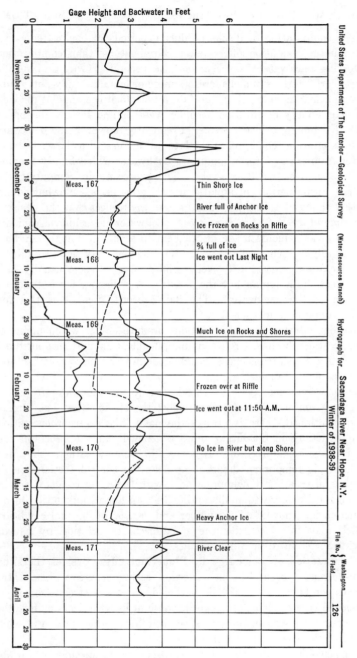

United States Department of The Interior — Geological Survey   (Water Resources Branch)   Hydrograph for   Sacandaga River Near Hope, N.Y.   Winter of 1938-39   File No. { Washington   { Field   126

Gage Height and Backwater in Feet

Meas. 167   Thin Shore Ice

River full of Anchor Ice

Ice Frozen on Rocks on Riffle

¾ full of Ice

Meas. 168   Ice went out Last Night

Meas. 169   Much Ice on Rocks and Shores

Frozen over at Riffle

Ice went out at 11:50 A.M.

Meas. 170   No Ice in River but along Shore

Heavy Anchor Ice

Meas. 171   River Clear

FIG. 82. Winter hydrograph, showing recorded mean daily gage heights, backwater, and effective mean daily gage heights.

The computation of discharge during periods of backwater caused by aquatic vegetation offers fewer complications than computations involving backwater from ice, because vegetal growth that usually starts early in the summer increases more or less uniformly and gradually to a maximum early in the fall, after which the amount of backwater gradually declines with colder weather and largely disappears with the coming of heavy frosts. Frequently, however, the backwater from vegetation remaining in the late fall merges with the early backwater from ice to form a composite backwater which finally becomes backwater from ice exclusively. The procedure in computing discharge during periods of aquatic vegetal growths is somewhat similar to that followed during periods of ice, in the respect that the basis for the computations is the amount of backwater determined from discharge measurements made at frequent intervals during the summer. The results of such discharge measurements generally serve to indicate the backwater curve fairly well. Sharp rises in stage usually have the effect of flattening out the weeds and reducing, for a time, the amount of the backwater. The daily record of stage is therefore highly important in such a study.

Various other abnormal conditions produce effects which make the normal stage-discharge relation inapplicable. In northern latitudes, log jams and fish traps cause variable backwater, and various methods must be devised in each instance to ascertain the discharge while such abnormal conditions persist. In addition to the backwater from high lake or tributary stream stages below the station that has already been mentioned, there is always the possibility at recorder stations of obstructions in the intake pipes which will cause appreciable lags in the gage-height records. If a river is used by bathers, they may build crude temporary dams at or near the control section for the purpose of creating a swimming pool, with the usual result of accomplishing little more than disrupting the station rating until the obstruction is removed. The number and variety of unusual conditions which may interfere with the stage-discharge relation by causing backwater seem to be almost endless.

Computation of Discharge by Slope Methods. Besides the situations already discussed where normal rating curves or loop rating curves for high stages will be obtained, there are streams on which the slope is variable at all stages because of low gradients or for other reasons. Such streams present special problems, the solution of which requires the use of special methods.

In general, the determination of discharge on streams of variable slope requires two continuous gage-height records, referred to the same datum, obtained with clocks showing the same time at two stations a known distance apart. The difference in gage height shown at any instant by these two records is the fall in the reach, and that fall divided by the length of the reach is the slope at that instant. For the conversion of a record of stage in this reach into a record of discharge, frequent discharge measurements made at different stages and slopes and referred to both gages are required. Although the discharge is a function of the slope, it is not a direct function, and a large variety of methods of utilizing the base data have been devised and used to obtain continuous records of discharge in particular situations. Three methods outlined below have been selected from this variety as reasonably typical. These methods are relatively simple and easily applied. For a more detailed presentation of this topic, reference should be made to "Stream Gaging Procedure," [7] in which M. C. Boyer has published an elaborate discussion of many aspects of the problems related to the determination of discharge, some of which are complex, that are created by variable slopes.

Square-Root-of-Fall Method. The basis of the square-root-of-fall method rests on the theory that the velocity of current is proportional to the square root of the fall. Since the length of the reach in which the fall is measured is constant, it is not essential to the computations involved in the method. The office procedure is about as follows:

1. List all discharge measurements showing discharge, mean gage heights at both upper and lower gages, the fall f in the reach, the square root of the fall, and the discharge divided by the square root of the fall.

2. Plot the values of discharge divided by the square root of the fall against the stage, preferably at the upper gage, although the stage at the lower gage or the average stage at the two gages may sometimes be used.

3. Draw a smooth curve through these points and compute a stage -$Q/\sqrt{f}$ table similar to the stage-discharge table used under normal stage-discharge conditions.

4. Compute mean daily gage heights at both gages, interpolating where necessary to obtain the required degree of accuracy. It is not customary to allow for the time of flow between the two gages.

5. List data on computation forms under the following headings:

    (a) Mean gage height at upper gage.
    (b) Mean gage height at lower gage.
    (c) Fall, or difference between the gage heights at the two gages.

[7] Bibliog. 14·5.

(d) Square root of fall.

(e) $Q/\sqrt{f}$ from curve, based on stage at upper gage.

(f) Value in column (e) multiplied by value in column (d). The product is the actual discharge.

6. List stages at one gage (preferably the upper) on a form similar to Geological Survey Form 9-192-a, and values from column (f) in the discharge column. Values of fall for the day may or may not be listed between the gage-height and discharge columns. If fall for the day is listed, a three-column form, similar to Geological Survey Form 9-192-b, should be used.

Routine adjustments for channel storage or for changing stage will, at times, be necessary. Corrections for backwater from ice, if required, may be made in several ways, such as corrections to the computed fall by use of temporary $Q/\sqrt{f}$ curves if the backwater effect is fairly stable.

Stage-Ratio Method. List all available discharge measurements, showing discharge and mean gage heights at both upper and lower gages at time of measurement. The results of these discharge measurements are then plotted on cross-section paper, using in this method gage heights at the lower gage.

A trial curve is then drawn somewhat to the right of all the points and usually farther to the right at the lower end than at the upper end of the curve but following their general trend. New gage heights for the measurements, called "effective gage heights," are then picked from this curve at points where vertical lines dropped from the plotted points intersect the trial curve.

The following ratios are then computed, of which (a) is a variable and (b) a constant:

(a) $\dfrac{\text{Effective gage height for measurement}}{\text{Observed gage height of measurement}}$ (Called "ratio E")

(b) $\dfrac{\text{Observed gage height for measurement at lower gage}}{\text{Observed gage height for measurement at upper gage}}$ = Stage ratio

(It should be noted that in this method it is not necessary that both gages be set to the same datum. If readings at the upper gage are numerically lower than those at the lower gage, an arbitrary amount should be added to the stages recorded by the upper gage or subtracted from those recorded by the lower gage. The approximate fall in the reach can serve as a general rule or guide in the selection of this amount.)

Values of stage ratio and of ratio E for each discharge measurement are then plotted respectively as ordinates and abscissas in the lower right corner of the rating curve form. The first trial plotting usually results in considerable scatter, but a trial curve (called the stage-ratio curve) is drawn through the points. New values of ratio E are taken from the trial stage-ratio curve where horizontal lines from the plotted points intersect the curve, and from these new values of ratio E new effective gage heights are computed for the discharge measurements by multiplying observed gage heights by ratio E.

The discharge measurements are now replotted, using the new effective gage heights and measured discharges, and a second trial curve is drawn, again slightly to the right of the plotted points. This entire procedure is repeated, several times if necessary, until a stage-ratio curve of such shape is obtained that the effective gage heights ascertained by means of it will cause the discharge measurements to plot on a smooth curve, similar to an ordinary rating curve except that the ordinates are effective gage heights rather than observed gage heights. The percentages by which the discharge measurements vary from this curve (or from the rating table deduced from it) may be computed in the usual manner.

Daily discharge values are computed on a suitable form. The first two columns of this form show the mean daily gage heights at the upper and lower gages, respectively; the third column, the stage ratio; the fourth, ratio E; the fifth, effective gage heights from curve or table; the sixth, discharge from the "effective" rating table. Where there is considerable daily range in stage it may be necessary to proceed on the basis of shorter intervals of time in order to keep within allowable limits of accuracy.

Backwater corrections for ice may be handled in several different ways in connection with this method. One way is to use a smaller value of ratio E than that shown by the open-water curve. Another is to correct values from a discharge hydrograph and discharge measurements based on open-water rating values.

Gage heights and discharge values are listed in the usual manner on an appropriate form similar to Geological Survey Form 9-192-a. Daily values for the fall in the reach may be listed if desired, on a three-column form.

Chezy Formula. The earliest formula for the flow in open channels was suggested by Chezy in 1775. This formula, which is usually written $v = c\sqrt{rs}$, is sometimes utilized in determining the discharge at gaging stations on small canals of variable slope where the flow is reasonably uniform but where because of the effect of vegetal

9-199-a. July 1927

Daily Gage Height, in Feet, and Discharge, in Second-Feet, of ....SACANDAGA........ River

Near ....HOPE, N. Y........ for the Year Ending September 30, 19.39.

Drainage Area ....491.... Square Miles. Water-Stage Recorder ...An 7-day... Ratio ..1.. : ..12..

Day	October		November		December		January		February		March	
	Gage height	Discharge	Gage height	Discharge	Gage height	Discharge	Gage height	Discharge	Gage height	Discharge	Gage height	Discharge
1	2.82	890	2.33	472	2.51	608	2.69	420	3.45	300	3.39	1,550
2	2.71	784	2.28	437	2.37	500	2.73	400	3.66	280	3.29	1,420
3	2.62	703	2.23	404	2.36	493	2.76	380	3.60	380	3.19	1,200
4	2.54	634	2.19	379	a/	934	2.96	360	3.41	260	3.10	1,100
5	2.47	577	2.20	385	a/	1,720	3.17	340	3.49	260	3.04	1,120
6	2.40	522	2.34	479	a/	6,830	3.17	500	3.57	260	3.24	1,360
7	2.33	472	2.39	515	a/	4,370	2.61	694	3.48	240	3.42	1,590
8	2.28	437	2.36	493	4.31	3,090	2.59	676	3.40	240	3.29	1,400
9	2.24	411	2.32	464	4.10	2,690	2.51	608	3.18	240	3.22	1,100
10	2.21	392	2.29	444	a/	4,860	2.53	626	3.21	240	3.12	1,100
11	2.17	367	2.25	418	a/	4,780	2.85	920	3.26	240	2.97	900
12	2.14	350	2.22	398	4.43	3,330	2.81	880	3.30	220	2.95	800
13	2.11	332	a/	452	4.07	2,640	2.69	766	3.21	220	2.88	750
14	2.09	321	2.78	851	3.78	2,130	2.68	757	3.14	220	2.80	700
15	2.08	315	2.74	813	3.34	1,480	2.58	668	3.31	280	2.72	650
16	2.05	300	2.64	721	3.22	1,330	2.61	650	4.13	750	2.69	600
17	2.02	284	2.60	685	3.19	1,300	2.66	600	4.44	1,000	2.64	550
18	2.00	273	2.58	668	3.14	1,240	2.68	550	4.51	1,100	2.57	500
19	1.98	264	a/	1,500	3.03	1,110	2.72	500	4.41	1,000	2.52	500
20	1.96	254	3.60	1,850	2.89	960	2.72	480	4.66	1,300	2.51	460
21	1.97	259	3.33	1,470	2.78	851	2.70	460	4.58	2,000	2.49	440
22	1.97	259	3.15	1,250	2.73	804	2.73	440	3.61	1,860	2.45	420
23	1.95	250	3.10	1,190	2.54	634	2.65	420	3.42	1,590	2.42	400
24	a/	593	2.99	1,070	2.65	700	2.69	400	3.31	1,440	2.42	400
25	3.35	1,500	2.78	851	2.60	650	2.81	380	3.23	1,350	2.59	400
26	3.06	1,150	2.67	748	2.46	500	2.81	360	3.20	1,310	a/	1,100
27	2.87	940	2.70	775	2.52	550	2.97	340	3.48	1,670	a/	3,000
28	2.73	804	2.63	712	2.44	500	3.21	340	3.46	1,640	4.56	3,600
29	2.60	685	2.60	685	2.40	480	3.19	320	-	--	4.15	2,780
30	2.49	592	2.59	676	2.52	460	3.17	320			3.94	2,400
31	2.40	522			2.58	440	3.28	300			3.97	2,460

		October	November	December	January	February	March
388,774	Total	16,436	22,255	52,964	15,855	21,790	36,850
1,065	Mean	530	742	1,709	511	778	1,189
2.17	Second-feet per square mile	1.08	1.51	3.48	1.04	1.58	2.42
29.44	Run-off in inches	1.24	1.68	4.01	1.20	1.64	2.79
	Run-off in acre-feet						
14,100	Maximum	1,500	1,850	6,830	920	2,000	3,600
73	Minimum	250	379	440	300	220	400

Calendar Year 1938

Left margin notes:

Backwater present from ice Jan.

(G. H. 7.13 ft). Max. G.H. 7.46 ft at noon on Feb. 21

(G. H. 3.25 ft). Min. G. H. _____ ft. on

Sec.-ft. at 11:30 on Apr. 25 — p.m.

Sec.-ft. on Sept. 25, 26

Note.— Discharge, Dec. 24–Jan. 6, Jan. 16–Feb. 21, Mar. 3, 4, 8.25, determined from gage heights corrected for ice effect. a/ Discharge averaged for intervals of day.

Max. Disch. 11,700

Min. Disch. 44

Fig. 83. Completed daily record of gage height and discharge for climato-

UNITED STATES
DEPARTMENT OF THE INTERIOR
GEOLOGICAL SURVEY
WATER RESOURCES BRANCH

File Number { Washington ....
District 126

Used rating table dated Mar.28,1939(Oct.1-Apr.28)
July 5,1940(Apr.28-Sept.30)

Gage heights used to hundredths throughout.

Gage ▮▮▮▮ inspected Once a Day by C. H. Parker

Day	April Gage height	April Discharge	May Gage height	May Discharge	June Gage height	June Discharge	July Gage height	July Discharge	August Gage height	August Discharge	September Gage height	September Discharge	Day	Year
1	3.88	2,300	5.24	5,670	2.90	1,100	2.34	529	1.61	125	1.51	97	1	
2	4.15	2,780	4.99	5,000	2.73	904	2.17	401	1.55	108	1.48	89	2	
3	3.96	2,440	4.73	4,360	2.57	739	2.06	329	1.52	100	1.45	82	3	
4	3.74	2,060	4.60	4,060	2.48	653	1.98	282	1.70	155	1.43	78	4	
5	3.58	1,820	4.49	3,820	2.37	554	1.94	261	1.95	266	1.42	76	5	
6	3.50	1,700	4.40	3,620	2.28	481	1.91	245	1.81	200	1.40	71	6	
7	3.46	1,640	4.30	3,410	2.18	407	1.89	236	1.69	152	1.38	67	7	
8	3.34	1,480	4.12	3,040	1.97	277	1.86	222	1.62	129	a/	98	8	
9	3.27	1,390	3.94	2,700	1.82	204	1.83	208	1.60	122	1.71	159	9	
10	3.16	1,260	3.89	2,600	1.80	195	1.77	183	1.59	119	1.64	135	10	
11	3.20	1,310	3.68	2,240	1.92	251	1.72	163	1.54	105	1.62	129	11	
12	3.32	1,460	3.50	1,940	2.02	305	1.69	152	1.50	94	1.60	122	12	
13	3.26	1,380	3.33	1,680	2.05	323	1.65	138	a/	108	1.54	105	13	
14	3.29	1,430	3.19	1,490	a/	569	1.69	152	1.86	222	1.50	94	14	
15	3.42	1,590	3.06	1,310	2.38	562	1.71	159	1.80	195	1.46	85	15	
16	3.43	1,600	2.94	1,150	2.29	488	1.69	152	1.73	167	1.43	78	16	
17	3.51	1,720	2.83	1,020	a/	1,030	1.64	135	1.66	142	1.40	71	17	
18	3.98	2,470	2.74	915	a/	1,110	1.61	125	1.61	125	1.37	65	18	
19	4.40	3,270	2.65	819	2.58	749	1.58	116	1.57	114	1.34	60	19	
20	4.82	4,180	2.58	749	2.41	588	1.56	111	1.61	135	1.33	58	20	
21	a/	3,930	2.55	720	2.30	496	1.53	102	1.63	132	1.33	58	21	
22	6.04	7,620	2.62	788	2.16	394	1.51	97	1.57	114	1.32	56	22	
23	5.77	6,770	2.84	1,030	a/	454	1.50	94	1.54	105	1.31	54	23	
24	5.33	5,460	2.85	1,040	2.43	607	1.47	87	a/	140	1.27	47	24	
25	a/	7,410	2.74	915	2.27	474	1.46	85	1.89	236	1.26	46	25	
26	6.70	10,400	2.63	799	2.17	401	1.43	78	1.78	187	1.26	46	26	
27	6.53	9,830	2.57	739	2.09	347	a/	83	1.73	167	1.30	52	27	
28	6.49	9,680	a/	1,120	a/	293	1.64	135	1.69	152	1.37	65	28	
29	5.97	7,880	3.51	1,960	1.97	277	1.51	97	1.64	135	1.38	67	29	
30	5.59	6,680	3.25	1,570	a/	433	1.51	97	1.59	119	1.41	73	30	
31			3.08	1,330			1.61	125	1.54	105			31	
		114,930		63,604		15,665		5,379		4,465		2,383		372,576
		3,831		2,052		522		174		144		79.4		1,021
		7.80		4.18		1.06		.354		.293		.162		2.08
		8.70		4.82		1.18		.41		.34		.18		28.19
		10,400		5,670		1,110		529		266		159		10,400
		1,260		720		195		78		94		46		46

logical year, on Geological Survey Form 9-192-a.   (See Figs. 84, 85, 86, 87.)

growth or for other reasons the value of c is variable. Two water-stage recorders installed at the ends of a reach are set to the same datum. Discharge measurements are made at frequent intervals at some cross section within the reach, at which section values of A, the cross-sectional area, and r, the hydraulic radius, are computed for all stages, s being used as the fall, instead of the slope, between the ends of the reach as determined from the difference between the two gage-height records. Since Q equals Av, all the factors in the Chezy formula are known from the results of the discharge measurement, except c, which can be computed. At the end of the year or season, values of c determined from the different discharge measurements are plotted with respect to time, and a smooth curve is drawn through the plotted points. From this curve the value of c is known for each day of record, and the mean daily discharge may be computed by substituting in the formula the various quantities for that day.

The different methods of computation of discharge from observations of slope which may be made to fit particular situations are of almost endless variety; the above examples are given merely to show typical methods which may be suited to certain conditions. Other methods may be devised to fit other conditions.

Completion of Discharge Record. The final step in the conversion of a gage-height record into a record of mean daily discharge consists of the tabulation, on an appropriate form, similar to Geological Survey Form 9-192-a (Fig. 83), in parallel columns by months, of the mean daily gage heights and the discharges corresponding to them. The mean daily gage heights, which have already been computed and recorded either in the observer's quarterly books or on the weekly recorder charts or continuous record sheets, are transferred to this form. Discharges for those days for which the figures were obtained by means of the integrator or by averaging discharges for parts of the day are entered in the discharge column, but no entry is made in the gage-height column under these circumstances. Values of mean daily discharge corresponding to the recorded mean daily gage heights are ascertained from the computer's table and entered in the discharge column, using three significant figures, except for discharges below 100 second-feet, for which two significant figures are ordinarily used. This practice with respect to significant figures has been followed by the Geological Survey for many years, since it has been considered that in general the quality and accuracy of the basic data seldom warrant greater refinement. The figures of mean daily gage height and discharge having been tabulated, both the copying of the gage heights from the original records and the discharge quantities taken from the computer's table are carefully checked, after which the discharge values are listed on a special form, using a standard adding machine. This listing fulfills the dual purpose of providing monthly totals of the discharge figures and by the same operation a copy of the year's discharge record which may later serve, if desired, as the printer's copy if the record is published.

The values ordinarily appearing in the monthly summary of mean daily discharge include the monthly mean, which is usually expressed to four significant figures, on the theory that the relative accuracy of the monthly mean is considerably greater than that of any of the individual daily figures in the month's record. If the drainage area above the gaging station is known, a value for discharge in second-feet per square mile is computed from the monthly mean, followed by an entry of equivalent inches in depth on the drainage area as runoff. In the eastern part of the country, runoff, or quantity, is generally expressed either in inches in depth on the drainage area, millions of gallons, or billions of cubic feet. The unit, inches in depth on the drainage area, is valuable for comparing the runoff from drainage basins of different sizes; millions of gallons is used to a considerable extent in connection with municipal water supplies, and billions of cubic feet is a large unit for indicating the contents of storage reservoirs. In the West, runoff is almost invariably expressed in terms of acre-feet, a unit which is well adapted to irrigation practice. Maximum and minimum daily discharges are listed for each month. The computation of the summary figures for each month having been completed, similar figures for the year's record are computed. After the monthly and yearly summaries have been checked, the record itself is complete.

For statistical purposes, it is customary to determine from the record made by the water-stage recorder, and subsequently to publish, both the maximum and minimum instantaneous stages, with corresponding discharge values. Information concerning maximum instantaneous stages may be of greater value than that relating to maximum instantaneous discharges because of the importance of such information in studies related to overflow and submergence as well as to flood control and flood prevention. Maximum stages may not necessarily be accompanied by maximum discharges, because such stages are frequently caused by backwater from ice. On the other hand, information relating to minimum instantaneous discharges may be of greater general interest than that related to the corresponding stages because of the frequent great importance of low flows in connection with municipal supplies and irrigation water.

In an ideal situation, a complete gage-height record is available throughout the year, and it is converted to a record of discharge by means of a rating table representing a stage-discharge relation that is stable except perhaps as it may be affected for certain periods by backwater from ice, aquatic vegetation, or debris. In practice, however, such a situation is the exception rather than the rule. Gage-height records obtained from a nonrecording gage may be interrupted by the failure of the observer to read the gage or may be defective by his reporting inaccurate readings. If a water-stage recorder is used, the instrument may fail to function during periods of varying length, the intake pipe may become wholly or partially obstructed, ice in the well may render the float inoperative, and record sheets may be lost in the mail. Because of these or other reasons, the gage-height record may be broken or defective. In many situations, too, the stage-discharge relation may pass through periods of such instability that it may not be possible to express adequately, even with several rating curves, all the changes which may have taken place.

If the gage-height record is missing, or so faulty or doubtful as to make its use inadvisable, it will be necessary to make estimates of gage height or discharge for periods of varying length in order to complete the discharge record for the year. In making such estimates, many methods and devices are employed, a few of which are cited below.

If only a few days of gage-height record are missing when the stage of the stream is changing in a uniform manner, as on a regular recession, mean daily gage heights may be estimated from a connecting straight-line stage hydrograph and corresponding values of discharge obtained. This method is practically an interpolation.

Water-stage recorders, even when not in operation because of clock stoppage, will generally record the extreme range in stage as a vertical "range line." By using corresponding water-stage recorder records from other gaging stations, together with the range in stage so recorded, it will frequently be possible to sketch on the recorder graph sheet an estimated gage-height graph from which estimated daily discharges can be computed with considerable assurance. Flood marks may sometimes be similarly utilized both at recording and nonrecording stations, if no other records during the period are available.

When the periods of missing records are longer, it may be possible to make estimates of daily discharge by comparison with records of discharge from a station or stations either on the same stream or on a stream in an adjacent drainage basin, assuming, of course, that there were no great differences in precipitation at the different stations. In such situations, periods of parallel record before and after the missing periods are compared and daily discharge ratios ascertained. These ratios generally follow a definite pattern and so may be extended through the period of missing record and estimates of discharge deduced therefrom.

On streams which have been developed for hydroelectric power, it may be possible to estimate daily discharge from a plant record of daily kilowatt output. If such data can be obtained for considerable periods before and after the period of missing record, kilowatt output and recorded discharge may be compared either by curves or by coefficients which will enable fair estimates of discharge during the missing period to be made, provided that there was no wastage of water at the hydroelectric plant during the period or that the amount of such wastage was known.

In situations where no facilities of any kind are available for comparative purposes, recourse must be had to whatever precipitation records, crude though they may be, are available or can be obtained. In the summer, when violent thunderstorms may occur at irregular intervals and over limited areas, little reliance can be placed on estimates of discharge based on precipitation records alone.

It is evident that much office time may be spent in attempting to estimate values of mean daily discharge during periods when the gage-height record was either faulty or missing, with results varying in quality from excellent to very poor, or worse. Obviously, therefore, much time and money may be saved and the value of the discharge records enhanced by insuring that the breaks that occur in the gage-height record may be of as short duration as possible, even though special visits to the gaging stations may be required to keep water-stage recorders in operation, intake pipes open, and the observers attending properly to their duties. The cost of such efforts will be more than offset by the resulting improved quality of the records. Estimated records are in general only a poor makeshift and inspire little confidence among engineers and others who may have occasion to use them.

Although shifts or changes in the stage-discharge relation occur occasionally at many stations and frequently at some stations, such shifts do not always take place in an orderly manner and at a definite time, but on most streams they usually occur at times of high stages or as the result of the scouring action of heavy ice. However, where the control section consists of naturally impermanent material, or because of some temporary condition, the stage-discharge relation may change progressively, usually between periods of greater or less length when it is relatively stable. In such situations, discharge is customarily ascertained by the "shifting-control method" or the so-called indirect method for shifting control. The proper use of this method requires that frequent discharge measurements be made during the period of instability in much the same manner as during periods of backwater from ice or other cause since any condition of backwater is quite analogous to one of shifting control. Such discharge measurements will show, on the basis of the rating table which was in use prior to the period of instability, departures from that rating table by either plus or minus amounts of gage height until such time as a stable stage-discharge relation is again reached, when a new rating table may become applicable. Based on the results of these discharge measurements, and, if possible, through the auxiliary aid of a discharge hydrograph for a nearby station, appropriate shift corrections may be calculated which when applied to the observed mean daily gage heights will give correct daily discharges. These shift corrections are usually shown on a form corresponding to Geological Survey Form 9-192-a or Form 9-192-b in an auxiliary column between the columns of gage height and discharge.

The shifting-control method is sometimes used for a few days to effect a smooth transition between different rating tables at times when changes in the stage-discharge relation are known to have taken place, on the theory that such changes or shifts do not take place instantaneously. Of course, such transitions will be unnecessary if the two rating tables show substantially the same discharge for the gage height at the time of shift.

Reference was made above to the drainage area above the gaging station, and this area is measured for each gaging station if possible. Drainage areas can be most accurately and reliably determined from standard Geological Survey topographic maps, scale 1 : 62,500, or approximately 1 inch to the mile. Most of the eastern states have been mapped fairly completely, so that frequently it is possible to outline complete drainage areas on these maps and to measure the areas so outlined by means of a planimeter. The great majority of the other states have been mapped only in a fragmentary way so that recourse must be had, if a determination of drainage area is desired, to whatever maps may be available. Needless to say, determinations of drainage area on maps other than the standard topographic sheets leave much to be desired from the standpoint of accuracy.

Intercomparison of Records for Different Stations. After tne discharge computations have been completed, or frequently during the process of computation, it is customary to plot a daily discharge hydrograph for the year of record. Such a hydrograph is useful in helping to detect gross errors in discharge which have previously been unnoticed. It is valuable also for comparative purposes in connection with similar hydrographs for records from other stations either on the same stream or on streams in adjacent drainage basins. Several daily discharge hydrographs may be plotted in contrasting colors on the same sheet with or without individual discharge scales, or they may be plotted on separate sheets and compared on a "light table." Hydrographs for stations on the same stream will usually bear a close resemblance to each other, and those for stations on other streams in the same general region will usually show at least a general resemblance (Fig. 84). Aside from its use in connection with the making of estimates of daily discharge for periods of no gage-height record, this relationship may be utilized in verifying the computed discharge record during periods of backwater from ice or other cause. It is common practice at present to plot these daily discharge hydrographs on semilog paper with three vertical cycles, since logarithmic scale plotting provides a distortion of the record which is most helpful in studying the hydograph and in drawing conclusions therefrom.

The evidence obtained by a comparative study of hydrographs is important in verifying the consistency of the respective daily discharge records. Hydrographs, however, though generally indicating similarity of form, provide less reliable information with respect to relative magnitudes. Because of this fact, it is customary, whenever there are several stations in various parts of a drainage basin, to make a critical study of at least the monthly and yearly figures on the basis of both the total and the unit discharge from intervening areas. For instance, when there are two stations on a stream, mean monthly discharge values for the intervening area may be obtained by subtraction and from them unit discharge figures in second-feet per square mile determined. If these figures of unit discharge for the intervening area are consistent with the corresponding figures for the upper and lower stations, a good check on the accuracy of both records is afforded. In making such studies, which, in situations involving large river systems, may be complex and involved, due allowance must be made for, and consideration given to, the possible effects of storage and diversion if either occurs within the basin. However, it should be recognized that in this process the errors in the figures for the upper and lower stations are carried to the smaller figures of the difference; that if such errors are of the same sign, and if the difference is not relatively small, the percentage error in the difference will not be great; but that

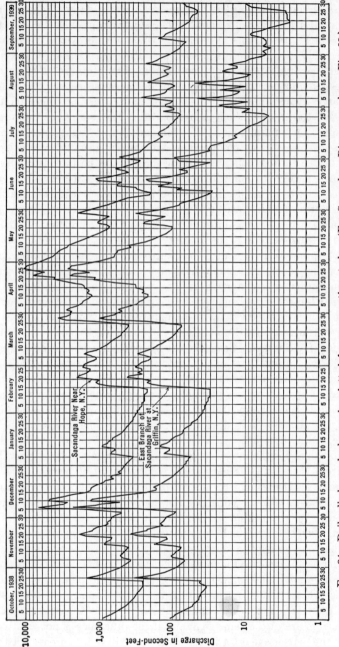

FIG. 84. Daily discharge hydrographs plotted for comparative study. (For Sacandaga River record, see Fig. 83.)

if such errors are of opposite sign, even though small when applied to the figures to which they properly pertain, they may be large when applied to the smaller figures of the difference. For example, a 1 per cent error in Q, the lower record, and a 1 per cent error of the opposite sign in $\frac{3}{4}Q$, the upper record, may cause a 7 per cent error in the difference; if the original errors are 2 per cent, the error in the difference will be 14 per cent; if 3 per cent, the error will be 21 per cent of the difference. Any study or determination in which consistency of differences becomes a criterion of evaluation may appear to indicate surprising inaccuracies even among excellent basic figures.

In the humid regions of the country, except in very dry periods, river discharge will generally increase from the source to the mouth, while the unit discharge in second-feet per square mile will decrease. Since there is generally more than sufficient tributary inflow to balance the losses arising from evaporation, transpiration, and infiltration, the study of discharge and runoff from intervening areas is given added significance. Stream-flow records are data that will be used for many years to come, and important court decisions may be based upon them. It is therefore highly important that, even after such records have been carefully checked, every possible test should be applied to them in order to provide assurance of their consistency with respect to similar records at different points on the same stream or on streams in adjacent drainage basins.

Publication of Records. A majority of the systematic stream-flow records collected in the continental United States represent the work of the Geological Survey; these records are now published annually in fourteen parts, each part covering an area whose boundaries coincide with natural drainage features, as indicated below:

PART
1. North Atlantic slope basins (St. John River to York River).
2. South Atlantic Slope and eastern Gulf of Mexico basins (James River to Mississippi River).
3. Ohio River Basin.
4. St. Lawrence River Basin.
5. Hudson Bay and upper Mississippi River Basins.
6. Missouri River Basin.
7. Lower Mississippi River Basin.
8. Western Gulf of Mexico basins.
9. Colorado River Basin.
10. The Great Basin.
11. Pacific slope basins in California.
12. Pacific slope basins in Washington and upper Columbia River Basin.
13. Snake River Basin.
14. Pacific slope basins in Oregon and lower Columbia River Basin.

Sacandaga River near Hope, N. Y.

Location.- Water-stage recorder, lat. 43°21'10", long. 74°16'15", 1¼ miles downstream from confluence of East and West Branches and 4¼ miles upstream from Hope, Hamilton County.

Drainage area.- 491 square miles.

Records available.- September 1911 to September 1939.

Average discharge.- 28 years, 1,122 second-feet.

Extremes.- Maximum discharge during year, 11,700 second-feet Apr. 25; maximum gage height, 7.46 feet Feb. 21 (ice jam); minimum discharge, 44 second-feet Sept. 25, 26 (gage height, 1.25 feet).

1911-39: Maximum discharge, 32,000 second-feet Mar. 27, 1913 (gage height, 11.0 feet, from floodmarks); minimum, about 16 second-feet Sept. 30, 1913 (gage height, 1.17 feet).

Remarks.- Records excellent except those for periods of ice effect, Dec. 24 to Jan. 6, Jan. 16 to Feb. 21, Mar. 3, 4, 8-15, which were computed on basis of five discharge measurements, gage heights, observer's and engineers' notes, and weather records and are good. Occasional diurnal fluctuation caused by operation of small dams.

Rating tables, water year 1938-39 except periods of ice effect (gage height, in feet, and discharge, in second-feet)

Oct. 1 to Apr. 25				Apr. 26 to Sept. 30					
1.8	185	3.5	1,700	1.2	36	1.7	155	2.4	579	4.9	4,780
2.0	273	4.0	2,510	1.3	52	1.8	195	2.7	870	5.8	7,330
2.2	385	4.5	3,470	1.4	71	1.9	240	3.0	1,230	6.7	10,450
2.4	522	5.0	4,600	1.5	94	2.0	293	3.5	1,940		
2.7	775	5.5	5,950	1.6	122	2.2	421	4.1	3,000		
3.0	1,080	6.1	7,820								

Discharge, in second-feet, water year October 1938 to September 1939

Day	Oct.	Nov.	Dec.	Jan.	Feb.	Mar.	Apr.	May	June	July	Aug.	Sept.
1	890	472	608	420	300	1,550	2,300	5,670	1,100	529	125	97
2	784	437	500	400	280	1,420	2,780	5,000	904	401	108	89
3	703	404	493	380	280	1,200	2,440	4,360	739	329	100	82
4	634	379	934	360	260	1,100	2,060	4,060	653	282	155	78
5	577	385	1,720	340	260	1,120	1,820	3,820	554	261	266	76
6	522	479	6,830	500	260	1,360	1,700	3,620	481	245	200	71
7	472	515	4,370	694	240	1,590	1,640	3,410	407	236	152	67
8	437	493	3,090	676	240	1,400	1,480	3,040	277	222	129	98
9	411	464	2,690	608	240	1,100	1,390	2,700	204	208	122	159
10	392	444	4,860	626	240	1,000	1,260	2,600	195	183	119	135
11	367	418	4,780	920	240	900	1,310	2,240	251	163	105	129
12	350	398	3,330	880	220	800	1,460	1,940	305	152	94	122
13	332	452	2,640	766	220	750	1,380	1,680	325	138	108	105
14	321	851	2,130	757	220	700	1,420	1,490	569	152	222	94
15	315	813	1,480	668	280	650	1,590	1,310	562	159	195	85
16	300	721	1,330	650	750	600	1,600	1,150	488	152	167	78
17	284	685	1,300	600	1,000	550	1,720	1,020	1,030	135	142	71
18	273	668	1,240	550	1,100	500	2,470	915	1,110	125	125	65
19	264	1,500	1,110	500	1,000	500	3,270	819	749	116	114	60
20	254	1,850	960	480	1,300	460	4,180	749	588	111	125	58
21	259	1,470	851	460	2,000	440	3,930	720	496	102	132	58
22	259	1,250	804	440	1,860	420	7,620	788	394	97	114	56
23	250	1,190	634	420	1,590	400	6,770	1,030	454	94	105	54
24	593	1,070	700	400	1,440	400	5,460	1,040	607	87	140	47
25	1,500	851	650	380	1,350	600	7,410	915	474	85	236	46
26	1,150	748	500	360	1,310	1,100	10,400	799	401	78	187	46
27	940	775	550	340	1,670	3,000	9,830	739	347	83	167	52
28	804	712	500	340	1,640	3,600	9,680	1,120	293	135	152	65
29	685	685	480	320	-	2,780	7,880	1,960	277	97	135	67
30	592	676	460	320	-	2,400	6,680	1,570	433	97	119	73
31	522	-	440	300	-	2,460	-	1,330	-	125	105	-

Month	Second-foot-days	Maximum	Minimum	Mean	Per square mile	Run-off in inches
October..........................	16,436	1,500	250	530	1.08	1.24
November.........................	22,255	1,850	379	742	1.51	1.69
December.........................	52,964	6,830	440	1,709	3.48	4.01
Calendar year 1938	388,774	14,100	73	1,065	2.17	29.44
January..........................	15,855	920	300	511	1.04	1.20
February.........................	21,790	2,000	220	778	1.58	1.64
March............................	36,850	3,600	400	1,189	2.42	2.79
April............................	114,930	10,400	1,260	3,831	7.80	8.70
May..............................	63,604	5,670	720	2,052	4.18	4.82
June.............................	15,665	1,110	195	522	1.06	1.18
July.............................	5,379	529	78	174	.354	.41
August...........................	4,465	266	94	144	.293	.34
September........................	2,383	159	46	79.4	.162	.18
Water year 1938-39..........	372,576	10,400	46	1,021	2.08	28.19

Peak discharge.- Dec. 6 (12:20 p.m.) 8,360 sec.-ft.; Apr. 22 (5:30 p.m.) 8,470 sec.-ft.; Apr. 25 (11:30 p.m.) 11,700 sec.-ft.; Apr. 28 (1:30 a.m.) 11,100 sec.-ft.

FIG. 85. Reproduction of page from *Water Supply Paper*. (See Fig. 83.)

The completed records are forwarded from the various district offices to the Washington Office as soon as they are computed after the end of each report year on September 30. In the Washington Office, the records are reviewed in the Section of Reports in the approximate order in which they are scheduled to be published. Since the records are published on the basis of drainage basins rather than state boundaries, records collected by one district office may not all be published in one *Water Supply Paper*. This situation makes necessary the careful scheduling by the Washington Office of the preparatory work in the district offices in order that publication of any particular *Water Supply Paper* may not be unduly delayed by a district office that has only a few records to be published in that paper.

The reviewers in the Section of Reports examine the list of discharge measurements, the rating curves and tables, and the station analysis submitted in connection with each station record in order to assure themselves that there are no inconsistencies in the basic data upon which the final record of discharge depends. For each station record there is published a station description, a skeleton rating table or tables based on the actual tables used in the computation of discharge, a table of mean daily discharge for the water year, and a table of monthly and yearly figures showing second-foot days, maximum, minimum, and mean figures, discharge in second-feet per square mile, and runoff in inches, for both the climatological and calendar years. Special mention is made of those portions of the record for which special methods of computation were used, such as periods of backwater, periods of faulty or missing gage-height record, or other periods when the daily discharge figures did not represent normal conditions of stage-discharge relationship. When the reviewer of a particular record is satisfied that the station manuscript contains no inconsistencies or errors, it is submitted to the editor, who makes such editorial changes as may be necessary to bring the manuscript into conformity with standard government style, after which it is typed and reproduced as a *Water Supply Paper*.

BIBLIOGRAPHY 15

1. B. E. Jones, Flow in Tennessee Checked against Hydraulic Formulas, *Engineering News-Record*, Vol. 89, p. 610.
2. Kessler, Briggs, and Peterson, The Discharge Integrator—Instructions for Operation, *U.S.G.S. Mimeographed Circular*, 1928.
3. Hall, Hall, and Pierce, A Method of Determining the Daily Discharge of Rivers of Variable Slope, *U.S.G.S. Water Supply Paper* 345-E.
4. Murray Blanchard, A Discharge Diagram for Uniform Flow in Open Channels, *Trans. Am. Soc. C. E.*, Vol. 96, pp. 865-886.

CHAPTER 16

ANALYSIS AND PRESENTATION OF STREAM-FLOW RECORDS FOR SPECIFIC USE

Requirements. The tabular chronological statistics of stage, discharge, and runoff of rivers and other streams as they are regularly published, for example, in the *Water Supply Papers* of the Geological Survey, with totals, maxima, minima, and means, are through necessity not so variously arranged or so informatively grouped as best to serve many important purposes. However, in the form in which they are published they may serve many other purposes satisfactorily, while satisfying the general requirement by engineers that published records be so orderly and uniform that they can be readily rearranged and combined with other records to meet the needs of any use that may arise. In the studies related to many hydrologic and hydraulic problems and in the evaluation of projected developments that involve the use of rivers or the occupation of river channels and flood plains and in the design, erection, and operation of structures built or to be built for the use or control of rivers, it will be necessary to rearrange, average, combine, and analyze the available and applicable stream-flow records and related information in such ways as best to serve the problems or projects under consideration. Rearrangement, analysis, and study of river records are, therefore, essential to their utilization for many purposes.

The analyses and studies having been made, the results must be presented so clearly that they can be readily comprehended by administrative officials, lawyers, financiers, and other individuals—groups which may include many persons who are not engineers. In engineering studies related to the quantities of water flowing in rivers in which essential accuracy must be sought, meticulous precision is not generally warranted because of the wide variations that normally occur in precipitation and runoff, and the certainty that river records, whatever their length or degree of accuracy, do not disclose exactly the true maxima, minima, and mean discharges. The engineer, therefore, must distinguish between that kind or degree of accuracy which is essential to the work in hand and a precision with respect to computations which is not essential thereto. In many situations, the accuracy represented by the use of four-place logarithms, or of a good 10-inch slide rule, is sufficient; in others, a somewhat greater degree of precision may be required. The requirements of use lead to many problems in both engineering analysis and technical and nontechnical writing that arise in connection with the work of all engineers who are called upon to use stream-flow records, to report on projects for the control, utilization, and administration of river waters, and to evaluate or adjudicate water rights therein. These problems involve not only critical analysis but also effective presentation of the results obtained, in order that the facts and deductions shall be sound and that they shall be easily grasped by men who may not be able to comprehend readily the technical meaning of engineering terms or to follow the steps of mathematical analysis. It cannot be too strongly emphasized that, if these ends are to be realized, engineers must be proficient not only in mathematical and engineering analysis and in the making of tables and graphs, but also in the preparation of well-arranged texts that are written in clear, nontechnical language.

Because of the wide range in problems and in the methods utilized in their study, detailed descriptions of such problems and methods are not attempted in this book, which is designed to treat primarily of the instruments, equipment, and processes employed in the field work related to the collection of systematic records of river discharge, and of the office procedures utilized in computing, checking, and preparing such records for publication and use. Many references are made to reports and discussions in current engineering literature, however, which those who are interested should consult for more detailed and better information than could practicably be included in a book that is not devoted primarily to those topics. The student is cautioned that these references are intended to be typical and not exhaustive.

Basic Information. Statistical river records, as they are collected and published, are arranged chronologically in tables and summaries which show mean daily discharges and monthly and yearly maxima, minima, and means, generally in second-feet, and monthly and annual runoff, generally in acre-feet, depth in inches, or millions of gallons (Fig. 85). Similarly, the records of precipitation in inches and of temperature in degrees Fahrenheit are published in tables arranged chronologically, with summaries, totals, and means for seasons and years and for the periods of record. The arrangement of statistical data in chronological sequence is best for many needs, especially those related to analyses, coordinations, and intercomparisons. Other records and pertinent information that engineers must analyze and co-ordinate with the climatic and stream-flow records vary widely and may appear in many types of reports composed of text, tables, diagrams, and maps, and may be concerned with many and varied features of rivers and their control and utilization, such as water rights, navigational aspects, construction of dams, process uses of water in industry and the problems related thereto, municipal water requirements, irrigation water demands, generation of power by falling water or by steam, the transmission and marketing of electric power, regulation of river discharge, control of floods, drainage of wet lands, and many other aspects of the occupation, utilization, or administration of rivers and their channels and valleys. A reliable report on any proposal to use a river's water, channel, or valley may involve the necessity of analyzing, correlating, and presenting information along one or several of these and other lines in addition to the essential facts obtained from statistical records of water supply.

Since possible problems related to the analysis and presentation of information with respect to rivers are infinite in their variations, no specific rules with respect to procedures can be laid down. The engineer must study the facts and the ends sought and must make his own plans, utilizing, however, the experiences of others as they have been published in many valuable reports on investigations, surveys, and projects for development, and on construction, operation, and administration as related to such projects.

The complications which lead to the wide variety in problems may be illustrated by a single example. Consider the questions which may be at issue with reference to the quantity of water available or that can be made available at the point in a river where it is proposed to divert or use water. The average of the mean annual discharges recorded for a series of years fixes the limit of the total amount of water that could have been obtained (assuming no importation of water) at the site of a gaging station during those particular years, and that quantity or something approaching it could be utilized only if hydraulic works of sufficient capacities were built to utilize all rates of discharge or if sufficient storage capacity were to be created to convert the varying day-by-day flow into the mean flow for those years or into the regimen of flow needed in connection with the proposed use. However, even if adequate storage capacity should be created, that gross quantity of water could not be obtained because losses of water from evaporation, and infiltration resulting from the substitution of water surfaces for land surfaces, would be involved in the creation of the reservoir capacities needed for converting a normally varying flow into a regulated flow.

Generally, it is not feasible to build reservoirs of sufficient capacity to convert the normal daily discharges into the mean discharge for a year, much less for a period of years. There is, of course, an occasional notable exception such as Lake Mead, the reservoir created by Boulder Dam on the Colorado River, which has a gross capacity equivalent to the runoff of the river in two average years, and even in that extreme situation the drawdown of the reservoir prior to the arrival of any flood must be sufficient to provide capacity for storing that portion of the runoff of the flood period that is in excess of the demand for use during that period.

On most rivers, only partial conversion of the varying daily flow to the mean flow can be made because of the lack of feasible reservoir sites at or near the place or places where effective conversion could be made. The available information must be analyzed, therefore, to determine what storage is economically feasible of development in view of the cost of constructing and operating the reservoir or reservoirs, the value of the results that may be obtained because of the proposed change in regimen of flow, and the best effect, in terms of operation of the proposed development, that could be obtained by means of such reservoirs. All such problems are further complicated by the fact that the places where it is proposed to divert or use the water are seldom coincident with gaging-station sites. Generally, therefore, the river records must be converted from one site to another on the basis of drainage-area ratios, modified by differences in the assumed or known water yield of different parts of the basin.[1] This relatively simple illustration suggests only a few of the very many problems and types of problems that engineers, when called upon, must study, evaluate, and present clearly to laymen.

Forms of Expression. The forms of expression that are available and commonly utilized are text (presentation in words), tables (generally numerical quantities arranged in tabular form), and graphs (diagrams and maps). Each of these forms of expression varies widely in utilization with the nature and complexity of the information to be presented and the audience to be reached. Engineers should be able to use all of them effectively.

Some kinds of information might be presented in any of the three ways, and that way should be selected for presenting any piece or type of information that will best serve the purpose sought. How-

[1] Bibliog. 16·37.

ever, the same information should not be presented in more than one form; that is, it should not appear in both table and graph, and if presented in either of these forms it should not be repeated in text. The whole exposition should combine texts, tables, and graphs in such ways and proportions as to constitute an attractive, readable, clear, and convincing report.

TEXT. Whatever aids may be utilized in the form of tables and illustrations, practically every report, whether oral or written, must have a basic text consisting of words and phrases, arranged properly into sentences and paragraphs. An engineer should discriminate in his use of words with respect to their definiteness of meaning, and should so assemble them into sentences and paragraphs as to produce a report [2] that has character and leads to a definite objective, without the use of unnecessary words or of words that do not convey the exact meaning that is intended.

Given the availability of an essential basis of facts, the quality of the report will depend wholly on the engineer's ability to arrange in an orderly way the facts and his ideas with respect to them, to analyze, correlate, and discuss the facts, to draw sound conclusions from them, and to prepare the text in clear, concise, and convincing language.[3] A hazy report made on the basis of adequate facts must be presumed to be the product of a mind that is either hazy in its thinking or is untrained in logical analysis and the use of language.

TABLES. Much statistical information can be presented most concisely and clearly in the form of tables, of which there are many kinds. Some information might be presented with equal facility and effectiveness in two or more different kinds of tables. Obviously, a table should be so arranged that the facts will be presented clearly and in the most usable form. To that end, careful attention should be given to the column and side headings. In some instances, the width of the pages of the report will limit the number of columns and so largely determine the form and, perhaps, the substance of a table. In preparing many tables, however, there will be free choice as to arrangement. Under such circumstances, an inversion of a table, that is, the change of column headings to side headings, and vice versa, may be found greatly to improve its appearance and utility, and, to that end, thought should always be given to the most effective arrangement.

Although the presentation of data in tabular form is both orderly and concise, it generally does not enable the lay reader to grasp easily the essential aspects of such data. Long tables, valuable though

[2] Chapter 18.
[3] Bibliog. 16·27.

they may be, are mainly repositories for statistical data and certainly make difficult reading, especially for laymen to whom columns of figures may have little of significance and less of interest. Therefore the engineer should know his audience and should so vary the methods of presenting the data that his report or oral presentation will command the maximum amount of attention and interest while serving adequately the purpose for which it was prepared.

For some purposes, it will be desirable to rearrange stream-flow records so that the discharges will appear in the order of magnitude, leading to *duration tables,* showing the number of days in which any selected rate of flow is available, and *deficiency tables,*[4] showing the number of days in which there is deficiency in any selected rate of flow. If the year (365 days) serves as the basis of these tables, days shown in either table may be obtained by subtracting from 365 the corresponding days in the other table. Many other tabular rearrangements of river records are utilized for purposes of information, argument, or emphasis, and numberless instances of the use of tables of many kinds, statistical, correlative, comparative, and summary, may be found in easily accessible engineering literature. Naturally, tables should be designed and prepared as needed and in such appropriate forms as will serve best the text of each report. So used, tables are generally valuable as they tend to promote conciseness and clarity.

GRAPHS. Graphs enable the engineer to bring to his readers in an effective and readily understandable form, or to his hearers, if an oral presentation is being made with lantern slides, facts, comparisons, and conclusions that otherwise might be difficult or even impracticable to convey to those who have not devoted considerable time to their study. Since graphs are also common aids in many forms of analyses and computations, they are widely used and may be found in many engineering reports. They vary in nature and form with the problems under consideration, the controlling features of the problems, the information available, and the readers or audience for whom they are prepared. The graphs used in reports are generally simple; those in engineering studies may be very complex.

In the preparation of graphs, the data to be plotted and the scales chosen are of major importance in their relation to the points or conclusions sought or presented. In general, the data to be plotted must be reasonably adapted to such form of presentation, and the scales of plotting should be so selected that all the information will fall within the limits of the paper and the plotted graphs or diagrams will clearly

[4] Bibliog. 16·26.

disclose the significant characteristics or features that are to be demonstrated. If a graph is to be manifolded or published, photographic reduction of as much as 50 per cent or even more must be provided for, and all parts of it, including especially the lettering, must be of such size and width of line that they will remain clear and sharp even after great reduction.

From the many graphs used by engineers, six types, hydrograph, mass curve, frequency curve, probability curve, duration curve, and unit graph, described below, have been selected for mention as typical of those commonly connected with river records.

Hydrograph. The *stage hydrograph* is a simple and valuable diagram for presenting information with respect to the stages of rivers, lakes, or reservoirs. It is produced automatically by a graphic water-stage recorder, or it may be made by plotting the stages observed on any gage on the vertical axis and time on the horizontal axis. A convenient stage hydrograph which is much used involves the plotting, on one sheet, of mean daily gage heights for a calendar or climatological year. If the range in stage is great, two-cycle or three-cycle semilog paper is suitable; otherwise, rectangular-scale plotting may be preferred. Since it presents stages in the order of the time in which they occur the stage hydrograph is valuable, for example, in showing when and by how much a critical stage has been exceeded, such as bankful stage in a river or the stage of a reservoir at which spilling begins. It has the outstanding characteristics of simplicity and clarity for the presentation of river and reservoir records in their relation to those types of hydraulic problems that are directly related to stage.

The *discharge hydrograph* (Fig. 84) differs from the stage hydrograph by the substitution of discharge, expressed in any appropriate unit, for stage. As with the stage hydrograph, plotting may be either by logarithmic scale or by rectangular scale. One of these two forms of hydrographs, perhaps, is as simple and as easily understood as the other. They serve different purposes, however, the discharge hydrograph having more definite value in connection with studies of power capacities of possible sites of development or of the reservoir capacities that may be needed for insuring any minimum discharge below the annual mean, and the stage hydrograph being more valuable for studies related to problems of overflow and submergence in which discharge is not necessarily a factor.

The discharge hydrograph shows increments of flow in the time sequence in which they occur, in contrast with the duration curve, which shows increments of discharge in order of magnitude. A discharge hydrograph might show, for example, the successive drafts on and replenishments of storage that might occur in a reservoir constructed or proposed for construction on a river. It is especially valuable, therefore, in connection with the study of storage-capacity requirements on rivers like those of the southeastern states where there are normally several periods of high discharge within each year. The discharge hydrograph is also much used in making studies of power capacities; a scale of horsepower per foot of fall or for any selected head, or a scale of horsepower-days or horsepower-months for a particular power site, may also be plotted on the vertical axis alongside the scale of discharge, since potential power is a direct function of discharge. Discharge hydrographs are extremely valuable in connection with studies and comparisons of the variations in flow in streams draining adjacent watersheds or at different points on the same stream. The plotting of two or more such hydrographs on the same sheet will facilitate such comparisons as relating both to the respective magnitudes of flow and to the discharge patterns.

Mass Curve. The *mass curve* or *summation diagram* (Fig. 86), apparently first developed in 1882 by Rippl,[5] is much used in connection with hydraulic problems, especially those related to reservoir capacities[6] and to power studies.[7] In this curve, increments in amounts of water, energy, or other factor that may be involved in a study are plotted progressively on the vertical axis, to an appropriate scale, with the particular unit of quantity that is applicable to the study being made; and units of time are plotted on the horizontal axis. The increments plotted on the vertical axis may represent gross quantities or the residuals left after deductions have been made for uses and losses. Differences in the quantities plotted may cause marked differences in the characteristics of the resulting mass curves, and those quantities will be selected for plotting which will best serve the purposes or ends of the studies that are being made.

Monthly increments are commonly utilized in the plotting, but daily, weekly, or even annual increments may be used. The resulting curve shows for any time the gross or net (depending on the quantities plotted) supply of the item plotted since the initial time. The slope of the curve at any point shows the rate of accretion at that point of time. The slope of the line connecting any two points on the curve shows the average accretion for the interval of time between the two points, and the projection of the line on the vertical axis shows the total accretion in that time.

[5] Bibliog. 16·31.   [7] Bibliog. 16·35.
[6] Bibliog. 16·27, 28.

If storage of water is being considered and the curve is horizontal at any point, the net runoff into the reservoir at that time is zero; if the curve slopes downward to the right, the depletions, comprising

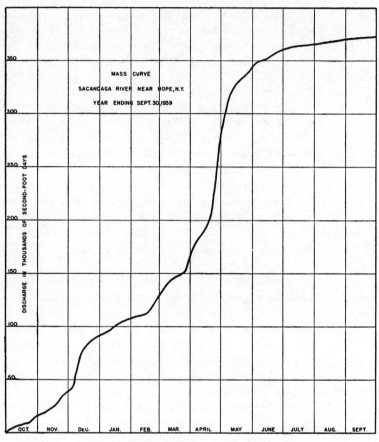

Fig. 86. Mass curve. (See Fig. 83.)

withdrawals and losses, are greater than the accretions. If a demand line, representing an actual or contemplated demand, is plotted intersecting the mass curve at two or more points, the greatest vertical distance between the line and the mass curve will represent, to scale, the quantity of effective storage needed to yield the supply of water represented by the demand line.

Frequency Curve. The *frequency curve* [8] shows the frequency with which specific recorded events have occurred. Either ordinary or logarithmic-scale plotting paper may be used in its construction. This type of curve has long been utilized by statisticians and engineers in the analysis of events of many kinds, including those shown on the discharge hydrograph.

Among the characteristics of river discharge of importance to engineers, those related to frequency of occurrence of stages and discharges of various magnitudes may have great significance. Obviously, an event that occurs on the average only once in fifty years has far less economic importance than one that recurs often. Damaging floods that recur annually present an economic situation that may warrant large expenditures for protection or control, but a flood that recurs only once in perhaps twenty years or fifty years would warrant much smaller expenditures or perhaps none.

Many engineers engaged in evaluating projects and in planning programs of work are, therefore, called upon to estimate the frequency of specific events in terms of seasons (construction periods), years, decades, or centuries. Such estimates [9] must be made and utilized even though it is recognized, for example, that an event that appears to occur normally only once in a century may recur within a decade or even within a year, and that the available records of river discharge are far too short to disclose satisfactorily the frequency of events that recur only in terms of decades, and even less satisfactorily those that recur only in terms of centuries. The relatively short available river records serve better, therefore, for the study of events of frequent occurrence than for those that occur only rarely, and the rarer the occurrence the less satisfactory will be the study of frequency. However unsatisfactory the basis may be, engineers must attempt to evaluate frequencies and probabilities; to that end, they must know the characteristics and significance of both frequency and probability curves.

Probability Curve. The *probability curve* [10] shows the probable frequency of occurrence of future events, in accordance with the mathematical law of probabilities. It is derived from the frequency curve, and it is commonly made by plotting the magnitudes of events on the vertical axis and time on the horizontal axis. In this plotting, probability paper is commonly used. The curve when so plotted falls nearly in a straight line and so may be extrapolated for a small distance with considerable assurance of reasonable reliability, at least

[8] Bibliog. 16·33.
[9] Bibliog. 16·27.
[10] Bibliog. 16·38, 39, 40, 41, 42, 43.

from a mathematical standpoint. Long extrapolations for the purpose, for example, of ascertaining the magnitudes of 1,000-year or even 10,000-year floods are interesting but unwarranted, both because of the paucity of basic data and because of the fact that such natural phenomena most certainly do not occur with mathematical precision.

Since no method of graphical or mathematical analysis can compensate for lack of records, engineers who must evaluate the probabilities of recurrence of river stages and discharges of various magnitudes are greatly handicapped by the relative shortness of reliable river records in their relation to the length of records needed for trustworthy predictions of the probabilities of those future events that recur infrequently. This situation does not remove the necessity for making such predictions and therefore of studying the curves and methods that have been utilized.

Duration Curve. A *duration curve* of discharge (Fig. 87) is obtained by plotting the rates of discharge of a river which have been arranged in order of magnitude in a duration table. It may be made on the basis of a year or any longer period up to the whole time of record. Rates of flow are plotted to the appropriate scale, generally in units of second-feet, on the vertical axis, and percentages of total time, or time in days, weeks, or months, on the horizontal axis.

The duration curve [11] is a very valuable graph for engineers. It is largely utilized in studies of power-plant design with special reference to spillway capacities, plant capacities, and primary power available or obtainable. For run-of-river plants, it shows the portion of the year or the percentage of time during which the discharge and, therefore, the possible output of energy is above or below any selected rate. It shows, at the half-way point in time, the median discharge for the period, which is generally considerably less than the mean discharge.

If the flow of a river had occurred in the order of magnitude, the discharge hydrograph and the duration curve would be of identical shape and the storage capacity needed in that year or period to yield any desired discharge below the mean would be shown, to the appropriate scale, by the area included between the line of the desired discharge and the part of the discharge hydrograph (or duration curve) that lies below it. Although such a circumstance would never occur, many rivers in the western states and in any region that has one well-defined annual rainy season have only one high-water period in a year. An annual duration curve for such a river shows the storage needed to convert the flow for that year into uniform flow or any

[11] Bibliog. 16·28, 34, 36.

regimen of flow that averages below the mean flow. For such a situation, a duration curve would serve adequately in studies of storage, although a discharge hydrograph might also do as well. If, on the other hand, the regimen of the river is such as to cause several or

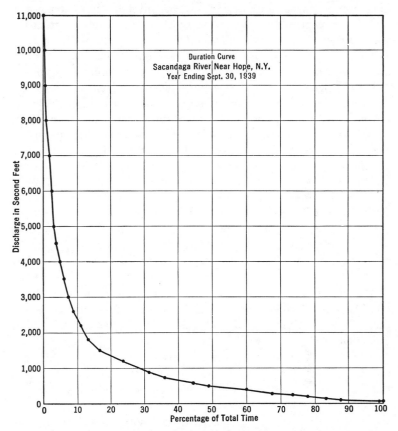

FIG. 87. Duration curve of discharge. (See Fig. 83.)

many peaks in the yearly discharge hydrograph and, therefore, several fillings or partial fillings of storage reservoirs during each year, the duration curve would indicate the necessity for storage capacities in excess of those actually needed, and the discharge hydrograph might better serve in studying problems related to storage.

Unit Graph. The necessity is constantly arising for estimating stages and discharges of rivers where no adequate basic records are available. Therefore, engineers must make such estimates on the basis of very meager information. Since the conditions under which estimates are made range through a wide variety, the estimates vary widely in probable accuracy. They include virtual guesses; computations made from observations of shorelines and debris and the slopes indicated by them; estimated extensions of short-time stream-flow records; attempted transposition and adaptation of records from the place of collection to another place on the same river [12] or nearby river in the same or in a neighboring drainage basin that has, as nearly as may be, the same characteristics of exposure, topography, geology, soil, and vegetation; and the computation of estimated stages and discharges from records of precipitation alone. There should be no thought that such estimates will have the accuracy or reliability of actual records, and they should be treated with full recognition of their limitations in these respects. However, through necessity, the design, cost, and safety of important hydraulic structures may rest on such estimates. To say that design and construction should await the availability of actual records covering a considerable period of years does not help in some situations because such delay is not always possible. However, developments made on the basis of estimated stream flow should have appropriately high factors of safety, which, of course, involve higher costs. Engineers, therefore, are on the alert for ways and means for increasing the reliability of such estimates. In making them, many methods have been proposed and tried,[13] and there have been gradual and in recent years hopeful improvements in these devices. Only one of these attempted improvements will be presented here.

In 1932, LeRoy K. Sherman advanced the concept of the *unit graph* [14] which was devised by him to show the characteristics of a drainage basin in terms of the distribution, with respect to time, of rates of runoff resulting from a unit depth of effective rainfall (rainfall that appears as surface runoff) occurring in a unit of time. In this graph, quantities of flow are plotted on the vertical axis and time on the horizontal axis. In connection with this plotting, Sherman undertook, by adding together the increments of runoff, to compute not only the rate of the maximum discharge caused by a recorded rainfall but also the probable discharge hydrograph of the resulting stream flow. Sherman's proposal led to prompt discussion [15] and trial by many engineers.

[12] Bibliog. 16·37.
[13] Bibliog. 16·29, 30, 32.
[14] Bibliog. 16·9.
[15] Bibliog. 16·20, 21.

In 1934, Merrill M. Bernard proposed [16] to make the unit graph more practical by supplementing it with the *distribution graph* and the *pluviagraph*. The distribution graph shows the typical distribution of runoff from a drainage basin in terms of the percentage of the total runoff that occurs in each of a number of equally spaced intervals of time; percentages of runoff are plotted on the vertical axis and time on the horizontal axis. The pluviagraph is a theoretical hydrograph which would result from a storm if the runoff were 100 per cent of the rainfall and if the proportions fixed by the distribution graph were applicable to the gross rainfall. It is in theory, therefore, a limiting hydrograph of the runoff that would be caused by that storm.

Bernard [17] and others [18] have presented detailed descriptions of the computations and of the diagrams that have been tried and found to be of assistance in connection with this method of estimating stream flow, which has now, in part at least, displaced the earlier and perhaps less reliable methods in those regions where it has been found to be reasonably applicable. The method and modifications of it have been proposed for use also in connection with storm transposition and flood routing.[19]

The unit-graph method of estimating river discharge and runoff is based on the observed facts that the unit graph for each river has a characteristic shape that is not generally modified essentially by the amount of the rainfall which produces it, or by the amount of antecedent rainfall and the resulting differences in stages of ground water. Confidence in the process rests on the essential confirmation of these facts by studies made by many engineers working independently. A continued lack of confidence among some is apparently based on the possible modifications in the shape of the unit graph due to variations in conditions which may include, among others, the nature of the storm, especially with respect to unevenness of rainfall within the storm period, and, to a lesser extent perhaps, to variations in the antecedent conditions, and to variations in the rates of vegetal growth within the year, especially in its relation to seasonal differences in transpiration. Lack of confidence may also arise because of recognition of the ever-present human tendency to place a high valuation on results obtained by elaborate computations in which the mathematical work is known to have been accurately done, and therefore to place, unconsciously, too great reliance on the accuracy of the results obtained by overlooking the important fact that elaborate and accurate

[16] Bibliog. 16·10.   [18] Bibliog. 16·2, 22, 23, 25.
[17] Bibliog. 16·10.   [19] Bibliog. 16·5, 6, 23.

computations cannot remove the intrinsic inaccuracies of the fundamental assumptions with respect to the reliability of the shapes of the unit graph, distribution graph, and pluviagraph.

BIBLIOGRAPHY 16

1. R. S. GOODRIDGE, A Graphic Method of Routing Floods through Reservoirs, *Trans. A. G. U.*, 1937, Part II, pp. 433–439.
2. F. F. SNYDER, Synthetic Unit-Graphs, *Trans. A. G. U.*, 1938, Part I, pp. 447–454.
3. R. T. ZOCH, The Mathematical Synthesis of the Flood-Hydrograph, *Trans. A. G. U.*, 1939, Part II, pp. 207–218.
4. J. C. GEYER, New Curve-Fitting Method for Analysis of Flood Records, *Trans. A. G. U.*, 1940, Part II, pp. 660–668.
5. LADEN, REILLY, and MINNOTTE, Synthetic Unit-Hydrographs, Distribution-Graphs, and Flood-Routing in the Upper Ohio River Basin, *Trans. A. G. U.*, 1940, Part II, pp. 649–659.
6. W. B. LANGBEIN, Channel-Storage and Unit-Hydrograph Studies, *Trans. A. G. U.*, 1940, Part II, pp. 620–627.
7. W. B. LANGBEIN, Determination of Manning's n from Vertical-Velocity Curves, *Trans. A. G. U.*, 1940, Part II, pp. 618–620.
8. H. A. THOMAS, Graphical Integration of the Flood-Wave Equations, *Trans. A. G. U.*, 1940, Part II, pp. 596–602.
9. L. K. SHERMAN, Stream-Flow from Rainfall by Unit-Graph Method, *Engineering News-Record*, Vol. 108, pp. 501–505 (April 7, 1932).
10. MERRILL BERNARD, An Approach to Determinate Stream Flow, *Trans. Am. Soc. C. E.*, Vol. 100, pp. 347–395.
11. RUTTER, GRAVES, and SNYDER, Flood Routing, *Trans. Am. Soc. C. E.*, Vol. 104, pp. 275–313.
12. E. F. BRATER, Unit Hydrograph Principle Applied to Small Watersheds, *Trans. Am. Soc. C. E.*, Vol. 105, pp. 1154–1192.
13. O. H. MEYER, Analysis of Runoff Characteristics, *Trans. Am. Soc. C. E.*, Vol. 105, pp. 83–141.
14. GUTHE and OWEN, A Proposed Method for Calculating Stream-Flow, *Trans. A. G. U.*, 1941, Part III, pp. 799–808.
15. R. E. HORTON, Virtual Channel-Inflow Graphs, *Trans. A. G. U.*, 1941, Part III, pp. 811–820.
16. R. E. HORTON, Flood-Crest Reduction by Channel-Storage, *Trans. A. G. U.*, 1941, Part III, pp. 820–835.
17. CARDWELL and DICKERSON, Runoff from Terraced Areas under Conditions of Extreme Flood, *Trans. A. G. U.*, 1941, Part III, pp. 856–862.
18. H. K. PALMER, A Method of Computing the Size of Spillway for a Dam, *Engineering News*, Vol. 67, pp. 524–525 (March 21, 1912).
19. W. T. WILSON, A Graphical Flood-Routing Method, *Trans. A. G. U.*, 1941, Part III, pp. 893–897.
20. BARROWS, HORTON, PIERCE, JARVIS, GRUNSKY, BOLIG, and CLYDE, A Discussion of the Unit-Hydrograph Method of Estimating Runoff, *Engineering News-Record*, Vol. 109, pp. 223–225 (Aug. 25, 1932).
21. HORNER, GAY, SAVILLE, and SHERMAN, Further Discussion of the Unit-Graph Method of Estimating Runoff, *Engineering News-Record*, Vol. 109, pp. 255–259 (Sept. 1, 1932).

22. C. E. SUDLER, Storage Required for the Regulation of Stream Flow, *Trans. Am. Soc. C. E.,* Vol. 91, pp. 622–704.
23. C. C. JACOB, Computing the Size of a Reservoir Spillway, *Engineering News,* Vol. 67, p. 1134 (June 13, 1912).
24. W. T. COLLINS, Runoff Distribution Graphs from Precipitation Occurring in More than One Time Unit, *Civil Engineering,* Vol. 9, No. 9, pp. 559–561 (September 1939).
25. L. K. SHERMAN, The Hydraulics of Surface Runoff, *Civil Engineering,* Vol. 10, No. 3, pp. 165–166 (March 1940).
26. PIERCE and DEAN, Surface Waters of Massachusetts, *U.S.G.S. Water Supply Paper* 415.
27. CREAGER and JUSTIN, *Hydroelectric Handbook,* John Wiley & Sons, New York, 1927.
28. H. K. BARROWS, *Water Power Engineering,* McGraw-Hill Book Co., New York, 2nd Edition, 1934.
29. C. E. GRUNSKY, Rainfall and Runoff Studies, *Trans. Am. Soc. C. E.,* Vol. 85, pp. 66–136.
30. A. F. MEYER, Computing Runoff from Rainfall and Other Physical Data, *Trans. Am. Soc. C. E.,* Vol. 79, pp. 1056–1224.
31. W. RIPPL. The Capacity of Storage Reservoirs for Water Supply, *Proc. Inst. Civil Eng.,* Vol. 71, p. 270.
32. Report by Committee on Floods, *Journal Boston Soc. Civil Eng.,* Vol. 17, pp. 293–464 (September 1930).
33. H. A. FOSTER, Theoretical Frequency Curves and Their Application to Engineering Problems, *Trans. Am. Soc. C. E.,* Vol. 87, pp. 142–203.
34. H. A. FOSTER, Duration Curves, *Trans. Am. Soc. C. E.,* Vol. 99, pp. 1213–1267.
35. J. W. HACKNEY, Energy Mass Diagrams for Power Studies, *Trans. Am. Soc. C. E.,* Vol. 104, pp. 1644–1658.
36. HICKOX and WESSENAUER, Application of Duration Curves to Hydroelectric Studies, *Trans. Am. Soc. C. E.,* Vol. 98, pp. 1276–1308.
37. H. W. DENNIS, A Method for Adapting the Records of Stream Flow at One Point to Another Point on the Same Stream, *Trans. Am. Soc. C. E.,* Vol. 84, pp. 551–569.
38. ALLEN HAZEN, Storage to Be Provided in Impounding Reservoirs for Municipal Water Supply, *Trans. Am. Soc. C. E.,* Vol. 77, pp. 1539–1669.
39. L. S. HALL, The Probable Variations in Yearly Runoff as Determined from a Study of California Streams, *Trans. Am. Soc. C. E.,* Vol. 84, pp. 191–257.
40. R. D. GOODRICH, Straight Line Plotting of Skew Frequency Data, *Trans. Am. Soc. C. E.,* Vol. 91, pp. 1–118.
41. W. E. FULLER, Flood Flows, *Trans. Am. Soc. C. E.,* Vol. 77, pp. 564–694.
42. J. J. SLADE, JR., An Asymmetric Probability Function, *Trans. Am. Soc. C. E.,* Vol. 101, pp. 35–104.
43. Report by Committee on Floods, *Journal Boston Soc. Civil Eng.,* Vol. 29, No. 1, Section 2 (January 1942).

CHAPTER 17

GOVERNMENTAL PUBLICATION OF RIVER RECORDS

Public Interest in Records. The public is interested in the governmental publication of river records for several substantial reasons: because they relate to a variable and limiting natural resource that is essential to the stability of localities, regions, and the nation; because their public availability is essential to the prevention of monopolistic control of water and its utilization and to the establishment and maintenance of justice with respect to the rights in availability and use; because they are needed currently in connection with problems of development, operation, and administration; because they should be published systematically and in uniform style in order to be reasonably usable; because they must be recognized as unbiased and reliable; because publication is essential to their preservation; because they have been collected at public expense and so belong to the public; and because they have no great public value and provide no direct return to the public for the money expended for their collection until they have been made readily available for use by all interested persons and agencies. These ends can be obtained only through publication by governmental agencies and, preferably, so far as may be practicable, by a single agency and in a single, well-known series of reports.

Governmental Publication. Reports related to rivers are published by several governmental agencies on many phases of rivers and their utilization, as described below.

Geological Survey. River records collected by the Geological Survey are published in its series of *Water Supply Papers* comprising in 1942 about 900 volumes. Several types of reports are included in the series:

(*a*) Reports of daily river discharge, each annual report consisting of 15 volumes, one for each of the 15 river basins or other geographic units into which the country is divided for publication purposes.

(*b*) Compilations of discharge records by basins or states, in which all records in a geographic unit for a series of years are compiled.

(*c*) Reports on the quantity, chemical quality, and availability of ground water.

(d) Reports on the chemical quality of waters from specified sources, with special reference to their utility in agriculture and industry.

(e) Reports on important topics or unusual phenomena, such as floods, droughts, and fluctuations in ground-water stages.

(f) Reports on the present and possible future utilization of rivers.

Weather Bureau. The Weather Bureau publishes in its *Monthly Weather Review* summaries of current records of precipitation and temperature which are, of course, closely related to river records because river flow is derived from precipitation and is at some seasons affected largely by temperature. The complete records of these meteorological phenomena are published by the offices of the several districts into which the Weather Bureau divides the country. From time to time these offices publish compilations of the records in their respective districts. The Weather Bureau publishes annually a volume entitled *River Stages,* containing the records of river stages observed at a large number of stations maintained primarily in connection with flood forecasting. In the *Monthly Weather Review* appear also special reports on unusual events, such as storms, floods, and droughts. Local offices of the Weather Bureau in many of the larger cities issue daily and monthly summaries of observed meteorological data and in some instances snowfall bulletins and other releases of current interest for the information of the public.

Corps of Engineers, U. S. Army. The Corps of Engineers, U. S. Army, and an affiliated agency, the Mississippi River Commission, publish an annual report of stages and discharges of the Mississippi River and from time to time compilations of such records for selected river stations or for particular periods of time. The Corps publishes many reports on river and harbor improvement projects that have been referred by Congress, also reports on floods or features related to flood control and navigation as occasion may arise. Such reports are published in the *Annual Reports of the Chief of Engineers* and in *Congressional Documents,* of which perhaps the most noteworthy is the series of reports prepared in response to House Document 308, 67th Congress, 1st Session, wherein the Corps was authorized and directed to report on many specified rivers of the country with respect to navigation, flood control, water power, and irrigation. These "308" reports cover the principal rivers of the country except those in the drainage basins of the Colorado River and Great Salt Lake.

Public Health Service. The publications of the Public Health Service that relate to rivers pertain to the pollution of interstate streams, to the sanitation of shellfish shipped in interstate commerce, and to water supplies used on interstate carriers.

Soil Conservation Service. The publications of the Soil Conservation Service relating to rivers pertain to erosion, transportation, and deposition, with special reference to the removal or depletion of soils and to the filling of stream channels and reservoirs by sand and silt. Many specific studies have been treated in published reports.

Bureau of Agricultural Engineering. The Bureau of Agricultural Engineering has published many reports on the measurement and utilization of water in agriculture. This bureau has been discontinued and its activities divided among other bureaus. Information about its reports may be obtained from the Department of Agriculture.

Forest Service. The few publications of the Forest Service that relate to rivers have to do with the effects of forests and other vegetation on stream flow.

Bureau of Reclamation. The publications of the Bureau of Reclamation relate to specific irrigation projects and to the subsidiary water power which may have been developed or be susceptible of development in connection with its irrigation operations, actual or proposed.

Bureau of Standards. The publications of the Bureau of Standards that relate to rivers include problems of flowing water in rivers, canals, and pipes, and of hydraulic structures.

Federal Power Commission. The Federal Power Commission publishes reports on the development and utilization of power, on power resources, and on the water-power industry and its relation to other industries and to interstate and foreign commerce.

Bureau of the Census. Every five years the Bureau of the Census publishes a census of the electrical industries, covering electric light and power plants and electric railways, and a census of manufactures showing the electric power used in manufacturing.

National Resources Planning Board. The National Resources Planning Board publishes reports relative to long-time plans and programs for the wise use and fullest development of the national resources, including rivers, and their utilization for all purposes.

States. Publication of river records by states is widely diverse both as to substance and form. Many states do not publish records of river discharge but rely on the publications of the Geological Survey to serve their needs. Other states publish compilations and summary reports, and a very few may still publish annual reports containing fairly complete records of river discharge. There appears to be a tendency as the years pass for states to publish fewer records of river discharge and to rely more and more on the series of *Water Supply Papers* for that information. Many old records, however, are contained in state reports, some of which are not available elsewhere. Some of the states, notably California, have published voluminous and valuable reports on special studies of rivers and their utilization. Massachusetts has many publications on matters of water supply in relation to public health. Several state universities maintain well-equipped hydraulic laboratories and publish the results of hydraulic experiments and studies made therein. The scope and availability of state reports can be learned only by correspondence with the respective state officials.

Municipalities. Municipalities have not commonly published river records, and such municipal publications as have been made are generally in summary form. A few may relate to stages and discharges, but they are more commonly concerned with extremes and means of chemical and bacterial quality in sources or proposed sources of supply or in the water after treatment as it is delivered to the consumer. In the aggregate, doubtless, many valuable special reports are published by municipalities or similar governmental agencies, as, for example, the reports on floods and their control at Pittsburgh, Pa.; the reports on studies of floods and their control, at Dayton, Ohio; the reports on the water supply for San Francisco, Calif., which preceded the construction of the Hetch Hetchy dam and aqueduct, and on the water supply for Los Angeles, which preceded the construction of the Owens River aqueduct. The nature and availability of municipal reports can generally be determined only from the officials of the respective cities.

Form of Publication. River records are generally published annually. The publication year used by the Geological Survey is October 1 to September 30, the so-called climatic year which is believed to have at least three important advantages: (1) the stages of ground water are more nearly uniform on October 1 in most sections of the United States than on any other fixed date, leading, in general, to fairly reliable comparisons of annual rainfall-runoff relations because of the relatively small errors due to annual differences in the ground-water table on that date; (2) in the arid and semiarid parts of the country, September 30 usually marks the end of the irrigation season, and in humid regions it marks the end of the growing season; and (3) there is a minimum probable error due to the effect of ice in the records of winter flow if the discharge for the winter period (November to April) is computed at one time. If the record were published on the basis of the calendar year, the computation of the flow for part of the period (January to April) would be made a year later than the computations for November and December of the same winter.

As much statistical information used in connection with river records is published on a calendar-year basis, the Geological Survey now includes in its regular annual reports the summaries, extremes, and means for the preceding calendar year in addition to those for the climatic year. The Weather Bureau regularly publishes its records of precipitation on a calendar-year basis. In addition, it now publishes also the summaries for the climatic year in order that they may be easily used in connection with the records of stream flow and runoff published by the Geological Survey, and with other computations by engineers on the basis of a climatic year, as is commonly desired in connection with problems of irrigation and other uses of water, especially in the arid and semiarid states.

Availability of Published Records. All federal reports are available for purchase at low prices, which, in accordance with law, are just sufficient to pay for stock, presswork, and binding. Editions are small, however, and many items are exhausted soon after issue. Thereafter they are available for consultation in many public and private libraries, or sometimes they may be purchased from dealers in second-hand books. Copies of records are therefore always to be had even after the editions for sale by the Government Printing Office are exhausted, but perhaps at the cost of photostating, photographing, or copying by hand or typewriter.[1]

Availability of Unpublished Records. Unpublished records are generally not readily available for public use although they may be opened for court and other important purposes. The unpublished routine river records of the Geological Survey may always be had by all who may need them. They are commonly made available by means of blueprint or photostat copies, the user being required by law to pay for the copies at the rate of 25 cents per letter-size page. Records that have not reached the stage at which they may be copied by these processes may be available for copying by hand. Under some conditions special information or reports by the Geological Survey needed by the public in advance of publication may be opened for inspection, copying, or other use, after the publication of an announcement that the files or report would be open at certain places, thus insuring against discrimination or favoritism as between different users or interests.

[1] Bibliog. 17·5.

BIBLIOGRAPHY 17

1. U. S. WEATHER BUREAU, *Daily River Stages at River Gage Stations on the Principal Rivers of the United States,* published annually.
2. MISSISSIPPI RIVER COMMISSION, *Stages and Discharges of the Mississippi River.*
3. CORPS OF ENGINEERS, U. S. ARMY, many *Congressional Documents.*
4. HOLLAND and JARVIS, Inventory of Unpublished Hydrologic Data, *U.S.G.S. Water Supply Paper* 837.
5. G. E. LARSON, Research for Flood Control Data, *Civil Engineering,* Vol. 12, No. 3, pp. 131–134 (March 1942).

CHAPTER 18

SPECIAL REPORTS

Purpose. Systematic reports of rainfall and of the stage and discharge of rivers consist largely of tabular statistics and do not generally discuss or interpret the data contained in them. These reports have great current and continuing value because they furnish an important part of the basic information needed in connection with problems related largely to utilization and administration and to the determination of equities in the rights to the use of water and to the benefits and damages resulting from the control and utilization of rivers. Like other statistical reports, however, they have small popular appeal.

Another type of report that is more descriptive, more interpretive, and less statistical treats of those phases of rivers and their utilization which are associated with public interests, and of the aspects of water in their relation to human activities. Such a special report is usually best prepared by a specialist in the field of water investigation and utilization who is qualified by education and experience to prepare an informative, readable, and reliable report. As the general investigations of water are commonly made by governmental agencies, many such specialists are engaged in statistical and regional studies of water for federal and state bureaus, and the descriptive and interpretive reports which they prepare are published by these governmental agencies.

Although, as we have seen, systematic statistical reports are almost exclusively of governmental origin, the major number of special reports are probably prepared by nongovernmental agencies and individuals and are published in both the popular and technical press. Such special nongovernmental reports range in scope from brief news items related to isolated current events to comprehensive treatises covering wide fields and also embrace a great variety of subjects, many of which may be extremely complex and technical. Many reports on water and rivers prepared by engineers and scientists are of principal value to particular groups and so are usually published in the technical press. Reports designed for more popular reading, whether written by engineers, scientists, or others, are published in newspapers, popular magazines, or books. The publication of any of these reports serves not only to inform the public concerning the topics treated but also to record valuable information in such permanent form that it will not be lost, since files of papers and magazines are commonly kept by publishers, and such files, as well as books, are also preserved in libraries, and so are always available to students and historians. Thus, these miscellaneous special reports may become important contributions to the historical and economic records of a region or country.

Governmental and private, or commercial, engineering reports related to rivers generally have different objectives. Special governmental engineering reports usually present matters, topics, or phases that are primarily of general public interest or importance. Such reports should not and commonly do not encroach on the recognized fields of commercial engineering. On the other hand, private, or commercial, engineering reports, which are not generally published or made widely available in other ways, commonly treat of specific projects or groups of projects with particular reference to economic feasibility of development and to the relations of these projects to local and regional needs. The two types of reports are, therefore, essentially different in object and scope. Private engineering reports, though they may contain much information of general public interest, treat primarily of technical and physical aspects and of the problems of development and operation and of probable commercial success or failure. Frequently governmental engineering reports contain significant information with respect to commercial projects, but their subject matter covers primarily only those aspects that are of broad public and social interest and importance, while the commercial aspects of economic feasibility of particular projects that are being considered or may possibly be considered for nongovernmental development or utilization are not discussed. Neither is designed to serve the purposes of the other, and neither should be made to do so.

Presumably, nontechnical reports, governmental or otherwise, are written for the general public and as such present aspects of rivers that are of broad general interest, although many of them have scarcely nominal value. Popular reports which are designed to be informative are widely diverse in subject matter and in style of presentation. Less emphasis is placed on statistics and more on description, interpretation, and argument with respect to projects in which the public is interested and to aspects of water that have human interest and appeal; for instance, in a flood report, the disastrous consequences of the flood and the degree of effectiveness of its physical control are stressed.

Engineering reports related to rivers are generally prepared for one of two purposes, administrative or technical. Administrative reports are designed to assist federal, state, municipal, and corporate officials in the performance of such administrative duties as the classification, administration, or disposal of public lands, in the administration of developments owned or controlled by governmental agencies, and in the adjudication and division of water among users whose rights may be conflicting. Technical reports are used as the bases for promoting, designing, financing, constructing, and operating hydraulic developments. Both the administrative and technical types of reports may contain much statistical information, and either may serve in whole or in part the purposes of the other.

The comprehensiveness of a report will be determined by the complexity of the situation or condition to which it relates and the particular purposes for which it is prepared, and these factors will to a considerable extent determine the amount of detail which must be included and discussed. Statistical information may be presented by text, table, or graphs, and that type of presentation should be selected which will be most effective and most concise. Generally, either a graph or a table is most desirable. The reports listed in the bibliography contain ample illustrations of each of these methods of presentation.

The engineer who prepares a report should keep in mind two important considerations. One is that much propaganda is abroad with respect to many topics and problems which, since it is reiterated so frequently and so loudly, is not easily recognized as such and so is liable to be accepted as fact without proper consideration of its source. Obviously, to the degree that unsound propaganda enters into any conclusion, that conclusion will be unsound. The second consideration is that facts are frequently inadequate for the purposes which they must serve and are therefore subject to interpretation and judgment, with the resulting danger that unsound conclusions may be drawn from them.

Nature. The nature of special nonstatistical reports with respect to rivers varies widely from news items to elaborate technical treatises related to high or low water, control of flood flows by means of reservoirs, levees, or vegetation, utilization of rivers for navigation, irrigation, or power, stocking rivers with fish, descriptions of exploration and adventure, water sports, and many other topics covering the whole range of human interests. They present many points of view, generally reliable as to fact but perhaps faulty as to reasoning and conclusions because of the propaganda they contain. The value of any special report to a particular individual depends largely on his interests and occupation. Engineers, like other citizens, are interested in the dangerous as well as in the enjoyable and usable characteristics of rivers, their usual as well as their unusual features, the extremes as well as the ordinary stages and discharges, and in many factors that affect human enjoyment and human activities in river control and utilization. They are, however, more interested in those reports made by other engineers, scientists, lawyers, and laymen on topics related to aspects of rivers that affect the successes or failures in their utility for any purpose. Obviously, it is not possible to discuss or even to list here or elsewhere the thousands of major and minor reports which can be mentioned only by groups or classes.

Technical Reports. The subject matter of special governmental reports relating to rivers varies widely, but all such reports should contain summaries and interpretations of the pertinent records that are published in regular order elsewhere and, in addition, many other facts collected and compiled specifically for the reports, if such facts are essential to any conclusions reached, or if they have probable future value and might otherwise be lost because of not having been published elsewhere.

Special governmental reports on stream-gaging methods, procedures, and accuracy [1] are of value in their relation to stream-gaging activities and are consequently much used by engineers and engineering students. These and similar reports are related to the activities of the Geological Survey in its studies of rivers and river flow. They serve not only to coordinate and improve field and office practices within the Geological Survey but also to improve the general technique of stream-gaging work in this and other countries, an improvement which is reflected in more accurate records of river stage and discharge.

Collection, compilation, interpretation, and publication in special reports of information concerning unusual events, such as floods and droughts, are essential to reliable permanent records of those events, their causes, the progress and magnitude of each flood as it moved downstream, and the resulting damages. Records of such events, which are erratic in occurrence, do not fit into and have no proper place in general statistical reports. Such records not only are informative but also serve as the bases for plans for flood amelioration or control. Reports incorporating these records should contain and interpret not only the information regularly collected during and immediately following the events but also additional pertinent information, not

[1] Bibliog. 18·2, 3; 14·1, 5.

published elsewhere, related to precipitation and stages and runoff of rivers. In order to be reasonably complete and to serve public needs, the miscellaneous information related to stage must be collected before the drift and other marks left by the floods have been eradicated by the elements and before observations made by individuals have been forgotten or otherwise lost. As long as the marks of the flood remain visible, slopes of the water surfaces at crest stage may be determined with fair accuracy for use in computing the probable velocity and discharge of the peak of the flood. At that time, approximate rates of rise and fall can sometimes be ascertained from individuals who were so situated and so inclined as to observe them with some degree of precision.

Reports of floods are of increasing importance because the damages caused by them are increasing, not, as many people believe, because the floods are now greater or occur more frequently than in the past, but because more lives and more property are exposed to flood hazards as a result of the increased occupation and use of flood plains for farms, industrial plants, towns, and cities. Such reports should include pertinent information about the intensities, variations, and amounts of precipitation, the fluctuations in temperature so far as they may be significant as relating to the form of precipitation, whether rain or snow, to the accumulation of snow on the ground, its consolidation into ice, its melting and resulting release of water to the streams, and about other aspects of the accumulation or synchronization of the flows of water from different tributaries. They should describe the storms that caused the floods, their extent, their movements, and the variations in wind velocities (if significant) and in temperature and precipitation as they moved across the country. They should describe the fluctuations of the stages and discharges of rivers, the rates of rise, the crest stages and discharges, the rates of recession, and the downstream movements of the flood waves. They should describe and evaluate the damages. They should compare each flood with previous floods in order to show its relative importance and, if possible, the apparent periodicity of floods of that magnitude with respect to years and seasons. Figures relating to unit rates of peak discharge at progressive points on the river are of particular value. No two floods are alike in timing, magnitude, and shape of crest, or rates of rise, recession, and progress downstream. A description of one flood will generally serve for no other, and therefore each major flood should be described.

Special reports on floods relate to both local cloudburst floods and to broad regional floods caused by great storms of wide extent. Although there is no dividing line between these two types of floods, the extremes of the two types are widely different in their characteristics. Cloudburst floods are caused by intense precipitation in limited areas and are therefore essentially flash floods. They come with little warning and subside quickly. Though they may occur anywhere, some regions are more subject to them than others. They are especially disastrous on small streams but have small significance on large rivers. Satisfactory reports on cloudburst floods are difficult to make because they seldom recur on the same streams and often occur in areas where there are no recording or even nonrecording rain gages, or on streams where there are no gaging stations. For records of the total precipitation, therefore, recourse must be had to accidental catches of the rain in buckets, tubs, barrels, or other nonstandard receptacles, commonly with no information as to the variations in intensity either by time or area, and to records of discharge computed by one or more of several methods, none of which has high accuracy. Although cloudburst floods occur with much greater frequency than broad regional floods, good reports on them are, for the reasons indicated, relatively few, and those reports that are available have correspondingly high value.[2]

By contrast with the conditions attending cloudburst floods, the waters of broad regional floods are accumulated into major river channels more slowly, and the progress of that accumulation and the travel of the flood wave can be followed for hours, days, or even weeks. There will be many records of precipitation within a large drainage basin from both recording and nonrecording rain gages, and many records of stage and discharge obtained at properly established and well-rated gaging stations. Generally, the information for satisfactory reports on such floods may, therefore, be collected as desired, and many such reports have been prepared and published.[3]

Reports on droughts relate to deficiencies in water. In them, records of temperature and precipitation, stages of rivers, and depletion and failure of wells are important. Temperature may be a factor of major significance in connection with the effect of the drought on agriculture because the combination of high temperatures with lack of moisture during the growing season may be extremely disastrous to vegetation. The records should make comparisons with previous droughts to disclose possible periodicity and relative importance. They should discuss the relations of the drought to agriculture, to domestic and municipal water supplies, to production of power by hydraulic and steam-power plants, and the damages caused in each kind of water

[2] Bibliog. 18·10, 11, 15.
[3] Bibliog. 18·9.

use. They should discuss the areal extent of the drought, its variations within the area, and its duration.[4]

Systematic records of ground-water stages and other reports having to do with ground water are increasingly in demand in connection with the problems related to the utilization of rivers because the ground-water stages determine the low-water flow of rivers. Stages and discharges during droughts have restrictive effects on the utility of rivers for all purposes, and reports on these aspects are correspondingly valuable. Because of these effects, efforts are now made to forecast low-water stages, and, since low-water flows are derived almost entirely from ground water, such forecasting is based largely on records of ground-water conditions and especially on statistical records of ground-water stages within a drainage basin. These records are therefore significant and valuable in studies of the discharge of rivers, especially with respect to low stages.[5]

The depth of snow on a drainage basin and its water content are directly related to the total runoff of rivers within that basin. The actual rates of runoff derived from the snow are, of course, determined by the temperature and its fluctuations. In many sections of the country, therefore, interest has developed in the amount of water that is stored in the form of snow, and snow surveys are now being made in regions of heavy snow during the latter part of each winter. By means of these surveys the depth and water content of the snow are observed over carefully selected snow-measuring courses that are used for that purpose from year to year. The measured runoff of a river which drains a measured snow field gives a relation between the water content of the snow and the total runoff derived therefrom, which, after several years of such surveys, establishes a general relationship that enables the engineers who operate irrigation systems or other hydraulic works to estimate with some assurance the probable total seasonal runoff from snow. This relationship may be seriously affected by a variety of hydrologic considerations. Regardless of its possible inaccuracies, however, this information is of great value in connection with the operating problems of water-supply systems of all kinds and with the maintenance of a proper regimen of river discharge where storage reservoirs are also available. Because of the significance of snow with respect to river stages and especially to runoff, the making of snow surveys has now become a part of the regular program of work of the Weather Bureau and to some extent of that of the Geological Survey. Snow surveys are also being carried on in a

[4] Bibliog. 18·19.
[5] Bibliog. 2·32.

systematic manner by various cooperative groups of agencies and individuals. The results of these snow surveys are made available promptly to the local public by means of special mimeographed reports and, in some instances, in the newspapers which circulate in the region. Such special reports are of great value both as current information and with respect to their long-time uses related to the determination of the ratios of runoff to snow accumulation; in the arid and semiarid regions that rely so largely on snow fields for their supplies of irrigation water, they are commonly given wide publicity in the daily and weekly press.

Other special reports relate, in a general way, to the utility of rivers, and it is especially within this field that great care must be exercised in distinguishing between the discussion of specific nongovernmental projects and those broader aspects of the utilization of rivers in navigation, production of mechanical and electric energy, irrigation, and public water supplies that have general public significance with respect to regional development and stability. Since the public is concerned with the full practicable development and utilization of rivers, it has a real interest in broad regional studies of river slopes, possible dam and reservoir sites, and the quantities and seasonal distribution of water available at each to the end that development as made shall be an integral and proper part of complete utilization.[6]

Closely related to the phases and functions of rivers are various questions pertaining to the hydrologic cycle: transpiration as one of nature's principal methods for transferring water from the earth to the air, and the effects of vegetation, especially of forests, on stream flow; the use of water in irrigation, the resulting increase in transpiration and decrease in stream flow; the storage of water in reservoirs, the resulting delays in runoff and decrease in total runoff because of the increased exposure of water to the effects of evaporation; and the artificial control of river stages and discharges in order to decrease flood flows or to increase the utility of the river for irrigation or power; snow storage and release and the effects produced on the regimen of streams. These and other aspects of the circulation in the hydrologic cycle and of minor modifications in it as the result of the activities or works of man are proper subjects for special governmental reports related to rivers. The studies leading to such reports involve the most painstaking care. If they are made under controlled conditions in the laboratory, the near-perfect simulation of and departures from natural conditions are highly important. If they are made under

[6] Bibliog. 18·1, 2.

the complex, variable, varying, and uncontrollable conditions of the field, great care must be exercised in the collection and analysis of the basic information to insure that definite and apparently final conclusions are not drawn from data that are inadequate or inaccurate because of failure to recognize the variability of and variations in the conditions that affect the hydrologic cycle and that are beyond human control. If reliable conclusions are to be drawn, the program of work must be carefully planned, the instrumental equipment must be precise, and the operations must be conducted in a methodical and painstaking manner. Many of the processes of the hydrologic cycle are complex, difficult to measure with accuracy, and variable with the geology, topography, vegetation, and climate of the region. Studies that will lead to correct conclusions are therefore extremely difficult to make.

Field Methods. The field methods employed in connection with the preparation of special reports vary with conditions and with the aspect or aspects of water to be considered. So far as practicable, the methods are those utilized in regular observational work, a major exception being flood reports, for which special surveys must be made after the floods have subsided and for which methods of procedure in both field and office must be adopted that would not be considered satisfactory under normal conditions. Observations of stage are made on such established gages as may be available, and these observations, if possible, are converted into values of discharge by means of previously developed rating curves. Elsewhere, the stages, cross sections, and slopes of flood discharges must be ascertained and measured by means of surveys of the channel and of drift and other high-water marks. The rates of flood discharge must be computed either by a slope method utilizing the slopes and cross sections thus determined or by means of the contracted-area method, utilizing the fall through contracted openings (between bridge abutments, for example) as ascertained from surveys of high-water marks above and below such openings, or by means of the subsequently determined head on a dam and the use of an appropriate formula by which the peak flow may be calculated, or through other methods which at best are liable to greater errors than would be permissible in connection with regular statistical work. Many flood reports [7] afford illustrations of the application of each of these methods.

It must be recognized that these emergency methods are liable to error, perhaps large, because of the unavoidable inaccuracy of obser-

[7] Bibliog. 18·10, 11, 15, 16.

vations made after floods have subsided, and because of the uncertainty with respect to coefficients used in computing the flow over dams of various shapes of crests and varying depths of submergence, and through contracted openings of many shapes and sizes. The determinations of slopes of water surfaces and of areas of cross sections of flowing water are subject to at least two other sources of error that may be great: (1) the drift left by a flood may show the height of waves which will always be present to some extent at flood stages and which, in some instances, may be much above the general slope that accompanied the flood crest; and (2) owing to the scour and fill, the size and shape of the channel at the crest stage may be considerably different from what they are when surveys are made after the flood has subsided.

With full appreciation of these and other sources of error, it is often necessary to adopt the relatively unsatisfactory methods of measurement and computation indicated above in lieu of more satisfactory methods. Explanations of exceptional methods and of their applications in specific instances are contained in the flood reports listed in the bibliography.

Language and Form.[8] A report should, above everything else, be clear; preferably it should be concise; it should be sufficiently comprehensive to accomplish its purpose, and obviously it should be sound as to facts and conclusions within the limitations of the basic data. Reports that meet all these specifications are not common. Much more attention and study should be given by engineers to report writing, not only with respect to substance and arrangement but also to the choice of words and the sentence structure.

To be effective, engineering reports must be readily understandable to financiers, lawyers, and business men; the engineer should recognize this fact and train himself to present technical information either orally or in writing in nontechnical language that can be readily understood by those executives who are not engineers. Simplicity and clarity in language, which make for easy reading, are therefore the first requisites of a good report, whatever its subject or purpose may be. To the extent that it fails in this important respect, it falls short of being a first-class report.

Many nongovernmental engineering reports must include much information, perhaps in great detail, and must discuss several different aspects of the project or development. For example, a report on a water-power site must discuss the quantity and seasonal distribution

[8] Chapter 16.

of water, the available head, dam site, pondage, power-house site, transmission line, costs, the market for power, and other aspects; a report on an irrigation project must discuss the lands to be irrigated, the amount of water needed, the sufficiency of the supply of water, water rights, transportation facilities, costs, and colonization problems. Many such reports must necessarily be long, and, since they are to be used by busy men, each report should contain, preferably on its first page, a brief summary of the project, the facts, and the conclusions. After the summary, the report should contain an introduction in which the situation or project is outlined and the reasons for and basis of the report are set forth; a section or sections in which the essential facts are presented clearly and in an orderly manner; a section or sections in which the facts are analyzed and discussed and arguments, if any, are made; and a section in which deductions and conclusions are drawn from the facts, analyses, and arguments. The report should have a title page, or at least an adequate title; appropriate center and side headings; and, if of considerable length, a table of contents, list of illustrations, and index.

Unnecessary words detract from the readability, clarity, and value of a report. Conciseness is obtained in part by the elimination of unnecessary words but to a greater extent by the proper assembling and presentation of facts, arguments, and conclusions. Experienced writers and speakers without exception testify that a satisfactory short article or short address on any topic is much more difficult to prepare than a long one. So, also, a concise report requires much more intensive study of the arrangement and wording than a long report. The effort involved in achieving conciseness, however, always results in improvement in the readability, clarity, and value of any report.

BIBLIOGRAPHY 18

1. E. C. LaRue, Colorado River and Its Utilization, *U.S.G.S. Water Supply Paper* 395.
2. E. C. LaRue, Water Power and Flood Control of Colorado River below Green River, Utah, *U.S.G.S. Water Supply Paper* 556.
3. Robert Follansbee, Upper Colorado River and Its Utilization, *U.S.G.S. Water Supply Paper* 617.
4. Hoyt and Troxell, Forests and Stream Flow, *Trans. Am. Soc. C. E.*, Vol. 99, pp. 1–111.
5. C. S. Jarvis, Flood-Flow Characteristics, *Trans. Am. Soc. C. E.*, Vol. 89, pp. 985–1104.
6. A. E. Morgan, Planned Utilization of Water Resources, *Civil Engineering*, Vol. 7, No. 4, pp. 255–259 (April 1937).
7. Paulsen and others, Hurricane Floods of September 1938, *U.S.G.S. Water Supply Paper* 867.

8. N. C. Grover, The Floods of March 1936, *U.S.G.S. Water Supply Papers* 798, 799, 800.

9. N. C. Grover, Floods of Ohio and Mississippi Rivers, January-February 1937, *U.S.G.S. Water Supply Paper* 838.

10. Hollister Johnson, The New York State Flood of July 1935, *U.S.G.S. Water Supply Paper* 773-E.

11. Tate Dalrymple, Major Texas Floods of 1936, *U.S.G.S. Water Supply Paper* 816.

12. Tate Dalrymple, Floods in the Canadian and Pecos River Basins of New Mexico, May and June 1937, *U.S.G.S. Water Supply Paper* 842.

13. Follansbee and Spiegel, Flood on Republican and Kansas Rivers, May and June 1935, *U.S.G.S. Water Supply Paper* 796-B.

14. Troxell and Peterson, Flood in La Cañada Valley, Calif., January 1, 1934, *U.S.G.S. Water Supply Paper* 796-C.

15. H. B. Kinnison, The New England Flood of November 1927, *U.S.G.S. Water Supply Paper* 636-C.

16. McGlashan and Briggs, The Floods of December 1937 in Northern California, *U.S.G.S. Water Supply Paper* 843.

17. Kirk Bryan, Geology of Reservoir and Dam Sites, *U.S.G.S. Water Supply Paper* 597-A.

18. J. C. Hoyt, Droughts of 1930–34, *U.S.G.S. Water Supply Paper* 680.

19. J. C. Hoyt, Drought of 1936, *U.S.G.S. Water Supply Paper* 820.

20. National Resources Committee, *The Future of the Great Plains*, p. 32, 1936.

21. W. E. Dickinson, Summary of Surface Water Supply of Colorado River Basin, *U.S.G.S. Water Supply Paper* (unpublished in 1942).

CHAPTER 19

ORGANIZATION IN FIELD AND OFFICE

Economic Aspects. The art of collecting systematic and reliable records of river discharge is both complicated and highly technical. It consists of a specialized technique based on a science that is complex through an infinite variety of conditions and combines to an unusual degree the procedures developed both by practice and by theoretical considerations of the flow of water in open channels. Although the art may be and has been greatly advanced by both abstract reasoning and laboratory experimentation, it can approach perfection only in combination with wide experience in the measurement and recording of the flow of water in natural channels under extremely varied conditions. This art, though based on a science, has nevertheless been developed as a result of trial and experience under a wide variety of field conditions as related to the selection of sites and to the establishment of gaging stations and their subsequent operation.

The collection of records of river discharge at a group of well-located and well-equipped gaging stations which are easily accessible to a force of trained engineering assistants in a headquarters office may be relatively easy, especially if there is no limit to the expense that may be incurred. Such conditions do not apply, however, in an extensive program of stream gaging in which the funds available for equipment and operation are limited. In such a program, which is typical, the field engineer usually works alone or occasionally with an untrained local assistant, except as he may have with him an engineering assistant in training. He will travel in an automobile which he must drive himself and must carry with him adequate instrumental equipment to meet the wide variety of conditions which obtain in streams of many types. He must be prepared to work from bridges, cableways, and boats, and by wading, and, because accidents sometimes occur, he must be able to swim. Gaging stations must be visited frequently, the interval of time between visits depending upon the different aspects of the stations in relation to equipment, to permanence of the control sections, and to variations in precipitation and in the operation of storage reservoirs. High stages, especially flood stages, may change rapidly, and they are not only the most difficult to measure but also the most difficult to reach, especially on small streams that may go through a complete cycle from low to high and back to low within a few hours. The economics of the establishment, maintenance, and operation of gaging stations, therefore, depends both on the organization of the personnel and on the location and equipment of the stations.

Field Personnel. No two streams are alike, and no two locations for gaging stations are alike. There are relatively few sites for first-class gaging stations on any river, but there are many sites that, even with the best equipment and most careful operation, will yield only unsatisfactory records of discharge. The selection of the site, the establishment of a gaging station, and the subsequent successful operation of the station all involve the exercise of expert judgment that is based on extensive field experience and on a thorough knowledge of theoretical and experimental hydraulics.

The field engineers who select sites and establish and operate gaging stations must therefore be well grounded technically and must have had such field experience as will enable them to meet each new situation as it arises. They must, on occasion, devise practical methods which are theoretically sound and must apply such methods under many conditions that may not be conducive to the obtaining of satisfactory records. Such engineers can be obtained only through the training of men who have a sound basis of knowledge in the sciences of hydraulics and hydrology. The experienced field engineers who have the responsibility for collecting river records may have as assistants engineers in various stages of training, who will later help to train others. In a well-balanced and growing organization, such training is always in progress as new engineers are recruited to fill vacancies or new positions. Of course, this training is expensive, but it is nevertheless a necessary part of the cost of the work, and a trained engineer consequently represents a considerable investment. While the training is in progress, the field forces must be so organized and operated, singly or in groups, as to obtain reliable records at minimum cost.

Since the accuracy and reliability of the final records of stage and discharge depend to a large extent on his work, a sense of responsibility is perhaps one of the most important qualities a field engineer can possess. Likewise, adaptability is essential in this work, since a field engineer is away from home, sometimes for long periods of time, and must adjust himself to living conditions on the road, to continued travel by automobile, and to working in all kinds of weather. Even while he is at home, unexpected emergencies may develop which will make necessary his immediate return to the field. In addition, the field engineer has constantly to keep in mind that he is the representative of his organization and that the impressions concerning the work of stream gaging will be favorable or unfavorable, depending upon both his tact and the intelligent handling of such contacts as he may have with the public. Indeed, in no other phase of stream-gaging work is a wider diversity of mental and physical qualities needed than in the successful handling of both the usual and unusual situations encountered in the field work related to the operation of gaging stations.

Office Personnel. The office personnel of a broad stream-gaging program includes both engineers and clerks. The office engineers must be familiar with the gaging stations of their districts and must know the peculiarities of each station. They must therefore have had prior experience in the field work of the districts in which they are on duty and preferably in the field work of other districts as well. They must receive, check, and record currently the field data, advising the field engineers promptly of any inconsistencies or deficiencies in the field records so that check observations and measurements may be made and faulty observational data avoided. They must keep the office records as nearly current as practicable, revise rating curves and tables, and compute and make available provisional figures of daily discharge for those gaging stations the records of which are needed currently by cooperating agencies, by federal and state officials, or by the engineering, legal, and financial public. The office engineer must combine ability with field experience and knowledge of office procedure; he must be methodical and a rapid and accurate computer, and must supplement such knowledge and ability with maturity of judgment.

The field office clerks in such a broad program should have a general knowledge of the routine processes of field work and of the instruments and equipment used, be able to check computations and records, and on their own initiative prepare correspondence with the observers, the field engineers, and the public. In the absence from the office of the whole engineering force on emergency field work, they should be qualified to prepare and sign all routine correspondence and to assist the field force by forwarding essential information, equipment, and supplies as they are needed and requisitioned from the field. Upon the field office clerks generally rests the responsibility for keeping books that will show the status of each of the district funds, which may be several in number, depending on the number of cooperating agencies in the district. In addition, the clerks must see that all fiscal forms are properly prepared in accordance with the requirements of the governmental organization, federal, state, or municipal, from whose funds the accounts will ultimately be paid. They must therefore be alert, resourceful, and competent, both in clerical and accounting duties and in such quasi-technical work as may be required of them.

Recruiting Personnel. Changes occur in the personnel of a large stream-gaging organization because of fluctuations in the available funds, resignations to accept more lucrative employment, lack of individual fitness and adaptability, and occasionally dissatisfaction with the exacting conditions under which the work is carried on.

Since the problems of recruiting, training, and maintaining an organization for any broad regional stream-gaging program would in essence be the same in any other governmental or corporate organization, except for the requirement of recruiting through the United States Civil Service Commission, the procedure of the Geological Survey will be described as illustrating the methods followed in their solution. Because of the technical nature of the work and the infinite variety of conditions that may be encountered, "rule-of-thumb" practices in stream gaging cannot be tolerated. The engineers must be broadly grounded in theory and practice in order to develop a proper basis for the judgment which must be exercised and on which the integrity of the resulting records will depend.

The engineering and clerical personnel of the Geological Survey is recruited by certification of the United States Civil Service Commission from lists of eligible persons established as a result of competitive examination in accordance with federal law and with Commission regulations thereunder. Candidates for employment must therefore pass the appropriate examinations as a prerequisite to the placing of their names on the registers from which certifications are made.

Recruiting is generally accomplished in the lower grades because training is expensive and its cost should be kept as low as practicable by holding it within the lower-salary groups. Being more adaptable, young employees are more readily trained than older ones, and of course have longer expectation of service. The work involves the development of resourcefulness, the exercise of judgment, and the assumption of full responsibility for the steps taken, as well as cheerful acceptance of the hardships that are unavoidably associated with it. A new appointee serves a year of probation in order to be given an opportunity to decide whether he likes the work and to give the responsible officers of the Survey ample time to test his fitness techni-

cally, physically, and temperamentally. Those who meet the test
of this trial year are given permanent appointments. They are gradually trained and promoted as experience and ability are acquired
and without further formal examinations by the Commission.

Training Personnel. The training of personnel is an important
function of any large organization, such as the Water Resources
Branch of the Geological Survey, that is engaged in stream-gaging
work.

Individual clerks are well qualified by basic training in stenography
and typing for ordinary office work, but they must be subsequently
trained in the special technical and fiscal procedures which are part
of the office work of the Geological Survey. Their training is usually
supervised by the district engineer or office engineer, except that in a
large district where there are several clerks the newer clerical employees are trained by the district clerk, who, as the result of long
experience, is thoroughly familiar with the requirements and procedures of that particular district office. The scope of the duties of
the clerical force is determined by the district engineer, whose aim
should be that as much as possible of the routine semi-technical office
work may be accomplished by the clerks, in addition to their strictly
clerical duties, in order that the technical employees may devote their
time to the more technical aspects and problems of stream gaging.

In the Geological Survey, for example, the training of engineering
personnel starts with graduates of engineering colleges and proceeds,
at first under direct supervision, from simple to more complex operations into work requiring independent judgment and involving only
indirect supervision, and finally to detached employment requiring a
high degree of judgment as well as expertness in stream-gaging procedures and in computing and preparing the records for publication.
Training is informal, but it is nevertheless deliberate and progressive
and involves the transfer among districts of promising young engineers in order to give them the best and most valuable training for
the higher and ultimately the major positions in the organization and
to enable them to acquire experience under varying field conditions.

The attainment among the different districts of uniformity in instruments, equipment, and field and office methods in connection with
a nationwide field activity is not easy. Engineers, by nature, education, and experience, are inclined to be individualistic, and this characteristic is accentuated under the conditions of field work which relate
to water investigation. New and unexpected problems are met and
solved as they arise, generally without opportunity for consultation

with others who may have found different solutions for similar problems.

The Water Resources Bulletin. In order to give publicity to and encourage the discussion of pertinent problems, solutions, and experiences, the *Water Resources Bulletin* is issued quarterly in mimeographed form for the engineers of the Water Resources Branch; each field man is urged to contribute to this bulletin original articles and discussions of articles prepared by others. As a result of such articles and discussions, field instruments, equipment, and methods have been improved and field and office practices perfected and unified. The editions of these bulletins are necessarily limited, and circulation is restricted to the personnel of the Branch, not because the contents are confidential, but because copies cannot be made available in sufficient number to warrant outside circulation which, if once inaugurated, could hardly be restricted, and the bulletin would thus become a "publication." In that event, it would necessarily become more formal; its contents would be edited and changed in tone; and inevitably its value as a means of developing and coordinating the work of the Branch would be greatly reduced. It is possible that means should be found for making some of the information contained in the bulletin available to the public, but if this is done some medium of publication other than the bulletin should be found in order that its present value shall not be impaired.

In addition to the bulletin, the Branch encourages the exchange of ideas by correspondence, assigns special problems for study by intrabranch committees, and issues circular letters to the personnel in which promising ideas and practices are presented and so made generally available for the vital tests of field use. If these suggestions do not meet such tests, they must be modified and improved or else discarded. The field engineer who must produce results satisfactorily and economically can never be convinced of the value of a new device or procedure until it has stood the test of trial by different groups of men under different field conditions.

Conferences. Among the valuable practical means for training the widely scattered field personnel of the Water Resources Branch and for improving and coordinating methods of field procedure are conferences of engineers. Such conferences are encouraged whenever and wherever practicable; in addition, the practice has been developed of having occasional (one to five years apart) formal conferences of the Survey's district engineers. These meetings are invariably held in Washington in order to afford opportunities, without added cost, for conferences with the Director and the accounting and other general

Survey officials and with officials of other bureaus. They continue throughout a full week, during which the discussions follow a carefully prepared program of important topics, which, however, does not exclude other timely topics which may arise. At the conferences, the district engineers become better acquainted with each other and with the problems and difficulties that arise in different sections of the country. As a result of these contacts, procedures and improvements are discussed, equipment and technique are improved, and an excellent *esprit de corps* is promoted. Abstracts of the proceedings of the conferences are mimeographed and made available to the entire Branch personnel.

Districts. Activities related to stream gaging are always local, although they may be conducted as part of a nationwide program. The stream-gaging work of the Geological Survey is organized into districts, in order that field forces shall know local conditions, needs, and problems better and be readily available for work within a restricted area and also in order that the local public may know the field employees personally and be familiar with the nature of their activities. Each district, comprising one or more states, is generally bounded by state lines. Such an organization insures a minimum cost of travel, the availability of engineers when and where needed, an intimate acquaintance by the engineers with the gaging stations which they operate, and a sense of personal responsibility for the reliability and cost of the records; consequently it is efficient and economical. The district engineers, some of the principal assistant engineers, and the district clerks are generally assigned indefinitely in their respective districts. By the district arrangement, cooperative accounting is simplified, records are readily available for use by cooperating state and municipal officials, and good relations with those officials and with the local public are promoted.

Relations of District and Central Offices. Stream gaging and other related investigations of the quantity, quality, and availability of water are essentially field activities. This work is conducted through district offices under the direction of trained district engineers who have the principal responsibility for the quality of the field work and, within the limits of available funds, for the adequacy of the results and the economy of their procurement.

The central office has as its principal function to support and aid the field forces. It also observes and coordinates procedures, handles fiscal papers in their relation to general governmental records and accounting, promotes relations with other branches of the Survey and with other federal bureaus and departments, prepares reports for release or publication, handles general correspondence, and in other ways protects and promotes the field activities in their relation to other governmental activities and to the public. It seldom directs the details of field work, but it is responsible for its integrity through control of the selection, training, and assignment of its personnel and the coordination and publication of the records.

CHAPTER 20

COORDINATION IN ADMINISTRATION AND FINANCING

Need for Reliable Records. Reliable records of the quantity and frequently of the quality of water are needed as a basis for developments that utilize water in any considerable amounts. Without such records, the stability of these developments cannot be assured because of the danger that hydraulic works of all kinds and industrial and other plants that utilize water for the generation of power or in processing will not be properly designed, constructed, and operated to utilize efficiently the available supply of water. Such plants may be unduly expensive either because they are too large by reason of overdevelopment, or because they are too small and so can utilize only a part of the resource. Also, they may be unprofitable and uneconomical in operation if they are not sufficiently flexible to utilize, for one or many purposes, much of the varying supply of water available at the site. With the aid of such records, the available water supply may be utilized as fully as may be economically justifiable, and stability in local and regional development will be promoted.

Plans for the utilization of a power or industrial site, therefore, must be based on known limits and fluctuations in the supply of water, and frequently on its quality as well, if there is to be such sound development that the resultant growth in local population may be of a stable, prosperous, and contented type. Directly or indirectly, the whole population of a region or even of a nation is concerned in that potential development which such knowledge of the natural water resources makes possible. In order that stable local and regional growth may take place, reliable records of the varying supply of water must be readily available to anyone who may be concerned with its utilization.

Records of the quantity, quality, and availability of water are needed for a wide variety of purposes by officials of federal, state, and municipal governments and by the general public represented, in part, by engineers, financiers, lawyers, and the courts. In order that such needs may be impartially served, it is necessary that the records be available to everyone on the same basis and that they be without bias in that they shall not have been collected for a particular purpose to the disadvantage or detriment of other meritorious uses. It is necessary, too, that they be essentially uniform, both in accuracy and as to style and units adopted for publication, and also that they be continuous over a period of years in order to show with some degree of certainty the probable means and extremes of occurrence. Finally, it is necessary that, if possible, they be currently available for the needs of administration, development, operation, and litigation; that they bear the stamp of reliability through collection and publication by a recognized governmental authority; and that they be made available promptly at a minimum uniform cost to all who may need them. These essential objectives can be attained only by a centralized control of collection and publication through a single agency with no construction, administrative, or other responsibilities to impair the acceptability or availability of the records.

Limitations of Individual Effort. The incentive for an individual to collect on his own initiative records of river stages, discharges, or quality of flowing water might arise either from a personal or public-spirited interest in statistical information concerning precipitation, temperature, or river fluctuations, or from the thought that such records might lead to increased utilization and so to enhancement of the value of his lands or other property. An individual who has a personal interest in the records he is collecting becomes a good observer, and his records are commonly of as good quality as his own qualifications and the precision, suitability, and stability of his instruments and equipment will allow. However, such records are usually not published and ordinarily serve no public purpose. They are not uniform with respect to other records and are generally irretrievably lost with the death or migration of the individual who has collected them. Few, if any, individuals have the knowledge, financial resources, and continuity of interest to enable them to serve satisfactorily in collecting and making available reliable, continuing records of any natural phenomena. Although their records may serve in some instances to supplement other information and so assume considerable value, they cannot meet the public requirements that arise in connection with records of the fluctuations of water or with its control and utilization.

Limitations of Private or Commercial Organizations. Commercial or private organizations and corporations are commonly operated for the sole purpose of earning money. They may specialize in problems related to water and may collect information, perhaps in great detail, concerning certain aspects of water at particular times and places. They are generally adequately equipped and financed to collect the information which may be required to meet corporate needs or which they may be employed to obtain for their clients. However, the corporation's funds are available only for purposes that relate to corporate activities; they cannot be expended to promote or satisfy general public interests except so far as such interests may be related to those of the corporation. There can be no assurance that records collected by private organizations or corporations will best serve public needs, that they will be both continuous and continuing, or that the personnel which collects them will be adequately trained by broad experience in the technique of obtaining records relating to the occurrence of water. In general, such records will not be published, either because corporate funds may not be available to defray the costs of publication or because some or all of the records must be held confidential for purposes of litigation or to prevent use by competitors. Moreover, such records are lacking in uniformity as between different corporations and are always *ex parte* and so liable to the charge of bias in the sense that they may have been collected for a particular purpose. They cannot, therefore, be relied upon to serve public requirements even though many of them may be exhaustive, and all of them may be reliable and of great value.

It should be recognized also that public records will not always fully serve private or corporate needs, particularly where intensive studies of local situations which may have little public appeal or value are needed for the purposes of design, construction, or operation of local plants that utilize water. Lacking such general public appeal or value, these studies should perhaps form no part of a program carried out at public expense, however great may be their interest and value to the relatively few individuals who are users of water in the vicinity or who are students of hydrology.

Limitations of States and Public Corporations. All state, municipal, and other public agencies are liable to variable appropriations and changes, both in personnel and in facilities for publication.

City officials often have no long tenure in office. As a result, municipal field and office personnel, however competent they may otherwise be, may not have the essential qualifications as to training and experience, without which, of course, they cannot acquire the recognized standing as investigators that is needed to make their records generally acceptable to other governmental agencies, to the public, and to the courts. Under such circumstances, it would be difficult at best to develop uniform standards for methods or records or to maintain that unbiased attitude with respect to nonmunicipal uses that is so essential in obtaining records satisfactory for all purposes, nor are proper facilities for regular and systematic publication commonly provided.

Although in many respects states are much better equipped than municipalities to collect information about water, they are frequently unable to develop trained and permanent staffs of engineers, to improve methods, to collect consistent, uniform, and reliable records over a period of years, or to make the records systematically and promptly available to the public. Frequently, too, the collection of such records is merely an incidental matter, to be assigned for a short period of time or as a part-time job to any engineering employee who may be available.

The results of state investigations may have a definite state bias in relation to nonstate and interstate problems. State officials must protect the state's interests, which on occasion may be in conflict with those of some of its own citizens and of the citizens of other states. States commonly lack personnel broadly trained in investigational methods and in the techniques of field and office work, and, since they often suffer from variable appropriations, disastrous breaks in the records occur. State employees are limited in their fields of activities by the boundaries of their respective states, whereas water flows along and across state lines and in many instances may be measured most advantageously in an adjoining state. Records collected by states are not coordinated with those of other states and are not consistent among the states either with respect to accuracy, form of publication, or general availability. Therefore, the records so collected are not the result of broad systematic planning, may not be well adapted to serve public needs, are not uniform among the states, are often not continuous, well balanced, or readily available, and consequently do not always satisfy the many requirements of records related to water that have broad and varying uses by a public with many diverse and in part conflicting interests.

Limitations and Advantages of Federal Agencies. It is true that federal agencies suffer from fluctuations in funds and personnel, they may lack legal authority, and their officials may be unfamiliar with local problems and needs. On the other hand, they have a much greater stability in personnel and so acquire a broader background of experience than nonfederal governmental agencies. They are generally dissociated from bias as among several users and uses except perhaps in those instances where their activities relate to the construction of hydraulic works, to the administration of water, or to the supervision of lands that depend upon water for their value. Federal agencies are able to give reasonable assurance of uniformity in methods and records and in general to make the records available more or less promptly to the public.

It is unthinkable that any individual or group of individuals or any private corporation or group of such corporations should have the custody and control of information so vital to the development, stability, and prosperity of the country as the records of rivers and smaller streams. The collection of records related to water is a function of government because of the public interests involved and because only governmental agencies are equipped to conduct the necessary investigations and to publish the results on a reasonably satisfactory basis. Considering the various possible governmental agencies, the qualifications of a federal agency appear to outweigh by far those of all state and municipal agencies.

Reasons for Cooperation. In order to collect systematic, unbroken, and continuing records of the quantity and quality of the water in rivers, adequate and continuing financing is all-important. To assure such financing, there must be coordination of effort among the many private, corporate, and governmental agencies interested in and charged with the control, administration, and utilization of water. Coordination in financing naturally involves also coordination in administration by segregating in one organization the control and direction of the work, the administration of available funds, and the selection, training, and direction of the personnel engaged in the conduct of both field and office work. Without such coordination, duplication of work, incomplete and inadequate records, and unnecessary and unwarranted high costs will result. Such coordination is not easily arranged between groups whose interests are diverse and perhaps conflicting and whose personnel often includes able and ambitious individuals who hesitate to relinquish any small part of their prerogatives or to modify their ideas in even a minor degree to meet the ideas and wishes of others.

There is, however, no single governmental agency with available funds sufficient for the accomplishment of the great amount of work required in connection with the nationwide collection of river records or with the necessary knowledge of local and regional needs related to these records to enable it to act satisfactorily alone. Pooling of funds, information, and effort, therefore, is sought as an expression of cooperation among the interested governmental agencies. This appears to be the most practicable method of serving all interests satisfactorily and economically.

Qualifications of Governmental Agencies for Leadership in Cooperation. There is not at present and perhaps never will be a governmental agency that, acting entirely alone, is qualified in all respects for leadership in cooperation in water-resources investigations. The qualifications of agencies that might be so considered vary widely.

The officials and employees of states and municipalities generally possess the qualifications that pertain to public service, and many of these public corporations have ample funds and able technical employees. City officials are well informed concerning local needs, especially those that relate to the projects and operations of their own city. These officials realize that water-supply records are needed for the construction and operation of municipal water and sewerage systems, for promoting local development, and for the abatement of pollution.

State officials are familiar with the needs of their states with respect to the administration of water, to stream pollution and its abatement, to questions arising along the borders of adjacent states, to stability in local and regional development, and to litigation of statewide or interstate significance. Particularly in arid regions, the states employ engineers who are concerned with the distribution of water, are informed as to water rights, uses, and needs, and are devoted to public service.

In general, federal bureaus lack both the broad congressional authority necessary for water-resources investigations and the funds needed for general or cooperative programs of study. Their funds are generally available for specified purposes only, and their employees are relatively untrained in stream gaging, ground-water investigations, and allied work. Generally, they have either administrative or construction responsibilities or both, a fact which leads to fears of bias among those whose interests run counter to those of such bureaus. These bureaus, therefore, are not generally acceptable as agencies for centralizing and directing far-reaching cooperative programs in which the final results serve many users whose interests may be in conflict.

Among the several possible federal agencies, the Geological Survey appears to be the best qualified as the coordinating and centralizing agency for pooling the efforts of all governmental agencies in the study of rivers. It has a well-trained and experienced personnel of reasonably assured stability, and standards that are followed uniformly throughout the country without bias as to projects, locality, or administration. It has also reasonable stability of funds and a broad outlook on interstate, national, and international problems, developments, and needs. Although it does not have sufficient funds for the accomplishment of all the needed investigational work with respect to water, or knowledge of many local, state, and municipal problems and requirements, it does have broad congressional authorization, including specific recognition of cooperation with states and municipalities in the following language which is included in each annual act making appropriations for water-resources investigations:

Provided, That no part of this appropriation shall be expended in cooperation with States or municipalities except upon the basis of the State or municipality bearing all of the expense incident thereto in excess of such an amount as is necessary for the Geological Survey to perform its share of general water resource investigations, such share of the Geological Survey in no case exceeding 50 per centum of the cost of the investigation.

The necessary pooling of interests and resources in the study of water has been accomplished in this country through cooperation by states and municipalities with the Geological Survey, acting through its Water Resources Branch as the responsible centralizing agency. The Geological Survey is authorized by specific congressional sanction, quoted above, to serve the public in centralizing and coordinating this important work of cooperation with states and municipalities and is qualified to render this service by its long experience as a fact-finding organization and by its broadly worded general authorization that is carried in the following language in each annual appropriation act:

For gaging streams and determining the water supply of the United States, the investigation of underground currents and artesian wells, and the preparation of reports upon the best methods of utilizing the water resources.

Thus, the study of both surface water and ground water, of their quality with respect to industry, and of their utilization for all purposes, together with the reporting thereon, are authorized. The Survey is engaged in no other activities that disqualify it for these investigational duties.

As a result of a succession of trials in which the causes of failure have gradually been eliminated and the merging of funds and centralization of control have been accomplished, the Geological Survey has become the accepted centralizing agency in the collection of river records. It cooperates widely with other federal bureaus and with states and municipalities; coordinates, systematizes, and stabilizes the activities related to water-resources investigations; publishes the results promptly and uniformly; and in these and other ways serves the public needs. By such cooperation, the stability of financing and consequently of personnel appears to be reasonably well protected, certainly better so than by any other procedure that has yet been tried or proposed; and the uniformity of methods and the continuity and public availability of records are thereby assured. Under this procedure, the cooperative arrangements may readily be changed to meet new and unforeseen conditions, and the records related to water are made consistent, reliable, and more or less currently available to all who need them. This cooperative procedure has superseded the uncoordinated efforts of federal, state, and municipal agencies, private corporations and individuals, each acting independently of the others, whereby broken, nonuniform, and generally unsatisfactory records were collected. Such records, at least in part, were unpublished and to that extent were largely lost in many different offices and forgotten files. The ways and means which enable the Geological Survey to perform this important public function have been developed by a series of trials in which there were both successes and failures but in which there were also mutual perseverance and forbearance until workable cooperative arrangements were found and adopted. Had it been properly authorized by Congress, some other federal bureau might have been organized or developed to carry on the investigational work which the Geological Survey is now doing, and it is possible that at some future time such another bureau will be so organized or developed. If and when such a bureau appears, it should be an investigational agency allied with other investigational agencies having no administrative or construction responsibilities. Before it can accomplish what the Geological Survey is now doing, it must have developed a personnel possessing the spirit of scientific investigation whereby facts are sought and published without bias. It must have merited and acquired public confidence in the soundness of its work; it must possess the ability to cooperate with many agencies under a wide variety of laws and regulations and with changing personnels, and it must have the confidence of Congress in the nature and soundness of its work—in other words, it must acquire all the present qualifications of the Geological Survey.

Cooperative Financing. Before cooperation between any two parties can be arranged, there must be some mutual interest in the subject matter of the cooperation and the conditions of cooperation must be reasonably attractive to both parties; in order that it may continue, the results must be valuable and acceptable to both parties in substance, availability, and form. There is mutual interest among municipal, state, and federal agencies in studying the quantity, quality, and availability of water, and to that extent at least there is a continuing basis for cooperation. Satisfactory terms are reached by an equitable division of the costs, by mutual agreement as to what work is to be done, by utilization of the recognized standard methods of the Geological Survey, and by placing with the Geological Survey the responsibility for the integrity, direction, and control of the work. Congress has prescribed that the federal participation in such cooperation shall not exceed one-half of the cost of the work, and on this basis cooperation has been successfully carried on for many years. The personnel is generally recruited through the United States Civil Service Commission, thus insuring as well as may be the conditions of stability under which employees may be trained with assurance of continued availability and under which methods may be improved and applied uniformly throughout the country. The accounting for state and municipal funds, of course, must be in accordance with applicable state or municipal laws and regulations, and that for federal funds in accordance with federal requirements. The results of the work are currently available before publication to all parties to the cooperation.

Publication of Cooperative Records. The information collected by the Geological Survey is uniform in substance and form, regardless of whether it was financed through cooperation or otherwise. Cooperative and noncooperative records are, therefore, generally combined and published in the series of *Water Supply Papers*, where they are available to one and all. Cooperative records may be published by a state or municipality for local use and because of local reasons. It seems desirable, however, that the records contained in *Water Supply Papers* be essentially complete, because that series is now recognized as the repository for information with respect to water as a resource; there the information bears the stamp of the Federal Government and is in the most convenient form for engineers, financiers, lawyers, and the courts. Wherever published, the cooperative records carry the information that they are the result of cooperation between the appropriate states, municipalities, or other federal agencies and the Geological Survey.

INDEX

CATALOGUE OF DOVER BOOKS

PHYSICS

General physics

FOUNDATIONS OF PHYSICS, R. B. Lindsay & H. Margenau. Excellent bridge between semi-popular works & technical treatises. A discussion of methods of physical description, construction of theory; valuable for physicist with elementary calculus who is interested in ideas that give meaning to data, tools of modern physics. Contents include symbolism, mathematical equations; space & time foundations of mechanics; probability; physics & continua; electron theory; special & general relativity; quantum mechanics; causality. "Thorough and yet not overdetailed. Unreservedly recommended," NATURE (London). Unabridged, corrected edition. List of recommended readings. 35 illustrations. xi + 537pp. 5⅜ x 8.
S377 Paperbound **$2.75**

FUNDAMENTAL FORMULAS OF PHYSICS, ed. by D. H. Menzel. Highly useful, fully inexpensive reference and study text, ranging from simple to highly sophisticated operations. Mathematics integrated into text—each chapter stands as short textbook of field represented. Vol. 1: Statistics, Physical Constants, Special Theory of Relativity, Hydrodynamics, Aerodynamics, Boundary Value Problems in Math. Physics; Viscosity, Electromagnetic Theory, etc. Vol. 2: Sound, Acoustics, Geometrical Optics, Electron Optics, High-Energy Phenomena, Magnetism, Biophysics, much more. Index. Total of 800pp. 5⅜ x 8.　　　Vol. 1 S595 Paperbound **$2.00**
Vol. 2 S596 Paperbound **$2.00**

MATHEMATICAL PHYSICS, D. H. Menzel. Thorough one-volume treatment of the mathematical techniques vital for classic mechanics, electromagnetic theory, quantum theory, and relativity. Written by the Harvard Professor of Astrophysics for junior, senior, and graduate courses, it gives clear explanations of all those aspects of function theory, vectors, matrices, dyadics, tensors, partial differential equations, etc., necessary for the understanding of the various physical theories. Electron theory, relativity, and other topics seldom presented appear here in considerable detail. Scores of definitions, conversion factors, dimensional constants, etc. "More detailed than normal for an advanced text . . . excellent set of sections on Dyadics, Matrices, and Tensors," JOURNAL OF THE FRANKLIN INSTITUTE. Index. 193 problems, with answers. x + 412pp. 5⅜ x 8.　　　　　　　　S56 Paperbound **$2.00**

THE SCIENTIFIC PAPERS OF J. WILLARD GIBBS. All the published papers of America's outstanding theoretical scientist (except for "Statistical Mechanics" and "Vector Analysis"). Vol I (thermodynamics) contains one of the most brilliant of all 19th-century scientific papers—the 300-page "On the Equilibrium of Heterogeneous Substances," which founded the science of physical chemistry, and clearly stated a number of highly important natural laws for the first time; 8 other papers complete the first volume. Vol II includes 2 papers on dynamics, 8 on vector analysis and multiple algebra, 5 on the electromagnetic theory of light, and 6 miscellaneous papers. Biographical sketch by H. A. Bumstead. Total of xxxvi + 718pp. 5⅝ x 8⅜.
S721 Vol I Paperbound **$2.50**
S722 Vol II Paperbound **$2.00**
The set **$4.50**

BASIC THEORIES OF PHYSICS, Peter Gabriel Bergmann. Two-volume set which presents a critical examination of important topics in the major subdivisions of classical and modern physics. The first volume is concerned with classical mechanics and electrodynamics: mechanics of mass points, analytical mechanics, matter in bulk, electrostatics and magnetostatics, electromagnetic interaction, the field waves, special relativity, and waves. The second volume (Heat and Quanta) contains discussions of the kinetic hypothesis, physics and statistics, stationary ensembles, laws of thermodynamics, early quantum theories, atomic spectra, probability waves, quantization in wave mechanics, approximation methods, and abstract quantum theory. A valuable supplement to any thorough course or text.
Heat and Quanta: Index. 8 figures. x + 300pp. 5⅜ x 8½.　　　　　　S968 Paperbound **$2.00**
Mechanics and Electrodynamics: Index. 14 figures. vii + 280pp. 5⅜ x 8½.
S969 Paperbound **$1.75**

THEORETICAL PHYSICS, A. S. Kompaneyets. One of the very few thorough studies of the subject in this price range. Provides advanced students with a comprehensive theoretical background. Especially strong on recent experimentation and developments in quantum theory. Contents: Mechanics (Generalized Coordinates, Lagrange's Equation, Collision of Particles, etc.), Electrodynamics (Vector Analysis, Maxwell's equations, Transmission of Signals, Theory of Relativity, etc.), Quantum Mechanics (the Inadequacy of Classical Mechanics, the Wave Equation, Motion in a Central Field, Quantum Theory of Radiation, Quantum Theories of Dispersion and Scattering, etc.), and Statistical Physics (Equilibrium Distribution of Molecules in an Ideal Gas, Boltzmann statistics, Bose and Fermi Distribution, Thermodynamic Quantities, etc.). Revised to 1961. Translated by George Yankovsky, authorized by Kompaneyets. 137 exercises. 56 figures. 529pp. 5⅜ x 8½.　S972 Paperbound **$2.50**

ANALYTICAL AND CANONICAL FORMALISM IN PHYSICS, André Mercier. A survey, in one volume, of the variational principles (the key principles—in mathematical form—from which the basic laws of any one branch of physics can be derived) of the several branches of physical theory, together with an examination of the relationships among them. Contents: the Lagrangian Formalism, Lagrangian Densities, Canonical Formalism, Canonical Form of Electrodynamics, Hamiltonian Densities, Transformations, and Canonical Form with Vanishing Jacobian Determinant. Numerous examples and exercises. For advanced students, teachers, etc. 6 figures. Index. viii + 222pp. 5⅜ x 8½.　　　　　　S1077 Paperbound **$1.75**

Acoustics, optics, electricity and magnetism, electromagnetics, magneto-hydrodynamics

THE THEORY OF SOUND, Lord Rayleigh. Most vibrating systems likely to be encountered in practice can be tackled successfully by the methods set forth by the great Nobel laureate, Lord Rayleigh. Complete coverage of experimental, mathematical aspects of sound theory. Partial contents: Harmonic motions, vibrating systems in general, lateral vibrations of bars, curved plates or shells, applications of Laplace's functions to acoustical problems, fluid friction, plane vortex-sheet, vibrations of solid bodies, etc. This is the first inexpensive edition of this great reference and study work. Bibliography. Historical introduction by R. B. Lindsay. Total of 1040pp. 97 figures. 5⅜ x 8.
S292, S293, Two volume set, paperbound, **$4.70**

THE DYNAMICAL THEORY OF SOUND, H. Lamb. Comprehensive mathematical treatment of the physical aspects of sound, covering the theory of vibrations, the general theory of sound, and the equations of motion of strings, bars, membranes, pipes, and resonators. Includes chapters on plane, spherical, and simple harmonic waves, and the Helmholtz Theory of Audition. Complete and self-contained development for student and specialist; all fundamental differential equations solved completely. Specific mathematical details for such important phenomena as harmonics, normal modes, forced vibrations of strings, theory of reed pipes, etc. Index. Bibliography. 86 diagrams. viii + 307pp. 5⅜ x 8.
S655 Paperbound **$1.50**

WAVE PROPAGATION IN PERIODIC STRUCTURES, L. Brillouin. A general method and application to different problems: pure physics, such as scattering of X-rays of crystals, thermal vibration in crystal lattices, electronic motion in metals; and also problems of electrical engineering. Partial contents: elastic waves in 1-dimensional lattices of point masses. Propagation of waves along 1-dimensional lattices. Energy flow. 2 dimensional, 3 dimensional lattices. Mathieu's equation. Matrices and propagation of waves along an electric line. Continuous electric lines. 131 illustrations. Bibliography. Index. xii + 253pp. 5⅜ x 8.
S34 Paperbound **$2.00**

THEORY OF VIBRATIONS, N. W. McLachlan. Based on an exceptionally successful graduate course given at Brown University, this discusses linear systems having 1 degree of freedom, forced vibrations of simple linear systems, vibration of flexible strings, transverse vibrations of bars and tubes, transverse vibration of circular plate, sound waves of finite amplitude, etc. Index. 99 diagrams. 160pp. 5⅜ x 8.
S190 Paperbound **$1.35**

LIGHT: PRINCIPLES AND EXPERIMENTS, George S. Monk. Covers theory, experimentation, and research. Intended for students with some background in general physics and elementary calculus. Three main divisions: 1) Eight chapters on geometrical optics—fundamental concepts (the ray and its optical length, Fermat's principle, etc.), laws of image formation, apertures in optical systems, photometry, optical instruments etc.; 2) 9 chapters on physical optics—interference, diffraction, polarization, spectra, the Rayleigh refractometer, the wave theory of light, etc.; 3) 23 instructive experiments based directly on the theoretical text. "Probably the best intermediate textbook on light in the English language. Certainly, it is the best book which includes both geometrical and physical optics," J. Rud Nielson, PHYSICS FORUM. Revised edition. 102 problems and answers. 12 appendices. 6 tables. Index. 270 illustrations. xi +489pp. 5⅜ x 8½.
S341 Paperbound **$2.50**

PHOTOMETRY, John W. T. Walsh. The best treatment of both "bench" and "illumination" photometry in English by one of Britain's foremost experts in the field (President of the International Commission on Illumination). Limited to those matters, theoretical and practical, which affect the measurement of light flux, candlepower, illumination, etc., and excludes treatment of the use to which such measurements may be put after they have been made. Chapters on Radiation, The Eye and Vision, Photo-Electric Cells, The Principles of Photometry, The Measurement of Luminous Intensity, Colorimetry, Spectrophotometry, Stellar Photometry, The Photometric Laboratory, etc. Third revised (1958) edition. 281 illustrations. 10 appendices. xxiv + 544pp. 5½ x 9¼.
S319 Clothbound **$10.00**

EXPERIMENTAL SPECTROSCOPY, R. A. Sawyer. Clear discussion of prism and grating spectrographs and the techniques of their use in research, with emphasis on those principles and techniques that are fundamental to practically all uses of spectroscopic equipment. Beginning with a brief history of spectroscopy, the author covers such topics as light sources, spectroscopic apparatus, prism spectroscopes and graphs, diffraction grating, the photographic process, determination of wave length, spectral intensity, infrared spectroscopy, spectrochemical analysis, etc. This revised edition contains new material on the production of replica gratings, solar spectroscopy from rockets, new standard of wave length, etc. Index. Bibliography. 111 illustrations. x + 358pp. 5⅜ x 8½.
S1045 Paperbound **$2.25**

FUNDAMENTALS OF ELECTRICITY AND MAGNETISM, L. B. Loeb. For students of physics, chemistry, or engineering who want an introduction to electricity and magnetism on a higher level and in more detail than general elementary physics texts provide. Only elementary differential and integral calculus is assumed. Physical laws developed logically, from magnetism to electric currents, Ohm's law, electrolysis, and on to static electricity, induction, etc. Covers an unusual amount of material; one third of book on modern material: solution of wave equation, photoelectric and thermionic effects, etc. Complete statement of the various electrical systems of units and interrelations. 2 Indexes. 75 pages of problems with answers stated. Over 300 figures and diagrams. xix +669pp. 5⅜ x 8.
S745 Paperbound **$2.75**

MATHEMATICAL ANALYSIS OF ELECTRICAL AND OPTICAL WAVE-MOTION, Harry Bateman. Written by one of this century's most distinguished mathematical physicists, this is a practical introduction to those developments of Maxwell's electromagnetic theory which are directly connected with the solution of the partial differential equation of wave motion. Methods of solving wave-equation, polar-cylindrical coordinates, diffraction, transformation of coordinates, homogeneous solutions, electromagnetic fields with moving singularities, etc. Index. 168pp. 5⅜ x 8. S14 Paperbound **$1.75**

PRINCIPLES OF PHYSICAL OPTICS, Ernst Mach. This classical examination of the propagation of light, color, polarization, etc. offers an historical and philosophical treatment that has never been surpassed for breadth and easy readability. Contents: Rectilinear propagation of light. Reflection, refraction. Early knowledge of vision. Dioptrics. Composition of light. Theory of color and dispersion. Periodicity. Theory of interference. Polarization. Mathematical representation of properties of light. Propagation of waves, etc. 279 illustrations, 10 portraits. Appendix. Indexes. 324pp. 5⅜ x 8. S178 Paperbound **$2.00**

THE THEORY OF OPTICS, Paul Drude. One of finest fundamental texts in physical optics, classic offers thorough coverage, complete mathematical treatment of basic ideas. Includes fullest treatment of application of thermodynamics to optics; sine law in formation of images, transparent crystals, magnetically active substances, velocity of light, apertures, effects depending upon them, polarization, optical instruments, etc. Introduction by A. A. Michelson. Index. 110 illus. 567pp. 5⅜ x 8. S532 Paperbound **$2.45**

ELECTRICAL THEORY ON THE GIORGI SYSTEM, P. Cornelius. A new clarification of the fundamental concepts of electricity and magnetism, advocating the convenient m.k.s. system of units that is steadily gaining followers in the sciences. Illustrating the use and effectiveness of his terminology with numerous applications to concrete technical problems, the author here expounds the famous Giorgi system of electrical physics. His lucid presentation and well-reasoned, cogent argument for the universal adoption of this system form one of the finest pieces of scientific exposition in recent years. 28 figures. Index. Conversion tables for translating earlier data into modern units. Translated from 3rd Dutch edition by L. J. Jolley. x + 187pp. 5½ x 8¾. S909 Clothbound **$6.00**

ELECTRIC WAVES: BEING RESEARCHES ON THE PROPAGATION OF ELECTRIC ACTION WITH FINITE VELOCITY THROUGH SPACE, Heinrich Hertz. This classic work brings together the original papers in which Hertz—Helmholtz's protegé and one of the most brilliant figures in 19th-century research—probed the existence of electromagnetic waves and showed experimentally that their velocity equalled that of light, research that helped lay the groundwork for the development of radio, television, telephone, telegraph, and other modern technological marvels. Unabridged republication of original edition. Authorized translation by D. E. Jones. Preface by Lord Kelvin. Index of names. 40 illustrations. xvii + 278pp. 5⅜ x 8½. S57 Paperbound **$1.75**

PIEZOELECTRICITY: AN INTRODUCTION TO THE THEORY AND APPLICATIONS OF ELECTRO-MECHANICAL PHENOMENA IN CRYSTALS, Walter G. Cady. This is the most complete and systematic coverage of this important field in print—now regarded as something of scientific classic. This republication, revised and corrected by Prof. Cady—one of the foremost contributors in this area—contains a sketch of recent progress and new material on Ferroelectrics. Time Standards, etc. The first 7 chapters deal with fundamental theory of crystal electricity. 5 important chapters cover basic concepts of piezoelectricity, including comparisons of various competing theories in the field. Also discussed: piezoelectric resonators (theory, methods of manufacture, influences of air-gaps, etc.); the piezo oscillator; the properties, history, and observations relating to Rochelle salt; ferroelectric crystals; miscellaneous applications of piezoelectricity; pyroelectricity; etc. "A great work," W. A. Wooster, NATURE. Revised (1963) and corrected edition. New preface by Prof. Cady. 2 Appendices. Indices. Illustrations. 62 tables. Bibliography. Problems. Total of 1 + 822pp. 5⅜ x 8½.
S1094 Vol. I Paperbound **$2.50**
S1095 Vol. II Paperbound **$2.50**
Two volume set Paperbound **$5.00**

MAGNETISM AND VERY LOW TEMPERATURES, H. B. G. Casimir. A basic work in the literature of low temperature physics. Presents a concise survey of fundamental theoretical principles, and also points out promising lines of investigation. Contents: Classical Theory and Experimental Methods, Quantum Theory of Paramagnetism, Experiments on Adiabatic Demagnetization. Theoretical Discussion of Paramagnetism at Very Low Temperatures, Some Experimental Results, Relaxation Phenomena. Index. 89-item bibliography. ix + 95pp. 5⅜ x 8.
S943 Paperbound **$1.25**

SELECTED PAPERS ON NEW TECHNIQUES FOR ENERGY CONVERSION: THERMOELECTRIC METHODS; THERMIONIC; PHOTOVOLTAIC AND ELECTRICAL EFFECTS; FUSION, Edited by Sumner N. Levine. Brings together in one volume the most important papers (1954-1961) in modern energy technology. Included among the 37 papers are general and qualitative descriptions of the field as a whole, indicating promising lines of research. Also: 15 papers on thermoelectric methods, 7 on thermionic, 5 on photovoltaic, 4 on electrochemical effect, and 2 on controlled fusion research. Among the contributors are: Joffe, Maria Telkes, Herold, Herring, Douglas, Jaumot, Post, Austin, Wilson, Pfann, Rappaport, Morehouse, Domenicali, Moss, Bowers, Harman, Von Doenhoef. Preface and introduction by the editor. Bibliographies. xxviii + 451pp. 6⅛ x 9¼. S37 Paperbound **$3.00**

SUPERFLUIDS: MACROSCOPIC THEORY OF SUPERCONDUCTIVITY, Vol. I, Fritz London. The major work by one of the founders and great theoreticians of modern quantum physics. Consolidates the researches that led to the present understanding of the nature of super-conductivity. Prof. London here reveals that quantum mechanics is operative on the macro-scopic plane as well as the submolecular level. Contents: Properties of Superconductors and Their Thermodynamical Correlation; Electrodynamics of the Pure Superconducting State; Relation between Current and Field; Measurements of the Penetration Depth; Non-Viscous Flow vs. Superconductivity; Micro-waves in Superconductors; Reality of the Domain Structure; and many other related topics. A new epilogue by M. J. Buckingham discusses developments in the field up to 1960. Corrected and expanded edition. An appreciation of the author's life and work by L. W. Nordheim. Biography by Edith London. Bibliography of his publica-tions. 45 figures. 2 Indices. xviii + 173pp. 5⅝ x 8⅜.   S44 Paperbound **$1.45**

SELECTED PAPERS ON PHYSICAL PROCESSES IN IONIZED PLASMAS, Edited by Donald H. Menzel, Director, Harvard College Observatory. 30 important papers relating to the study of highly ionized gases or plasmas selected by a foremost contributor in the field, with the assistance of Dr. L. H. Aller. The essays include 18 on the physical processes in gaseous nebulae, covering problems of radiation and radiative transfer, the Balmer decrement, electron temperatures, spectrophotometry, etc. 10 papers deal with the interpretation of nebular spectra, by Bohm, Van Vleck, Aller, Minkowski, etc. There is also a discussion of the intensities of "forbidden" spectral lines by George Shortley and a paper concern-ing the theory of hydrogenic spectra by Menzel and Pekeris. Other contributors: Goldberg, Hebb, Baker, Bowen, Ufford, Liller, etc. viii + 374pp. 6⅛ x 9¼.   S60 Paperbound **$2.95**

THE ELECTROMAGNETIC FIELD, Max Mason & Warren Weaver. Used constantly by graduate engineers. Vector methods exclusively: detailed treatment of electrostatics, expansion meth-ods, with tables converting any quantity into absolute electromagnetic, absolute electrostatic, practical units. Discrete charges, ponderable bodies, Maxwell field equations, etc. Introduc-tion. Indexes. 416pp. 5⅜ x 8.   S185 Paperbound **$2.00**

THEORY OF ELECTRONS AND ITS APPLICATION TO THE PHENOMENA OF LIGHT AND RADIANT HEAT, H. Lorentz. Lectures delivered at Columbia University by Nobel laureate Lorentz. Unabridged, they form a historical coverage of the theory of free electrons, motion, absorption of heat, Zeeman effect, propagation of light in molecular bodies, inverse Zeeman effect, optical phenomena in moving bodies, etc. 109 pages of notes explain the more advanced sections. Index. 9 figures. 352pp. 5⅜ x 8.   S173 Paperbound **$1.85**

FUNDAMENTAL ELECTROMAGNETIC THEORY, Ronold P. King, Professor Applied Physics, Harvard University. Original and valuable introduction to electromagnetic theory and to circuit theory from the standpoint of electromagnetic theory. Contents: Mathematical Description of Matter—stationary and nonstationary states; Mathematical Description of Space and of Simple Media—Field Equations, Integral Forms of Field Equations, Electromagnetic Force, etc.; Transformation of Field and Force Equations; Electromagnetic Waves in Unbounded Regions; Skin Effect and Internal Impedance—in a solid cylindrical conductor, etc.; and Electrical Circuits—Analytical Foundations, Near-zone and quasi-near zone circuits, Balanced two-wire and four-wire transmission lines. Revised and enlarged version. New preface by the author. 5 appendices (Differential operators: Vector Formulas and Identities, etc.). Problems. Indexes. Bibliography. xvi + 580pp. 5⅜ x 8½.   S1023 Paperbound **$2.75**

Hydrodynamics

A TREATISE ON HYDRODYNAMICS, A. B. Basset. Favorite text on hydrodynamics for 2 genera-tions of physicists, hydrodynamical engineers, oceanographers, ship designers, etc. Clear enough for the beginning student, and thorough source for graduate students and engineers on the work of d'Alembert, Euler, Laplace, Lagrange, Poisson, Green, Clebsch, Stokes, Cauchy, Helmholtz, J. J. Thomson, Love, Hicks, Greenhill, Besant, Lamb, etc. Great amount of docu-mentation on entire theory of classical hydrodynamics. Vol I: theory of motion of frictionless liquids, vortex, and cyclic irrotational motion, etc. 132 exercises. Bibliography. 3 Appendixes. xii + 264pp. Vol II: motion in viscous liquids, harmonic analysis, theory of tides, etc. 112 exercises, Bibliography. 4 Appendixes. xv + 328pp. Two volume set. 5⅜ x 8.
S724 Vol I Paperbound **$1.75**
S725 Vol II Paperbound **$1.75**
The set **$3.50**

HYDRODYNAMICS, Horace Lamb. Internationally famous complete coverage of standard refer-ence work on dynamics of liquids & gases. Fundamental theorems, equations, methods, solutions, background, for classical hydrodynamics. Chapters include Equations of Motion, Integration of Equations in Special Gases, Irrotational Motion, Motion of Liquid in 2 Dimen-sions, Motion of Solids through Liquid-Dynamical Theory, Vortex Motion, Tidal Waves, Surface Waves, Waves of Expansion, Viscosity, Rotating Masses of liquids. Excellently planned, ar-ranged; clear, lucid presentation. 6th enlarged, revised edition. Index. Over 900 footnotes, mostly bibliographical. 119 figures. xv + 738pp. 6⅛ x 9¼.   S256 Paperbound **$3.75**

HYDRODYNAMICS, H. Dryden, F. Murnaghan, Harry Bateman. Published by the National Research Council in 1932 this enormous volume offers a complete coverage of classical hydrodynamics. Encyclopedic in quality. Partial contents: physics of fluids, motion, turbulent flow, compressible fluids, motion in 1, 2, 3 dimensions; viscous fluids rotating, laminar motion, resistance of motion through viscous fluid, eddy viscosity, hydraulic flow in channels of various shapes, discharge of gases, flow past obstacles, etc. Bibliography of over 2,900 items. Indexes. 23 figures. 634pp. 5⅜ x 8.   S303 Paperbound $2.75

Mechanics, dynamics, thermodynamics, elasticity

MECHANICS, J. P. Den Hartog. Already a classic among introductory texts, the M.I.T. professor's lively and discursive presentation is equally valuable as a beginner's text, an engineering student's refresher, or a practicing engineer's reference. Emphasis in this highly readable text is on illuminating fundamental principles and showing how they are embodied in a great number of real engineering and design problems: trusses, loaded cables, beams, jacks, hoists, etc. Provides advanced material on relative motion and gyroscopes not usual in introductory texts. "Very thoroughly recommended to all those anxious to improve their real understanding of the principles of mechanics." MECHANICAL WORLD. Index. List of equations. 334 problems, all with answers. Over 550 diagrams and drawings. ix + 462pp. 5⅜ x 8.
S754 Paperbound $2.00

THEORETICAL MECHANICS: AN INTRODUCTION TO MATHEMATICAL PHYSICS, J. S. Ames, F. D. Murnaghan. A mathematically rigorous development of theoretical mechanics for the advanced student, with constant practical applications. Used in hundreds of advanced courses. An unusually thorough coverage of gyroscopic and baryscopic material, detailed analyses of the Coriolis acceleration, applications of Lagrange's equations, motion of the double pendulum, Hamilton-Jacobi partial differential equations, group velocity and dispersion, etc. Special relativity is also included. 159 problems. 44 figures. ix + 462pp. 5⅜ x 8.
S461 Paperbound $2.25

THEORETICAL MECHANICS: STATICS AND THE DYNAMICS OF A PARTICLE, W. D. MacMillan. Used for over 3 decades as a self-contained and extremely comprehensive advanced undergraduate text in mathematical physics, physics, astronomy, and deeper foundations of engineering. Early sections require only a knowledge of geometry; later, a working knowledge of calculus. Hundreds of basic problems, including projectiles to the moon, escape velocity, harmonic motion, ballistics, falling bodies, transmission of power, stress and strain, elasticity, astronomical problems. 340 practice problems plus many fully worked out examples make it possible to test and extend principles developed in the text. 200 figures. xvii + 430pp. 5⅜ x 8.   S467 Paperbound $2.00

THEORETICAL MECHANICS: THE THEORY OF THE POTENTIAL, W. D. MacMillan. A comprehensive, well balanced presentation of potential theory, serving both as an introduction and a reference work with regard to specific problems, for physicists and mathematicians. No prior knowledge of integral relations is assumed, and all mathematical material is developed as it becomes necessary. Includes: Attraction of Finite Bodies; Newtonian Potential Function; Vector Fields, Green and Gauss Theorems; Attractions of Surfaces and Lines; Surface Distribution of Matter; Two-Layer Surfaces; Spherical Harmonics; Ellipsoidal Harmonics; etc. "The great number of particular cases . . . should make the book valuable to geophysicists and others actively engaged in practical applications of the potential theory," Review of Scientific Instruments. Index. Bibliography. xiii + 469pp. 5⅜ x 8.   S486 Paperbound $2.50

THEORETICAL MECHANICS: DYNAMICS OF RIGID BODIES, W. D. MacMillan. Theory of dynamics of a rigid body is developed, using both the geometrical and analytical methods of instruction. Begins with exposition of algebra of vectors, it goes through momentum principles, motion in space, use of differential equations and infinite series to solve more sophisticated dynamics problems. Partial contents: moments of inertia, systems of free particles, motion parallel to a fixed plane, rolling motion, method of periodic solutions, much more. 82 figs. 199 problems. Bibliography. Indexes. xii + 476pp. 5⅜ x 8.   S641 Paperbound $2.50

MATHEMATICAL FOUNDATIONS OF STATISTICAL MECHANICS, A. I. Khinchin. Offering a precise and rigorous formulation of problems, this book supplies a thorough and up-to-date exposition. It provides analytical tools needed to replace cumbersome concepts, and furnishes for the first time a logical step-by-step introduction to the subject. Partial contents: geometry & kinematics of the phase space, ergodic problem, reduction to theory of probability, application of central limit problem, ideal monatomic gas, foundation of thermo-dynamics, dispersion and distribution of sum functions. Key to notations. Index. viii + 179pp. 5⅜ x 8.
S147 Paperbound $1.50

ELEMENTARY PRINCIPLES IN STATISTICAL MECHANICS, J. W. Gibbs. Last work of the great Yale mathematical physicist, still one of the most fundamental treatments available for advanced students and workers in the field. Covers the basic principle of conservation of probability of phase, theory of errors in the calculated phases of a system, the contributions of Clausius, Maxwell, Boltzmann, and Gibbs himself, and much more. Includes valuable comparison of statistical mechanics with thermodynamics: Carnot's cycle, mechanical definitions of entropy, etc. xvi + 208pp. 5⅜ x 8.   S707 Paperbound $1.45

Catalogue of Dover Books

PRINCIPLES OF MECHANICS AND DYNAMICS, Sir William Thomson (Lord Kelvin) and Peter Guthrie Tait. The principles and theories of fundamental branches of classical physics explained by two of the greatest physicists of all time. A broad survey of mechanics, with material on hydrodynamics, elasticity, potential theory, and what is now standard mechanics Thorough and detailed coverage, with many examples, derivations, and topics not included in more recent studies. Only a knowledge of calculus is needed to work through this book. Vol. I (Preliminary): Kinematics; Dynamical Laws and Principles; Experience (observation, experimentation, formation of hypotheses, scientific method); Measures and Instruments; Continuous Calculating Machines. Vol. II (Abstract Dynamics): Statics of a Particle— Attraction; Statics of Solids and Fluids. Formerly Titled "Treatise on Natural Philosophy." Unabridged reprint of revised edition. Index. 168 diagrams. Total of xlii + 1035pp. 5⅜ x 8½.
Vol. I: S966 Paperbound **$2.35**
Vol. II: S967 Paperbound **$2.35**
Two volume Set Paperbound **$4.70**

INVESTIGATIONS ON THE THEORY OF THE BROWNIAN MOVEMENT, Albert Einstein. Reprints from rare European journals. 5 basic papers, including the Elementary Theory of the Brownian Movement, written at the request of Lorentz to provide a simple explanation. Translated by A. D. Cowper. Annotated, edited by R. Fürth. 33pp. of notes elucidate, give history of previous investigations. Author, subject indexes. 62 footnotes. 124pp. 5⅜ x 8.
S304 Paperbound **$1.25**

MECHANICS VIA THE CALCULUS, P. W. Norris, W. S. Legge. Covers almost everything, from linear motion to vector analysis: equations determining motion, linear methods, compounding of simple harmonic motion, Newton's laws of motion, Hooke's law, the simple pendulum, motion of a particle in 1 plane, centers of gravity, virtual work, friction, kinetic energy of rotating bodies, equilibrium of strings, hydrostatics, sheering stresses, elasticity, etc. 550 problems. 3rd revised edition. xii + 367pp. 6 x 9.
S207 Clothbound **$4.95**

THE DYNAMICS OF PARTICLES AND OF RIGID, ELASTIC, AND FLUID BODIES; BEING LECTURES ON MATHEMATICAL PHYSICS, A. G. Webster. The reissuing of this classic fills the need for a comprehensive work on dynamics. A wide range of topics is covered in unusually great depth, applying ordinary and partial differential equations. Part I considers laws of motion and methods applicable to systems of all sorts; oscillation, resonance, cyclic systems, etc. Part 2 is a detailed study of the dynamics of rigid bodies. Part 3 introduces the theory of potential; stress and strain, Newtonian potential functions, gyrostatics, wave and vortex motion, etc. Further contents: Kinematics of a point; Lagrange's equations; Hamilton's principle; Systems of vectors; Statics and dynamics of deformable bodies; much more, not easily found together in one volume. Unabridged reprinting of 2nd edition. 20 pages of notes on differential equations and the higher analysis. 203 illustrations. Selected bibliography. Index. xi + 588pp. 5⅜ x 8.
S522 Paperbound **$2.45**

A TREATISE ON DYNAMICS OF A PARTICLE, E. J. Routh. Elementary text on dynamics for beginning mathematics or physics student. Unusually detailed treatment from elementary definitions to motion in 3 dimensions, emphasizing concrete aspects. Much unique material important in recent applications. Covers impulsive forces, rectilinear and constrained motion in 2 dimensions, harmonic and parabolic motion, degrees of freedom, closed orbits, the conical pendulum, the principle of least action, Jacobi's method, and much more. Index. 559 problems, many fully worked out, incorporated into text. xiii + 418pp. 5⅜ x 8.
S696 Paperbound **$2.25**

DYNAMICS OF A SYSTEM OF RIGID BODIES (Elementary Section), E. J. Routh. Revised 7th edition of this standard reference. This volume covers the dynamical principles of the subject, and its more elementary applications: finding moments of inertia by integration, foci of inertia, d'Alembert's principle, impulsive forces, motion in 2 and 3 dimensions, Lagrange's equations, relative indicatrix, Euler's theorem, large tautochronous motions, etc. Index. 55 figures. Scores of problems. xv + 443pp. 5⅜ x 8.
S664 Paperbound **$2.50**

DYNAMICS OF A SYSTEM OF RIGID BODIES (Advanced Section), E. J. Routh. Revised 6th edition of a classic reference aid. Much of its material remains unique. Partial contents: moving axes, relative motion, oscillations about equilibrium, motion. Motion of a body under no forces, any forces. Nature of motion given by linear equations and conditions of stability. Free, forced vibrations, constants of integration, calculus of finite differences, variations, precession and nutation, motion of the moon, motion of string, chain, membranes. 64 figures. 498pp. 5⅜ x 8.
S229 Paperbound **$2.45**

DYNAMICAL THEORY OF GASES, James Jeans. Divided into mathematical and physical chapters for the convenience of those not expert in mathematics, this volume discusses the mathematical theory of gas in a steady state, thermodynamics, Boltzmann and Maxwell, kinetic theory, quantum theory, exponentials, etc. 4th enlarged edition, with new material on quantum theory, quantum dynamics, etc. Indexes. 28 figures. 444pp. 6⅛ x 9¼.
S136 Paperbound **$2.65**

THE THEORY OF HEAT RADIATION, Max Planck. A pioneering work in thermodynamics, providing basis for most later work, Nobel laureate Planck writes on Deductions from Electrodynamics and Thermodynamics, Entropy and Probability, Irreversible Radiation Processes, etc. Starts with simple experimental laws of optics, advances to problems of spectral distribution of energy and irreversibility. Bibliography. 7 illustrations, xiv + 224pp. 5⅜ x 8.
S546 Paperbound **$1.75**

FOUNDATIONS OF POTENTIAL THEORY, O. D. Kellogg. Based on courses given at Harvard this is suitable for both advanced and beginning mathematicians. Proofs are rigorous, and much material not generally avaliable elsewhere is included. Partial contents: forces of gravity, fields of force, divergence theorem, properties of Newtonian potentials at points of free space, potentials as solutions of Laplace's equations, harmonic functions, electrostatics, electric images, logarithmic potential, etc. One of Grundlehren Series. ix + 384pp. 5⅜ x 8.
S144 Paperbound **$1.98**

THERMODYNAMICS, Enrico Fermi. Unabridged reproduction of 1937 edition. Elementary in treatment; remarkable for clarity, organization. Requires no knowledge of advanced math beyond calculus, only familiarity with fundamentals of thermometry, calorimetry. Partial Contents: Thermodynamic systems; First & Second laws of thermodynamics; Entropy; Thermodynamic potentials: phase rule, reversible electric cell; Gaseous reactions: van't Hoff reaction box, principle of LeChatelier; Thermodynamics of dilute solutions: osmotic & vapor pressures, boiling & freezing points; Entropy constant. Index. 25 problems. 24 illustrations. x + 160pp. 5⅜ x 8.
S361 Paperbound **$1.75**

THE THERMODYNAMICS OF ELECTRICAL PHENOMENA IN METALS and A CONDENSED COLLECTION OF THERMODYNAMIC FORMULAS, P. W. Bridgman. Major work by the Nobel Prizewinner: stimulating conceptual introduction to aspects of the electron theory of metals, giving an intuitive understanding of fundamental relationships concealed by the formal systems of Onsager and others. Elementary mathematical formulations show clearly the fundamental thermodynamical relationships of the electric field, and a complete phenomenological theory of metals is created. This is the work in which Bridgman announced his famous "thermomotive force" and his distinction between "driving" and "working" electromotive force. We have added in this Dover edition the author's long unavailable tables of thermodynamic formulas, extremely valuable for the speed of reference they allow. Two works bound as one. Index. 33 figures. Bibliography. xviii + 256pp. 5⅜ x 8. S723 Paperbound **$1.65**

TREATISE ON THERMODYNAMICS, Max Planck. Based on Planck's original papers this offers a uniform point of view for the entire field and has been used as an introduction for students who have studied elementary chemistry, physics, and calculus. Rejecting the earlier approaches of Helmholtz and Maxwell, the author makes no assumptions regarding the nature of heat, but begins with a few empirical facts, and from these deduces new physical and chemical laws. 3rd English edition of this standard text by a Nobel laureate. xvi + 297pp. 5⅜ x 8.
S219 Paperbound **$1.75**

THE MATHEMATICAL THEORY OF ELASTICITY, A. E. H. Love. A wealth of practical illustration combined with thorough discussion of fundamentals—theory, application, special problems and solutions. Partial Contents: Analysis of Strain & Stress, Elasticity of Solid Bodies, Elasticity of Crystals, Vibration of Spheres, Cylinders, Propagation of Waves in Elastic Solid Media, Torsion, Theory of Continuous Beams, Plates. Rigorous treatment of Volterra's theory of dislocations, 2-dimensional elastic systems, other topics of modern interest. "For years the standard treatise on elasticity," AMERICAN MATHEMATICAL MONTHLY. 4th revised edition. Index. 76 figures. xviii + 643pp. 6⅛ x 9¼.
S174 Paperbound **$3.25**

STRESS WAVES IN SOLIDS, H. Kolsky, Professor of Applied Physics, Brown University. The most readable survey of the theoretical core of current knowledge about the propagation of waves in solids, fully correlated with experimental research. Contents: Part I—Elastic Waves: propagation in an extended plastic medium, propagation in bounded elastic media, experimental investigations with elastic materials. Part II—Stress Waves in Imperfectly Elastic Media: internal friction, experimental investigations of dynamic elastic properties, plastic waves and shock waves, fractures produced by stress waves. List of symbols. Appendix. Supplemented bibliography. 3 full-page plates. 46 figures. x + 213pp. 5⅜ x 8½.
S1098 Paperbound **$1.75**

Relativity, quantum theory, atomic and nuclear physics

SPACE TIME MATTER, Hermann Weyl. "The standard treatise on the general theory of relativity" (Nature), written by a world-renowned scientist, provides a deep clear discussion of the logical coherence of the general theory, with introduction to all the mathematical tools needed: Maxwell, analytical geometry, non-Euclidean geometry, tensor calculus, etc. Basis is classical space-time, before absorption of relativity. Partial contents: Euclidean space, mathematical form, metrical continuum, relativity of time and space, general theory. 15 diagrams. Bibliography. New preface for this edition. xviii + 330pp. 5⅜ x 8.
S267 Paperbound **$2.00**

ATOMIC SPECTRA AND ATOMIC STRUCTURE, G. Herzberg. Excellent general survey for chemists, physicists specializing in other fields. Partial contents: simplest line spectra and elements of atomic theory, building-up principle and periodic system of elements, hyperfine structure of spectral lines, some experiments and applications. Bibliography. 80 figures. Index. xii + 257pp. 5⅜ x 8.
S115 Paperbound **$2.00**

Catalogue of Dover Books

THE PRINCIPLE OF RELATIVITY, A. Einstein, H. Lorentz, H. Minkowski, H. Weyl. These are the 11 basic papers that founded the general and special theories of relativity, all translated into English. Two papers by Lorentz on the Michelson experiment, electromagnetic phenomena. Minkowski's SPACE & TIME, and Weyl's GRAVITATION & ELECTRICITY. 7 epoch-making papers by Einstein: ELECTROMAGNETICS OF MOVING BODIES, INFLUENCE OF GRAVITATION IN PROPAGATION OF LIGHT, COSMOLOGICAL CONSIDERATIONS, GENERAL THEORY, and 3 others. 7 diagrams. Special notes by A. Sommerfeld. 224pp. 5⅜ x 8.
S81 Paperbound **$1.75**

EINSTEIN'S THEORY OF RELATIVITY, Max Born. Revised edition prepared with the collaboration of Gunther Leibfried and Walter Biem. Steering a middle course between superficial popularizations and complex analyses, a Nobel laureate explains Einstein's theories clearly and with special insight. Easily followed by the layman with a knowledge of high school mathematics, the book has been thoroughly revised and extended to modernize those sections of the well-known original edition which are now out of date. After a comprehensive review of classical physics, Born's discussion of special and general theories of relativity covers such topics as simultaneity, kinematics, Einstein's mechanics and dynamics, relativity of arbitrary motions, the geometry of curved surfaces, the space-time continuum, and many others. Index. Illustrations, vii + 376pp. 5⅜ x 8.
S769 Paperbound **$2.00**

ATOMS, MOLECULES AND QUANTA, Arthur E. Ruark and Harold C. Urey. Revised (1963) and corrected edition of a work that has been a favorite with physics students and teachers for more than 30 years. No other work offers the same combination of atomic structure and molecular physics and of experiment and theory. The first 14 chapters deal with the origins and major experimental data of quantum theory and with the development of conceptions of atomic and molecular structure prior to the new mechanics. These sections provide a thorough introduction to atomic and molecular theory, and are presented lucidly and as simply as possible. The six subsequent chapters are devoted to the laws and basic ideas of quantum mechanics: Wave Mechanics, Hydrogenic Atoms in Wave Mechanics, Matrix Mechanics, General Theory of Quantum Dynamics, etc. For advanced college and graduate students in physics. Revised, corrected republication of original edition, with supplementary notes by the authors. New preface by the authors. 9 appendices. General reference list. Indices. 228 figures. 71 tables. Bibliographical material in notes, etc. Total of xxiii + 810pp. 5⅜ x 8⅜.
S1106 Vol. I Paperbound **$2.50**
S1107 Vol. II Paperbound **$2.50**
Two volume set Paperbound **$5.00**

WAVE MECHANICS AND ITS APPLICATIONS, N. F. Mott and I. N. Sneddon. A comprehensive introduction to the theory of quantum mechanics; not a rigorous mathematical exposition it progresses, instead, in accordance with the physical problems considered. Many topics difficult to find at the elementary level are discussed in this book. Includes such matters as: the wave nature of matter, the wave equation of Schrödinger, the concept of stationary states, properties of the wave functions, effect of a magnetic field on the energy levels of atoms, electronic spin, two-body problem, theory of solids, cohesive forces in ionic crystals, collision problems, interaction of radiation with matter, relativistic quantum mechanics, etc. All are treated both physically and mathematically. 68 illustrations. 11 tables. Indexes. xii + 393pp. 5⅜ x 8½.
S1070 Paperbound **$2.25**

BASIC METHODS IN TRANSFER PROBLEMS, V. Kourganoff, Professor of Astrophysics, U. of Paris. A coherent digest of all the known methods which can be used for approximate or exact solutions of transfer problems. All methods demonstrated on one particular problem —Milne's problem for a plane parallel medium. Three main sections: fundamental concepts (the radiation field and its interaction with matter, the absorption and emission coefficients, etc.); different methods by which transfer problems can be attacked; and a more general problem—the non-grey case of Milne's problem. Much new material, drawing upon declassified atomic energy reports and data from the USSR. Entirely understandable to the student with a reasonable knowledge of analysis. Unabridged, revised reprinting. New preface by the author. Index. Bibliography. 2 appendices. xv + 281pp. 5⅜ x 8½.
S1074 Paperbound **$2.00**

PRINCIPLES OF QUANTUM MECHANICS, W. V. Houston. Enables student with working knowledge of elementary mathematical physics to develop facility in use of quantum mechanics, understand published work in field. Formulates quantum theory in terms of Schroedinger's wave mechanics. Studies evidence for quantum theory, for inadequacy of classical mechanics, 2 postulates of quantum mechanics; numerous important, fruitful applications of quantum mechanics in spectroscopy, collision problems, electrons in solids; other topics. "One of the most rewarding features . . . is the interlacing of problems with text," Amer. J. of Physics. Corrected edition. 21 illus. Index. 296pp. 5⅜ x 8. S524 Paperbound **$2.00**

PHYSICAL PRINCIPLES OF THE QUANTUM THEORY, Werner Heisenberg. A Nobel laureate discusses quantum theory; Heisenberg's own work, Compton, Schroedinger, Wilson, Einstein, many others. Written for physicists, chemists who are not specialists in quantum theory, only elementary formulae are considered in the text; there is a mathematical appendix for specialists. Profound without sacrifice of clarity. Translated by C. Eckart, F. Hoyt. 18 figures. 192pp. 5⅜ x 8.
S113 Paperbound **$1.25**

ENGINEERING AND TECHNOLOGY

General and mathematical

ENGINEERING MATHEMATICS, Kenneth S. Miller. A text for graduate students of engineering to strengthen their mathematical background in differential equations, etc. Mathematical steps very explicitly indicated. Contents: Determinants and Matrices, Integrals, Linear Differential Equations, Fourier Series and Integrals, Laplace Transform, Network Theory, Random Function . . . all vital requisites for advanced modern engineering studies. Unabridged republication. Appendices: Borel Sets; Riemann-Stieltjes Integral; Fourier Series and Integrals. Index. References at Chapter Ends. xii + 417pp. 6 x 8½.　　　　S1121 Paperbound **$2.00**

MATHEMATICAL ENGINEERING ANALYSIS, Rufus Oldenburger. A book designed to assist the research engineer and scientist in making the transition from physical engineering situations to the corresponding mathematics. Scores of common practical situations found in all major fields of physics are supplied with their correct mathematical formulations—applications to automobile springs and shock absorbers, clocks, throttle torque of diesel engines, resistance networks, capacitors, transmission lines, microphones, neon tubes, gasoline engines, refrigeration cycles, etc. Each section reviews basic principles of underlying various fields: mechanics of rigid bodies, electricity and magnetism, heat, elasticity, fluid mechanics, and aerodynamics. Comprehensive and eminently useful. Index. 169 problems, answers. 200 photos and diagrams. xiv + 426pp. 5⅜ x 8½.　　　　S919 Paperbound **$2.50**

MATHEMATICS OF MODERN ENGINEERING, E. G. Keller and R. E. Doherty. Written for the Advanced Course in Engineering of the General Electric Corporation, deals with the engineering use of determinants, tensors, the Heaviside operational calculus, dyadics, the calculus of variations, etc. Presents underlying principles fully, but purpose is to teach engineers to deal with modern engineering problems, and emphasis is on the perennial engineering attack of set-up and solve. Indexes. Over 185 figures and tables. Hundreds of exercises, problems, and worked-out examples. References. Two volume set. Total of xxxiii + 623pp. 5⅜ x 8.

S734 Vol I Paperbound **$1.85**
S735 Vol II Paperbound **$1.85**
The set **$3.70**

MATHEMATICAL METHODS FOR SCIENTISTS AND ENGINEERS, L. P. Smith. For scientists and engineers, as well as advanced math students. Full investigation of methods and practical description of conditions under which each should be used. Elements of real functions, differential and integral calculus, space geometry, theory of residues, vector and tensor analysis, series of Bessel functions, etc. Each method illustrated by completely-worked-out examples, mostly from scientific literature. 368 graded unsolved problems. 100 diagrams. x + 453pp. 5⅝ x 8⅜.　　　　S220 Paperbound **$2.00**

THEORY OF FUNCTIONS AS APPLIED TO ENGINEERING PROBLEMS, edited by R. Rothe, F. Ollendorff, and K. Pohlhausen. A series of lectures given at the Berlin Institute of Technology that shows the specific applications of function theory in electrical and allied fields of engineering. Six lectures provide the elements of function theory in a simple and practical form, covering complex quantities and variables, integration in the complex plane, residue theorems, etc. Then 5 lectures show the exact uses of this powerful mathematical tool, with full discussions of problem methods. Index. Bibliography. 108 figures. x + 189pp. 5⅜ x 8.

S733 Paperbound **$1.35**

Aerodynamics and hydrodynamics

AIRPLANE STRUCTURAL ANALYSIS AND DESIGN, E. E. Sechler and L. G. Dunn. Systematic authoritative book which summarizes a large amount of theoretical and experimental work on structural analysis and design. Strong on classical subsonic material still basic to much aeronautic design . . . remains a highly useful source of information. Covers such areas as layout of the airplane, applied and design loads, stress-strain relationships for stable structures, truss and frame analysis, the problem of instability, the ultimate strength of stiffened flat sheet, analysis of cylindrical structures, wings and control surfaces, fuselage analysis, engine mounts, landing gears, etc. Ol ̣nally published as part of the CALCIT Aeronautical Series. 256 illustrations. 47 study problems. Indexes. xi + 420pp. 5⅜ x 8½.

S1043 Paperbound **$2.25**

FUNDAMENTALS OF HYDRO- AND AEROMECHANICS, L. Prandtl and O. G. Tietjens. The well-known standard work based upon Prandtl's lectures at Goettingen. Wherever possible hydrodynamics theory is referred to practical considerations in hydraulics, with the view of unifying theory and experience. Presentation is extremely clear and though primarily physical, mathematical proofs are rigorous and use vector analysis to a considerable extent. An Enginering Society Monograph, 1934. 186 figures. Index. xvi + 270pp. 5⅜ x 8.

S374 Paperbound **$1.85**

Catalogue of Dover Books

FLUID MECHANICS FOR HYDRAULIC ENGINEERS, H. Rouse. Standard work that gives a coherent picture of fluid mechanics from the point of view of the hydraulic engineer. Based on courses given to civil and mechanical engineering students at Columbia and the California Institute of Technology, this work covers every basic principle, method, equation, or theory of interest to the hydraulic engineer. Much of the material, diagrams, charts, etc., in this self-contained text are not duplicated elsewhere. Covers irrotational motion, conformal mapping, problems in laminar motion, fluid turbulence, flow around immersed bodies, transportation of sediment, general charcteristics of wave phenomena, gravity waves in open channels, etc. Index. Appendix of physical properties of common fluids. Frontispiece + 245 figures and photographs. xvi + 422pp. 5⅜ x 8. S729 Paperbound **$2.25**

WATERHAMMER ANALYSIS, John Parmakian. Valuable exposition of the graphical method of solving waterhammer problems by Assistant Chief Designing Engineer, U.S. Bureau of Reclamation. Discussions of rigid and elastic water column theory, velocity of waterhammer waves, theory of graphical waterhammer analysis for gate operation, closings, openings, rapid and slow movements, etc., waterhammer in pump discharge caused by power failure, waterhammer analysis for compound pipes, and numerous related problems. "With a concise and lucid style, clear printing, adequate bibliography and graphs for approximate solutions at the project stage, it fills a vacant place in waterhammer literature," WATER POWER. 43 problems. Bibliography. Index. 113 illustrations. xiv + 161pp. 5⅜ x 8½. S1061 Paperbound **$1.65**

AERODYNAMIC THEORY: A GENERAL REVIEW OF PROGRESS, William F. Durand, editor-in-chief. A monumental joint effort by the world's leading authorities prepared under a grant of the Guggenheim Fund for the Promotion of Aeronautics. Intended to provide the student and aeronautic designer with the theoretical and experimental background of aeronautics. Never equalled for breadth, depth, reliability. Contains discussions of special mathematical topics not usually taught in the engineering or technical courses. Also: an extended two-part treatise on Fluid Mechanics, discussions of aerodynamics of perfect fluids, analyses of experiments with wind tunnels, applied airfoil theory, the non-lifting system of the airplane, the air propeller, hydrodynamics of boats and floats, the aerodynamics of cooling, etc. Contributing experts include Munk, Giacomelli, Prandtl, Toussaint, Von Karman, Klemperer, among others. Unabridged republication. 6 volumes bound as 3. Total of 1,012 figures, 12 plates. Total of 2,186pp. Bibliographies. Notes. Indices. 5⅜ x 8. S328-S330 Clothbound, The Set **$17.50**

APPLIED HYDRO- AND AEROMECHANICS, L. Prandtl and O. G. Tietjens. Presents, for the most part, methods which will be valuable to engineers. Covers flow in pipes, boundary layers, airfoil theory, entry conditions, turbulent flow in pipes, and the boundary layer, determining drag from measurements of pressure and velocity, etc. "Will be welcomed by all students of aerodynamics," NATURE. Unabridged, unaltered. An Engineering Society Monograph, 1934. Index. 226 figures, 28 photographic plates illustrating flow patterns. xvi + 311pp. 5⅜ x 8. S375 Paperbound **$1.85**

SUPERSONIC AERODYNAMICS, E. R. C. Miles. Valuable theoretical introduction to the supersonic domain, with emphasis on mathematical tools and principles, for practicing aerodynamicists and advanced students in aeronautical engineering. Covers fundamental theory, divergence theorem and principles of circulation, compressible flow and Helmholtz laws, the Prandtl-Busemann graphic method for 2-dimensional flow, oblique shock waves, the Taylor-Maccoll method for cones in supersonic flow, the Chaplygin method for 2-dimensional flow, etc. Problems range from practical engineering problems to development of theoretical results. "Rendered outstanding by the unprecedented scope of its contents . . . has undoubtedly filled a vital gap," AERONAUTICAL ENGINEERING REVIEW. Index. 173 problems, answers. 106 diagrams. 7 tables. xii + 255pp. 5⅜ x 8. S214 Paperbound **$1.45**

HYDRAULIC TRANSIENTS, G. R. Rich. The best text in hydraulics ever printed in English . . . by one of America's foremost engineers (former Chief Design Engineer for T.V.A.). Provides a transition from the basic differential equations of hydraulic transient theory to the arithmetic intergration computation required by practicing engineers. Sections cover Water Hammer, Turbine Speed Regulation, Stability of Governing, Water-Hammer Pressures in Pump Discharge Lines, The Differential and Restricted Orifice Surge Tanks, The Normalized Surge Tank Charts of Calame and Gaden, Navigation Locks, Surges in Power Canals—Tidal Harmonics, etc. Revised and enlarged. Author's prefaces. Index. xiv + 409pp. 5⅜ x 8½. S116 Paperbound **$2.50**

HYDRAULICS AND ITS APPLICATIONS, A. H. Gibson. Excellent comprehensive textbook for the student and thorough practical manual for the professional worker, a work of great stature in its area. Half the book is devoted to theory and half to applications and practical problems met in the field. Covers modes of motion of a fluid, critical velocity, viscous flow, eddy formation, Bernoulli's theorem, flow in converging passages, vortex motion, form of effluent streams, notches and weirs, skin friction, losses at valves and elbows, siphons, erosion of channels, jet propulsion, waves of oscillation, and over 100 similar topics. Final chapters (nearly 400 pages) cover more than 100 kinds of hydraulic machinery: Pelton wheel, speed regulators, the hydraulic ram, surge tanks, the scoop wheel, the Venturi meter, etc. A special chapter treats methods of testing theoretical hypotheses: scale models of rivers, tidal estuaries, siphon spillways, etc. 5th revised and enlarged (1952) edition. Index. Appendix. 427 photographs and diagrams. 95 examples, answers. xv + 813pp. 6 x 9. S791 Clothbound **$8.00**

FLUID MECHANICS THROUGH WORKED EXAMPLES, D. R. L. Smith and J. Houghton. Advanced text covering principles and applications to practical situations. Each chapter begins with concise summaries of fundamental ideas. 163 fully worked out examples applying principles outlined in the text. 275 other problems, with answers. Contents: The Pressure of Liquids on Surfaces; Floating Bodies; Flow Under Constant Head in Pipes; Circulation; Vorticity; The Potential Function; Laminar Flow and Lubrication; Impact of Jets; Hydraulic Turbines; Centrifugal and Reciprocating Pumps; Compressible Fluids; and many other items. Total of 438 examples. 250 line illustrations. 340pp. Index. 6 x 8⅞.   S981 Clothbound **$6.00**

THEORY OF SHIP MOTIONS, S. N. Blagoveshchensky. The only detailed text in English in a rapidly developing branch of engineering and physics, it is the work of one of the world's foremost authorities—Blagoveshchensky of Leningrad Shipbuilding Institute. A senior-level treatment written primarily for engineering students, but also of great importance to naval architects, designers, contractors, researchers in hydrodynamics, and other students. No mathematics beyond ordinary differential equations is required for understanding the text. Translated by T. & L. Strelkoff, under editorship of Louis Landweber, Iowa Institute of Hydraulic Research, under auspices of Office of Naval Research. Bibliography. Index. 231 diagrams and illustrations. Total of 649pp. 5⅜ x 8½.   Vol. I: S234 Paperbound **$2.00**
Vol. II: S235 Paperbound **$2.00**

THEORY OF FLIGHT, Richard von Mises. Remains almost unsurpassed as balanced, well-written account of fundamental fluid dynamics, and situations in which air compressibility effects are unimportant. Stressing equally theory and practice, avoiding formidable mathematical structure, it conveys a full understanding of physical phenomena and mathematical concepts. Contains perhaps the best introduction to general theory of stability. "Outstanding," Scientific, Medical, and Technical Books. New introduction by K. H. Hohenemser. Bibliographical, historical notes. Index. 408 illustrations. xvi + 620pp. 5⅜ x 8⅜.   S541 Paperbound **$3.50**

THEORY OF WING SECTIONS, I. H. Abbott, A. E. von Doenhoff. Concise compilation of subsonic aerodynamic characteristics of modern NASA wing sections, with description of their geometry, associated theory. Primarily reference work for engineers, students, it gives methods, data for using wing-section data to predict characteristics. Particularly valuable: chapters on thin wings, airfoils; complete summary of NACA's experimental observations, system of construction families of airfoils. 350pp. of tables on Basic Thickness Forms, Mean Lines, Airfoil Ordinates, Aerodynamic Characteristics of Wing Sections. Index. Bibliography. 191 illustrations. Appendix. 705pp. 5⅜ x 8.   S558 Paperbound **$3.25**

WEIGHT-STRENGTH ANALYSIS OF AIRCRAFT STRUCTURES, F. R. Shanley. Scientifically sound methods of analyzing and predicting the structural weight of aircraft and missiles. Deals directly with forces and the distances over which they must be transmitted, making it possible to develop methods by which the minimum structural weight can be determined for any material and conditions of loading. Weight equations for wing and fuselage structures. Includes author's original papers on inelastic buckling and creep buckling. "Particularly successful in presenting his analytical methods for investigating various optimum design principles," AERONAUTICAL ENGINEERING REVIEW. Enlarged bibliography. Index. 199 figures. xiv + 404pp. 5⅝ x 8⅜.   S660 Paperbound **$2.50**

Electricity

TWO-DIMENSIONAL FIELDS IN ELECTRICAL ENGINEERING, L. V. Bewley. A useful selection of typical engineering problems of interest to practicing electrical engineers. Introduces senior students to the methods and procedures of mathematical physics. Discusses theory of functions of a complex variable, two-dimensional fields of flow, general theorems of mathematical physics and their applications, conformal mapping or transformation, method of images, freehand flux plotting, etc. New preface by the author. Appendix by W. F. Kiltner. Index. Bibliography at chapter ends. xiv + 204pp. 5⅜ x 8½.   S1118 Paperbound **$1.50**

FLUX LINKAGES AND ELECTROMAGNETIC INDUCTION, L. V. Bewley. A brief, clear book which shows proper uses and corrects misconceptions of Faraday's law of electromagnetic induction in specific problems. Contents: Circuits, Turns, and Flux Linkages; Substitution of Circuits; Electromagnetic Induction; General Criteria for Electromagnetic Induction; Applications and Paradoxes; Theorem of Constant Flux Linkages. New Section: Rectangular Coil in a Varying Uniform Medium. Valuable supplement to class texts for engineering students. Corrected, enlarged edition. New preface. Bibliography in notes. 49 figures. xi + 106pp. 5⅜ x 8.   S1103 Paperbound **$1.25**

INDUCTANCE CALCULATIONS: WORKING FORMULAS AND TABLES, Frederick W. Grover. An invaluable book to everyone in electrical engineering. Provides simple single formulas to cover all the more important cases of inductance. The approach involves only those parameters that naturally enter into each situation, while extensive tables are given to permit easy interpolations. Will save the engineer and student countless hours and enable them to obtain accurate answers with minimal effort. Corrected republication of 1946 edition. 58 tables. 97 completely worked out examples. 66 figures. xiv + 286pp. 5⅜ x 8½.   S974 Paperbound **$1.85**

GASEOUS CONDUCTORS: THEORY AND ENGINEERING APPLICATIONS, J. D. Cobine. An indispensable text and reference to gaseous conduction phenomena, with the engineering viewpoint prevailing throughout. Studies the kinetic theory of gases, ionization, emission phenomena; gas breakdown, spark characteristics, glow, and discharges; engineering applications in circuit interrupters, rectifiers, light sources, etc. Separate detailed treatment of high pressure arcs (Suits); low pressure arcs (Langmuir and Tonks). Much more. "Well organized, clear, straightforward," Tonks, Review of Scientific Instruments. Index. Bibliography. 83 practice problems. 7 appendices. Over 600 figures. 58 tables. xx + 606pp. 5⅜ x 8. S442 Paperbound **$3.25**

INTRODUCTION TO THE STATISTICAL DYNAMICS OF AUTOMATIC CONTROL SYSTEMS, V. V. Solovnikov. First English publication of text-reference covering important branch of automatic control systems—random signals; in its original edition, this was the first comprehensive treatment. Examines frequency characteristics, transfer functions, stationary random processes, determination of minimum mean-squared error, of transfer function for a finite period of observation, much more. Translation edited by J. B. Thomas, L. A. Zadeh. Index. Bibliography. Appendix. xxii + 308pp. 5⅜ x 8. S420 Paperbound **$2.25**

TENSORS FOR CIRCUITS, Gabriel Kron. A boldly original method of analyzing engineering problems, at center of sharp discussion since first introduced, now definitely proved useful in such areas as electrical and structural networks on automatic computers. Encompasses a great variety of specific problems by means of a relatively few symbolic equations. "Power and flexibility . . . becoming more widely recognized," Nature. Formerly "A Short Course in Tensor Analysis." New introduction by B. Hoffmann. Index. Over 800 diagrams. xix + 250pp. 5⅜ x 8. S534 Paperbound **$2.00**

SELECTED PAPERS ON SEMICONDUCTOR MICROWAVE ELECTRONICS, edited by Sumner N. Levine and Richard R. Kurzrok. An invaluable collection of important papers dealing with one of the most remarkable developments in solid-state electronics—the use of the p-n junction to achieve amplification and frequency conversion of microwave frequencies. Contents: General Survey (3 introductory papers by W. E. Danielson, R. N. Hall, and M. Tenzer); General Theory of Nonlinear Elements (3 articles by A. van der Ziel, H. E. Rowe, and Manley and Rowe); Device Fabrication and Characterization (3 pieces by Bakanowski, Cranna, and Uhlir, by McCotter, Walker and Fortini, and by S. T. Eng); Parametric Amplifiers and Frequency Multipliers (13 articles by Uhlir, Heffner and Wade, Matthaei, P. K. Tien, van der Ziel, Engelbrecht, Currie and Gould, Uenohara, Leeson and Weinreb, and others); and Tunnel Diodes (4 papers by L. Esaki, H. S. Sommers, Jr., M. E. Hines, and Yariv and Cook). Introduction. 295 Figures. xiii + 286pp. 6½ x 9¼. S1126 Paperbound **$2.25**

THE PRINCIPLES OF ELECTROMAGNETISM APPLIED TO ELECTRICAL MACHINES, B. Hague. A concise, but complete, summary of the basic principles of the magnetic field and its applications, with particular reference to the kind of phenomena which occur in electrical machines. Part I: General Theory—magnetic field of a current, electromagnetic field passing from air to iron, mechanical forces on linear conductors, etc. Part II: Application of theory to the solution of electromechanical problems—the magnetic field and mechanical forces in non-salient pole machinery, the field within slots and between salient poles, and the work of Rogowski, Roth, and Strutt. Formery titled "Electromagnetic Problems in Electrical Engineering." 2 appendices. Index. Bibliography in notes. 115 figures. xiv + 359pp. 5⅜ x 8½. S246 Paperbound **$2.25**

Mechanical engineering

DESIGN AND USE OF INSTRUMENTS AND ACCURATE MECHANISM, T. N. Whitehead. For the instrument designer, engineer; how to combine necessary mathematical abstractions with independent observation of actual facts. Partial contents: instruments & their parts, theory of errors, systematic errors, probability, short period errors, erratic errors, design precision, kinematic, semikinematic design, stiffness, planning of an instrument, human factor, etc. Index. 85 photos, diagrams. xii + 288pp. 5⅜ x 8. S270 Paperbound **$2.00**

A TREATISE ON GYROSTATICS AND ROTATIONAL MOTION: THEORY AND APPLICATIONS, Andrew Gray. Most detailed, thorough book in English, generally considered definitive study. Many problems of all sorts in full detail, or step-by-step summary. Classical problems of Bour, Lottner, etc.; later ones of great physical interest. Vibrating systems of gyrostats, earth as a top, calculation of path of axis of a top by elliptic integrals, motion of unsymmetrical top, much more. Index. 160 illus. 550pp. 5⅜ x 8. S589 Paperbound **$2.75**

MECHANICS OF THE GYROSCOPE, THE DYNAMICS OF ROTATION, R. F. Deimel, Professor of Mechanical Engineering at Stevens Institute of Technology. Elementary general treatment of dynamics of rotation, with special application of gyroscopic phenomena. No knowledge of vectors needed. Velocity of a moving curve, acceleration to a point, general equations of motion, gyroscopic horizon, free gyro, motion of discs, the damped gyro, 103 similar topics. Exercises. 75 figures. 208pp. 5⅜ x 8. S66 Paperbound **$1.75**

STRENGTH OF MATERIALS, J. P. Den Hartog. Distinguished text prepared for M.I.T. course, ideal as introduction, refresher, reference, or self-study text. Full clear treatment of elementary material (tension, torsion, bending, compound stresses, deflection of beams, etc.), plus much advanced material on engineering methods of great practical value: full treatment of the Mohr circle, lucid elementary discussions of the theory of the center of shear and the "Myosotis" method of calculating beam deflections, reinforced concrete, plastic deformations, photoelasticity, etc. In all sections, both general principles and concrete applications are given. Index. 186 figures (160 others in problem section). 350 problems, all with answers. List of formulas. viii + 323pp. 5⅜ x 8.   S755 Paperbound **$2.00**

PHOTOELASTICITY: PRINCIPLES AND METHODS, H. T. Jessop, F. C. Harris. For the engineer, for specific problems of stress analysis. Latest time-saving methods of checking calculations in 2-dimensional design problems, new techniques for stresses in 3 dimensions, and lucid description of optical systems used in practical photoelasticity. Useful suggestions and hints based on on-the-job experience included. Partial contents: strained and stress-strain relations, circular disc under thrust along diameter, rectangular block with square hole under vertical thrust, simply supported rectangular beam under central concentrated load, etc. Theory held to minimum, no advanced mathematical training needed. Index. 164 illustrations. viii + 184pp. 6⅛ x 9¼.   S720 Paperbound **$2.00**

APPLIED ELASTICITY, J. Prescott. Provides the engineer with the theory of elasticity usually lacking in books on strength of materials, yet concentrates on those portions useful for immediate application. Develops every important type of elasticity problem from theoretical principles. Covers analysis of stress, relations between stress and strain, the empirical basis of elasticity, thin rods under tension or thrust, Saint Venant's theory, transverse oscillations of thin rods, stability of thin plates, cylinders with thin walls, vibrations of rotating disks, elastic bodies in contact, etc. "Excellent and important contribution to the subject, not merely in the old matter which he has presented in new and refreshing form, but also in the many original investigations here published for the first time," NATURE. Index. 3 Appendixes. vi + 672pp. 5⅜ x 8.   S726 Paperbound **$3.25**

APPLIED MECHANICS FOR ENGINEERS, Sir Charles Inglis, F.R.S. A representative survey of the many and varied engineering questions which can be answered by statics and dynamics. The author, one of first and foremost adherents of "structural dynamics," presents distinctive illustrative examples and clear, concise statement of principles—directing the discussion at methodology and specific problems. Covers fundamental principles of rigid-body statics, graphic solutions of static problems, theory of taut wires, stresses in frameworks, particle dynamics, kinematics, simple harmonic motion and harmonic analysis, two-dimensional rigid dynamics, etc. 437 illustrations. xii + 404pp. 5⅜ x 8½. S1119 Paperbound **$2.00**

THEORY OF MACHINES THROUGH WORKED EXAMPLES, G. H. Ryder. Practical mechanical engineering textbook for graduates and advanced undergraduates, as well as a good reference work for practicing engineers. Partial contents: Mechanisms, Velocity and Acceleration (including discussion of Klein's Construction for Piston Acceleration), Cams, Geometry of Gears, Clutches and Bearings, Belt and Rope Drives, Brakes, Inertia Forces and Couples, General Dynamical Problems, Gyroscopes, Linear and Angular Vibrations, Torsional Vibrations, Transverse Vibrations and Whirling Speeds (Chapters on vibrations considerably enlarged from previous editions). Over 300 problems, many fully worked out. Index. 195 line illustrations. Revised and enlarged edition. viii + 280pp. 5⅝ x 8¾.   S980 Clothbound **$5.00**

THE KINEMATICS OF MACHINERY: OUTLINES OF A THEORY OF MACHINES, Franz Reuleaux. The classic work in the kinematics of machinery. The present thinking about the subject has all been shaped in great measure by the fundamental principles stated here by Reuleaux almost 90 years ago. While some details have naturally been superseded, his basic viewpoint has endured; hence, the book is still an excellent text for basic courses in kinematics and a standard reference work for active workers in the field. Covers such topics as: the nature of the machine problem, phoronomic propositions, pairs of elements, incomplete kinematic chains, kinematic notation and analysis, analyses of chamber-crank trains, chamber-wheel trains, constructive elements of machinery, complete machines, etc., with main focus on controlled movement in mechanisms. Unabridged republication of original edition, translated by Alexander B. Kennedy. New introduction for this edition by E. S. Ferguson. Index. 451 illustrations. xxiv + 622pp. 5⅜ x 8½.   S1124 Paperbound **$3.00**

ANALYTICAL MECHANICS OF GEARS, Earle Buckingham. Provides a solid foundation upon which logical design practices and design data can be constructed. Originally arising out of investigations of the ASME Special Research Committee on Worm Gears and the Strength of Gears, the book covers conjugate gear-tooth action, the nature of the contact, and resulting gear-tooth profiles of: spur, internal, helical, spiral, worm, bevel, and hypoid or skew bevel gears. Also: frictional heat of operation and its dissipation, friction losses, etc., dynamic loads in operation, and related matters. Familiarity with this book is still regarded as a necessary prerequisite to work in modern gear manufacturing. 263 figures. 103 tables. Index. x + 546pp. 5⅜ x 8½.   S1073 Paperbound **$2.75**

Optical design, lighting

THE SCIENTIFIC BASIS OF ILLUMINATING ENGINEERING, Parry Moon, Professor of Electrical Engineering, M.I.T. Basic, comprehensive study. Complete coverage of the fundamental theoretical principles together with the elements of design, vision, and color with which the lighting engineer must be familiar. Valuable as a text as well as a reference source to the practicing engineer. Partial contents: Spectroradiometric Curve, Luminous Flux, Radiation from Gaseous-Conduction Sources, Radiation from Incandescent Sources, Incandescent Lamps, Measurement of Light, Illumination from Point Sources and Surface Sources, Elements of Lighting Design. 7 Appendices. Unabridged and corrected republication, with additions. New preface containing conversion tables of radiometric and photometric concepts. Index. 707-item bibliography. 92-item bibliography of author's articles. 183 problems. xxiii + 608pp. 5⅜ x 8½. S242 Paperbound **$2.85**

OPTICS AND OPTICAL INSTRUMENTS: AN INTRODUCTION WITH SPECIAL REFERENCE TO PRACTICAL APPLICATIONS, B. K. Johnson. An invaluable guide to basic practical applications of optical principles, which shows how to set up inexpensive working models of each of the four main types of optical instruments—telescopes, microscopes, photographic lenses, optical projecting systems. Explains in detail the most important experiments for determining their accuracy, resolving power, angular field of view, amounts of aberration, all other necessary facts about the instruments. Formerly "Practical Optics." Index. 234 diagrams. Appendix. 224pp. 5⅜ x 8. S642 Paperbound **$1.75**

APPLIED OPTICS AND OPTICAL DESIGN, A. E. Conrady. With publication of vol. 2, standard work for designers in optics is now complete for first time. Only work of its kind in English; only detailed work for practical designer and self-taught. Requires, for bulk of work, no math above trig. Step-by-step exposition, from fundamental concepts of geometrical, physical optics, to systematic study, design, of almost all types of optical systems. Vol. 1: all ordinary ray-tracing methods; primary aberrations; necessary higher aberration for design of telescopes, low-power microscopes, photographic equipment. Vol. 2: (Completed from author's notes by R. Kingslake, Dir. Optical Design, Eastman Kodak.) Special attention to high-power microscope, anastigmatic photographic objectives. "An indispensable work," J., Optical Soc. of Amer. "As a practical guide this book has no rival," Transactions, Optical Soc. Index. Bibliography. 193 diagrams. 852pp. 6⅛ x 9¼. Vol. 1 S366 Paperbound **$3.50** Vol. 2 S612 Paperbound **$2.95**

Miscellaneous

THE MEASUREMENT OF POWER SPECTRA FROM THE POINT OF VIEW OF COMMUNICATIONS ENGINEERING, R. B. Blackman, J. W. Tukey. This pathfinding work, reprinted from the "Bell System Technical Journal," explains various ways of getting practically useful answers in the measurement of power spectra, using results from both transmission theory and the theory of statistical estimation. Treats: Autocovariance Functions and Power Spectra; Direct Analog Computation; Distortion, Noise, Heterodyne Filtering and Pre-whitening; Aliasing; Rejection Filtering and Separation; Smoothing and Decimation Procedures; Very Low Frequencies; Transversal Filtering; much more. An appendix reviews fundamental Fourier techniques. Index of notation. Glossary of terms. 24 figures. XII tables. Bibliography. General index. 192pp. 5⅜ x 8. S507 Paperbound **$1.85**

CALCULUS REFRESHER FOR TECHNICAL MEN, A. Albert Klaf. This book is unique in English as a refresher for engineers, technicians, students who either wish to brush up their calculus or to clear up uncertainties. It is not an ordinary text, but an examination of most important aspects of integral and differential calculus in terms of the 756 questions most likely to occur to the technical reader. The first part of this book covers simple differential calculus, with constants, variables, functions, increments, derivatives, differentiation, logarithms, curvature of curves, and similar topics. The second part covers fundamental ideas of integration, inspection, substitution, transformation, reduction, areas and volumes, mean value, successive and partial integration, double and triple integration. Practical aspects are stressed rather than theoretical. A 50-page section illustrates the application of calculus to specific problems of civil and nautical engineering, electricity, stress and strain, elasticity, industrial engineering, and similar fields.—756 questions answered. 566 problems, mostly answered. 36 pages of useful constants, formulae for ready reference. Index. v + 431pp. 5⅜ x 8. T370 Paperbound **$2.00**

METHODS IN EXTERIOR BALLISTICS, Forest Ray Moulton. Probably the best introduction to the mathematics of projectile motion. The ballistics theories propounded were coordinated with extensive proving ground and wind tunnel experiments conducted by the author and others for the U.S. Army. Broad in scope and clear in exposition, it gives the beginnings of the theory used for modern-day projectile, long-range missile, and satellite motion. Six main divisions: Differential Equations of Translatory Motion of a projectile; Gravity and the Resistance Function; Numerical Solution of Differential Equations; Theory of Differential Variations; Validity of Method of Numerical Integration; and Motion of a Rotating Projectile. Formerly titled: "New Methods in Exterior Ballistics." Index. 38 diagrams. viii + 259pp. 5⅜ x 8½. S232 Paperbound **$1.75**

LOUD SPEAKERS: THEORY, PERFORMANCE, TESTING AND DESIGN, N. W. McLachlan. Most comprehensive coverage of theory, practice of loud speaker design, testing; classic reference, study manual in field. First 12 chapters deal with theory, for readers mainly concerned with math. aspects; last 7 chapters will interest reader concerned with testing, design. Partial contents: principles of sound propagation, fluid pressure on vibrators, theory of moving-coil principle, transients, driving mechanisms, response curves, design of horn type moving coil speakers, electrostatic speakers, much more. Appendix. Bibliography. Index. 165 illustrations, charts. 411pp. 5⅜ x 8.   S588 Paperbound **$2.25**

MICROWAVE TRANSMISSION, J. C. Slater. First text dealing exclusively with microwaves, brings together points of view of field, circuit theory, for graduate student in physics, electrical engineering, microwave technician. Offers valuable point of view not in most later studies. Uses Maxwell's equations to study electromagnetic field, important in this area. Partial contents: infinite line with distributed parameters, impedance of terminated line, plane waves, reflections, wave guides, coaxial line, composite transmission lines, impedance matching, etc. Introduction. Index. 76 illus. 319pp. 5⅜ x 8.
S564 Paperbound **$1.50**

MICROWAVE TRANSMISSION DESIGN DATA, T. Moreno. Originally classified, now rewritten and enlarged (14 new chapters) for public release under auspices of Sperry Corp. Material of immediate value or reference use to radio engineers, systems designers, applied physicists, etc. Ordinary transmission line theory; attenuation; capacity; parameters of coaxial lines; higher modes; flexible cables; obstacles, discontinuities, and injunctions; tunable wave guide impedance transformers; effects of temperature and humidity; much more. "Enough theoretical discussion is included to allow use of data without previous background," Electronics. 324 circuit diagrams, figures, etc. Tables of dielectrics, flexible cable, etc., data. Index. ix + 248pp. 5⅜ x 8.   S459 Paperbound **$1.65**

RAYLEIGH'S PRINCIPLE AND ITS APPLICATIONS TO ENGINEERING, G. Temple & W. Bickley. Rayleigh's principle developed to provide upper and lower estimates of true value of fundamental period of a vibrating system, or condition of stability of elastic systems. Illustrative examples; rigorous proofs in special chapters. Partial contents: Energy method of discussing vibrations, stability. Perturbation theory, whirling of uniform shafts. Criteria of elastic stability. Application of energy method. Vibrating systems. Proof, accuracy, successive approximations, application of Rayleigh's principle. Synthetic theorems. Numerical, graphical methods. Equilibrium configurations, Ritz's method. Bibliography. Index. 22 figures. ix + 156pp. 5⅜ x 8.
S307 Paperbound **$1.85**

ELASTICITY, PLASTICITY AND STRUCTURE OF MATTER, R. Houwink. Standard treatise on rheological aspects of different technically important solids such as crystals, resins, textiles, rubber, clay, many others. Investigates general laws for deformations; determines divergences from these laws for certain substances. Covers general physical and mathematical aspects of plasticity, elasticity, viscosity. Detailed examination of deformations, internal structure of matter in relation to elastic and plastic behavior, formation of solid matter from a fluid, conditions for elastic and plastic behavior of matter. Treats glass, asphalt, gutta percha, balata, proteins, baker's dough, lacquers, sulphur, others. 2nd revised, enlarged edition. Extensive revised bibliography in over 500 footnotes. Index. Table of symbols. 214 figures. xviii + 368pp. 6 x 9¼.   S385 Paperbound **$2.45**

THE SCHWARZ-CHRISTOFFEL TRANSFORMATION AND ITS APPLICATIONS: A SIMPLE EXPOSITION, Miles Walker. An important book for engineers showing how this valuable tool can be employed in practical situations. Very careful, clear presentation covering numerous concrete engineering problems. Includes a thorough account of conjugate functions for engineers—useful for the beginner and for review. Applications to such problems as: Stream-lines round a corner, electric conductor in air-gap, dynamo slots, magnetized poles, much more. Formerly "Conjugate Functions for Engineers." Preface. 92 figures, several tables. Index. ix + 116pp. 5⅜ x 8½.   S1149 Paperbound **$1.25**

THE LAWS OF THOUGHT, George Boole. This book founded symbolic logic some hundred years ago. It is the 1st significant attempt to apply logic to all aspects of human endeavour. Partial contents: derivation of laws, signs & laws, interpretations, eliminations, conditions of a perfect method, analysis, Aristotelian logic, probability, and similar topics. xviii + 424pp. 5⅜ x 8.   S28 Paperbound **$2.00**

SCIENCE AND METHOD, Henri Poincaré. Procedure of scientific discovery, methodology, experiment, idea-germination—the intellectual processes by which discoveries come into being. Most significant and most interesting aspects of development, application of ideas. Chapters cover selection of facts, chance, mathematical reasoning, mathematics, and logic; Whitehead, Russell, Cantor; the new mechanics, etc. 288pp. 5⅜ x 8.   S222 Paperbound **$1.35**

FAMOUS BRIDGES OF THE WORLD, D. B. Steinman. An up-to-the-minute revised edition of a book that explains the fascinating drama of how the world's great bridges came to be built. The author, designer of the famed Mackinac bridge, discusses bridges from all periods and all parts of the world, explaining their various types of construction, and describing the problems their builders faced. Although primarily for youngsters, this cannot fail to interest readers of all ages. 48 illustrations in the text. 23 photographs. 99pp. 6⅛ x 9¼.
T161 Paperbound **$1.00**

Technological, historical

A DIDEROT PICTORIAL ENCYCLOPEDIA OF TRADES AND INDUSTRY, Manufacturing and the Technical Arts in Plates Selected from "L'Encyclopédie ou Dictionnaire Raisonné des Sciences, des Arts, et des Métiers" of Denis Diderot. Edited with text by C. Gillispie. This first modern selection of plates from the high point of 18th century French engraving is a storehouse of valuable technological information to the historian of arts and science. Over 2000 illustrations on 485 full-page plates, most of them original size, show the trades and industries of a fascinating era in such great detail that the processes and shops might very well be reconstructed from them. The plates teem with life, with men, women, and children·performing all of the thousands of operations necessary to the trades before and during the early stages of the industrial revolution. Plates are in sequence, and show general operations, closeups of difficult operations, and details of complex machinery. Such important and interesting trades and industries are illustrated as sowing, harvesting, bee-keeping, cheesemaking, operating windmills, milling flour, charcoal burning, tobacco process-ing, indigo, fishing, arts of war, salt extraction, mining, smelting, casting iron, steel, extracting mercury, zinc, sulphur, copper, etc., slating, tinning, silverplating, gilding, making gunpowder, cannons, bells, shoeing horses, tanning, papermaking, printing, dyeing, and more than 40 other categories. Professor Gillispie, of Princeton, supplies a full com-mentary on all the plates, identifying operations, tools, processes, etc. This material, pre-sented in a lively and lucid fashion, is of great interest to the reader interested in history of science and technology. Heavy library cloth. 920pp. 9 x 12.   T421 Two volume set **$18.50**

CHARLES BABBAGE AND HIS CALCULATING ENGINES, edited by P. Morrison and E. Morrison. Babbage, leading 19th century pioneer in mathematical machines and herald of modern operational research, was the true father of Harvard's relay computer Mark I. His Difference Engine and Analytical Engine were the first machines in the field. This volume contains a valuable introduction on his life and work; major excerpts from his autobiography, revealing his eccentric and unusual personality; and extensive selections from "Babbage's Calculating Engines," a compilation of hard-to-find journal articles by Babbage, the Countess of Lovelace, L. F. Menabrea, and Dionysius Lardner. 8 illustrations, Appendix of miscellaneous papers. Index. Bibliography. xxxviii + 400pp. 5⅜ x 8.   T12 Paperbound **$2.00**

HISTORY OF HYDRAULICS, Hunter Rouse and Simon Ince. First history of hydraulics and hydro-dynamics available in English. Presented in readable, non-mathematical form, the text is made especially easy to follow by the many supplementary photographs, diagrams, drawings, etc. Covers the great discoveries and developments from Archimedes and Galileo to modern giants—von Mises, Prandtl, von Karman, etc. Interesting browsing for the specialist; excellent intro-duction for teachers and students. Discusses such milestones as the two-piston pump of Ctesibius, the aqueducts of Frontius, the anticipations of da Vinci, Stevin and the first book on hydrodynamics, experimental hydraulics of the 18th century, the 19th-century expansion of practical hydraulics and classical and applied hydrodynamics, the rise of fluid mechanics in our time, etc. 200 illustrations. Bibliographies. Index. xii + 270pp. 5¾ x 8.
S1131 Paperbound **$2.00**

BRIDGES AND THEIR BUILDERS, David Steinman and Sara Ruth Watson. Engineers, historians, everyone who has ever been fascinated by great spans will find this book an endless source of information and interest. Dr. Steinman, recipient of the Louis Levy medal, was one of the great bridge architects and engineers of all time, and his analysis of the great bridges of history is both authoritative and easily followed. Greek and Roman bridges, medieval bridges, Oriental bridges, modern works such as the Brooklyn Bridge and the Golden Gate Bridge, and many others are described in terms of history, constructional prin-ciples, artistry, and function. All in all this book is the most comprehensive and accurate semipopular history of bridges in print in English. New, greatly revised, enlarged edition. 23 photographs, 26 line drawings. Index. xvii + 401pp. 5⅜ x 8.   T431 Paperbound **$2.00**

Prices subject to change without notice.

Dover publishes books on art, music, philosophy, literature, languages, history, social sciences, psychology, handcrafts, orientalia, puzzles and entertainments, chess, pets and gardens, books explaining science, inter-mediate and higher mathematics, mathematical physics, engineering, biological sciences, earth sciences, classics of science, etc. Write to:

Dept. catrr.
Dover Publications, Inc.
180 Varick Street, N.Y. 14, N.Y.

concrete ones. Such frost is troublesome in connection with the operation of a water-stage recorder because it tends to collect on moving
parts and may eventually stop the recorder. From the standpoint
of cost, there is little to be said in favor of either the wooden or the
concrete type of shelter construction. Figure 51 shows plans for a
typical wooden shelter and plain concrete well from which the details
of construction will readily be noted. Figures 50 and 52 show typical

Fig. 52. Typical installation, concrete well and wooden shelter, Cayuga Inlet
near Ithaca, N. Y. Note A-frame and cableway.

installations of this kind. One of the features of wooden-shelter construction is a boxed-in table upon which the water-stage recorder rests.
The floor is cut away underneath this table to an extent sufficient to
allow the float, in case of extremely high stages, to rise above the floor
and to be effective until it hits the under side of the table. In this
way, some 30 inches of additional head room is made available, which
may occasionally be utilized to very good advantage when extremely
high floods occur. The exteriors and roofs of wooden shelters may be
finished with asbestos, or composition shingles or clapboards may be
placed on the sides and wood shingles on the roofs. Composition
shingles are desirable because they require no painting. Since it is
customary to ceil wooden shelters on the inside, an air space is thus
provided which is quite effective in keeping shelters of this type rea-

sonably warm in winter and cool in summer. With a color scheme such as may be expressed in green shingles and door and white trim, structures of this type are quite attractive in appearance.

At certain sites and under certain conditions, it may be expedient and desirable to adopt other types of construction than those above referred to. In parks and other public places, shelters may be constructed either of natural stone or of brick with special ornamental

FIG. 53. Combination stone and concrete installation, Bennett Spring at Bennett Springs, Mo.

treatment. These considerations apply mainly to the exteriors of the structures, of course. The inside arrangements will be similar to those in other standard shelters. Figures 53 and 54 show examples of such special installations.

In dry climates and under circumstances where temporary recorder installations are required, a simple box 3 feet by 2 feet by 1½ feet in size, with one side hinged to form a door, may serve as a shelter. This type of installation (Fig. 45) was formerly quite common in the West but has been largely superseded except for stations on irrigation canals and ditches and on streams of minor importance.

Installation of Gages. The installation of a water-stage recorder involves its placement in the recorder shelter in such a position on a level support or shelf of fixed elevation that the float and counterweight will operate without interference with each other or contact with the walls of the well, at the same time being so far removed from the ladder that the engineer or observer may enter the well and work therein without interfering with the float and counterweight cables. If a float-tape gage is installed in the well, the matter of insuring the free operation of the recorder float is further complicated by the presence of another float and another counterweight. Great care should be taken in accurately locating and cutting the holes in the table for the clock weight and recorder float and counterweight cables,

Fig. 54. Combination concrete and brick installation, Cedar Swamp Creek at Glen Cove, L. I., N. Y. Note concrete artificial control.

since these cables must pass cleanly through the holes without rubbing on their edges.

A vertical staff gage (Figs. 7 and 12) is installed by attaching a timber back piece by anchor bolts or otherwise to the face of a pier, abutment, or other structure, or in rare instances to the face of a cliff, and fastening thereto a graduated scale in a vertical position. Preferably, the scale consists of one or more graduated enameled sections, or, if such sections are not available, a painted board graduated by coopers' staples to feet and tenths may be used and attached in the same manner to the backing timber. Whatever the type of gage, it should be accurately graduated, the enameled sections spaced correctly with the aid of a steel tape, and the whole gage set to station datum by means of an engineer's level.

The installation of an inclined staff gage differs from that of a vertical staff gage in that the graduation must be made by engineer's level after the bed piece and face board have been placed in position, since readings on the gage must relate to vertical distances and not to distances along its inclined face.

Staff gages may consist of vertical sections and inclined portions (Fig. 55) of different slopes that may best fit the topography and

Fig. 55. Staff gage installation, consisting of vertical and inclined sections.

facilities of a particular site. The only requirements are that the sections shall be securely placed, that the datum plane for every part of each section shall be the same, and that all parts shall show true vertical distances or changes in elevation.

As an inclined section of a staff gage will rest on two or more supports, it is especially subject to error in datum because each support may be liable to changes in elevation which can ordinarily be ascertained only by means of an engineer's level. Inclined staff gages, therefore, require more careful attention than vertical ones.